D1094319

THE CHEMISTRY AND MODE OF ACTION OF PLANT GROWTH SUBSTANCES

The Chemistry and Mode of Action of Plant Growth Substances

Proceedings of a Symposium held at Wye College (University of London) July 1955

Edited by

R. L. WAIN and F. WIGHTMAN

LONDON
BUTTERWORTHS SCIENTIFIC PUBLICATIONS
1956

BUTTERWORTHS PUBLICATIONS LTD.
88 KINGSWAY, LONDON, W.C.2

AFRICA: BUTTERWORTH & CO. (AFRICA) LTD.
DURBAN: 33/35 Beach Grove

AUSTRALIA: BUTTERWORTH & CO. (AUSTRALIA) LTD.
SYDNEY: 8 O'Connell Street
MELBOURNE: 430 Bourke Street
BRISBANE: 240 Queen Street

CANADA: BUTTERWORTH & CO. (CANADA) LTD.
TORONTO: 1367 Danforth Avenue

NEW ZEALAND: BUTTERWORTH & CO. (AUSTRALIA) LTD.
WELLINGTON: 49/51 Ballance Street
AUCKLAND: 35 High Street

U.S.A. Edition published by

ACADEMIC PRESS INC., PUBLISHERS
125 EAST 23RD STREET
NEW YORK 10, NEW YORK

Printed at The Universities Press, Belfast
by Sir Isaac Pitman & Sons, Ltd.

PREFACE

During the last twenty years, developments in the field of plant growth substances have been rapid and impressive. As is well known, some of these materials have found important and widespread uses in agriculture and horticulture and are playing a vital role in increasing the yield of crops. At the same time, research along more fundamental lines has not been neglected, and, although the precise mechanism's which underlie the growth response are not yet understood, much progress has been made in studies on physiological, chemical, and other aspects, and these investigations are being vigorously pursued in many countries. Furthermore, the development of paper chromatography has enabled critical investigations to be made on the auxin and auxin-inhibitor status of different plant tissues. Already the literature on all these fundamental aspects is very extensive and such is the rate of progress that it has become essential for specialized workers within these fields to have the opportunity of meeting from time to time to present and discuss their results.

In September 1953, the writer attended an International Conference on Plant Growth Substances at the University of Lund, Sweden, organized by Professor H. Burström. All those present were working within this field. The high level and great value of the papers and discussions led, two years later, to the idea of holding a similar Conference in England. This suggestion was well received, and, as a result, workers from seven countries met at Wye College from 17–22 July 1955. The present volume contains the papers read at this Conference.

For the purposes of historical record it is perhaps worth while to refer briefly to previous meetings of this kind. In this connection, the writer is indebted to Dr. P. Larsen for the reminder that the First International Conference on Growth Substances was held in Paris in 1937. This meeting was organized under the auspices of the League of Nations and the papers were published as a special volume, *Études et recherches sur les phytohormones* (Paris, 1938). Professor P. Boysen-Jensen was the President at this meeting and Professor V. J. Koningsberger and Dr. G. S. Avery were amongst those attending. The Second Growth Substance Conference, held in Wisconsin in 1949, was almost entirely American, Professor H. Burström being the only representative from Europe to present a paper. The contributions, edited by Professor F. Skoog and published in 1951 under the title *Plant Growth Substances*, have undoubtedly proved of great value to all workers in the field. Although only an abstract of the proceedings of the Lund Conference (1953) was published, the great success of this meeting must be recorded. The Wye Conference was organized along similar lines with the help of a grant kindly provided by the Governing Body of Wye College. Their generosity in this respect, and that of Sir William Slater, Secretary of the Agricultural Research Council, is gratefully acknowledged.

The following acted as Chairmen at the various sessions: Prof. H. Veldstra,

Dr. G. S. Avery, Prof. J. Bonner, Prof. T. A. Bennet-Clark, Prof. H. Burström, Dr. P. Larsen, and Prof. L. J. Audus. Their assistance in this connection was greatly appreciated. It is also a pleasure to record the help provided by all members of the Chemistry Department and Agricultural Research Council Growth Substance Unit at Wye in preparing for this meeting. Finally, warmest thanks are due to Dr. Frank Wightman, the Organizing Secretary, for all his efforts to ensure the smooth running of the Conference.

R. L. Wain

Wye College, University of London
16 *September* 1955

CONTENTS

Members of the Conference

Members of the Conference

D. L. Abbott, Long Ashton
B. Åberg, Uppsala, Sweden
L. J. Audus, London
G. A. Avery, Brooklyn, New York
H. W. B. Barlow, East Malling
G. E. Barnsley, Woodstock
J. A. Bentley, Manchester
T. A. Bennet-Clark, London
G. E. Blackman, Oxford
J. Bonner, Pasadena, California
R. C. Brian, Jealott's Hill
R. Brown, Oxford
H. Burström, Lund, Sweden
P. M. Cartwright, Wye
E. E. Cheesman, London
P. Dutton, Manchester
C. H. Fawcett, Wye
A. Fredga, Uppsala, Sweden
A. W. Galston, Pasadena, California
D. J. Galston, Pasadena, California
S. A. Gordon, Lemont, Illinois
B. Hansen, Lund, Sweden
C. R. Hancock, East Malling
E. S. J. Hatcher, East Malling
N. Heyes, Oxford
B. J. Heywood, Dagenham
S. Housley, Manchester
Å. Jönsson, Stockholm
K. Kaindl, Linz, Austria
V. J. Koningsberger, Utrecht
P. Larsen, Bergen, Norway
J. M. F. Leaper, Ambler, Pennsylvania
A. C. Leopold, Lafayette, Indiana
H. Linser, Linz, Austria
E. J. Maskell, Birmingham
H. Mayr, Linz, Austria
C. C. McCready, Oxford
D. G. Morgan, Hamburg
J. P. Nitsch, Harvard, Massachusetts
D. J. Osborne, Oxford
J. van Overbeek, Modesto, California
R. Pohl, Freiburg, Germany
R. D. Preston, Leeds
E. Raadts, Hamburg
L. Reinhold, Oxford
G. G. Samuel, London
W. W. Schwabe, Rothamsted
R. C. Seeley, Wye
Sir William Slater, London
H. Söding, Hamburg
M. S. Smith, Wye
D. M. Spencer, Wye
F. C. Steward, Ithaca, New York
N. Sunderland, Oxford
J. F. Sutcliffe, London
J. T. Sykes, Wye
F. Taylor, Wye
R. Thresh, London
A. J. Vlitos, New York
H. Veldstra, Amsterdam
D. Vince, Reading
R. L. Wain, Wye
R. L. Weintraub, Camp Detrick, Maryland
F. Wightman, Wye

I

NATURAL AUXINS

METHODS FOR THE INVESTIGATION OF NATURAL AUXINS AND GROWTH INHIBITORS†

J. P. Nitsch‡
Biological Laboratories, Harvard University

The field of knowledge of plant growth substances has developed tremendously, but unequally. Thus, the knowledge of synthetic compounds capable of modifying the growth of plants in a manner similar to native substances has accumulated at a prodigious pace, as have the horticultural and agricultural applications of this knowledge. One must admit, however, that the science of auxins rests upon the small and shaky foundation of the meagre and inadequate knowledge we have of the identity of the native substances at work in the plant. Moreover, the numerous attempts which have been made to explain how 'auxins' in general regulate growth may be futile unless we actually know the nature of all the auxins that occur in the normal development of plant tissues. It is high time that physiologists and chemists made a really comprehensive survey of the native growth-promoting and growth-inhibiting substances present in plants.

The main difficulty in such work arises from the extraordinarily low concentration of these substances in plants. Fortunately, the new techniques of paper chromatography and paper electrophoresis, recently applied to auxin problems by many different workers, show great promise as tools in this task. While trying to proceed in this direction, however, the plant scientist encounters many technical problems which have to be solved before any real advance can be made. Among these, one may list: a reliable extraction method, a good chromatographic technique, and a suitable bio-assay. Like other workers, we have been faced with these questions, and have tried to study the matter systematically. The results of our effort will be presented in this paper. We will consider successively the extraction of the active substances from the plant material, the purification of the extract, the chromatographic techniques, the bio-assay, and, finally, a technique for the chemical identification of the substances on the chromatograms.

THE EXTRACTION OF AUXINS FROM PLANT MATERIAL

When we extract something from the plant, we want the extraction to be complete; we want no more and no less than what is actually present in the tissues. This means that we do not want any synthesis of auxin to take place

† This work was supported in part by the American Cancer Society, Inc., as recommended by the Committee on Growth of the National Research Council, and in part by the National Science Foundation through grants-in-aid made to Professors R. H. Wetmore and K. V. Thimann of Harvard University. The author expresses his deep gratitude to Professor Wetmore and Professor Thimann for the facilities, help, and inspiration which they so generously provided, and to his wife, who performed a large number of the experiments.

‡ Present address: Department of Floriculture and Ornamental Horticulture, Cornell University, Ithaca, New York, U.S.A.

during the extraction procedure, nor do we want any destruction of these substances. It has been shown by many authors (Thimann *et al.*, 1940, 1942; Gustafson, 1941; van Overbeek *et al.*, 1947) that when ether is used, auxin can be generated from plant material over periods as long as a year. Temperature stimulates this generation (Wildman and Muir, 1949). That boiling stops the production indicates the enzymatic nature of the process. On the other hand, especially when tissues are ground or cut, the destruction of auxins during extraction may be extensive, depending on the kind of material used. This destruction is also an enzymatic phenomenon of the oxidative type (Tang and Bonner, 1947; Wagenknecht and Burris, 1950; Steeves *et al.*, 1953; Briggs *et al.*, 1955a,b). To obtain a reliable picture of the auxins present in the plant at the time of extraction, one has to stop this oxidative destruction of auxins.

Table 1 gives the results of a series of tests performed on the tuber tissue of Jerusalem artichoke. The extent of browning was taken as an index of the oxidative activity at the cut surfaces. Tissues in ether and ethyl acetate turned dark brown, indicating that these solvents do not stop the activity

Table 1

The prevention of tissue browning during auxin extraction

Jerusalem artichoke tuber tissues left overnight in the ice-box at about 5°C.

Extracting solvent	*Browning after* 18 *hours*
Absolute methanol	0
Absolute ethanol†	+
Acetone	+
Petroleum ether (boiling point: 30–65°C)	+++
Chloroform	+++++
Chloroform+8-hydroxyquinoline (2 mg/c.c.)	++++
Ethylacetate	+++++++
Ether	+++++++
Ether (95%)+absolute methanol (5%)	++++
Ether (70%)+absolute methanol (30%)	+++
Ether (50%)+absolute methanol (50%)	++
Ether (70%)+absolute ethanol (30%)	+++
Ether+$Na_2S_2O_4$ (1 mg/c.c. undissolved‡)	0
Ethylacetate (50%)+absolute methanol (50%)	++

† The tissues are shrivelled after extraction.
‡ Dissolves when the fresh tissue is put in the mixture.

of at least the polyphenoloxidase system. It is not surprising then, that previous workers have found that enzymes which produce auxins also are not inactivated by ether. Unless special precautions are taken, such as short time extraction and low temperatures, ether is not a reliable extracting solvent for auxins. According to *Table 1*, chloroform is slightly better than ether in preventing browning, but petroleum ether, acetone, and absolute ethanol are even better. The very best solvent, however, seems to be methanol, which yielded beautiful white tissues without the slightest trace of browning. To improve the ether solvent, several addenda were tried. The best one was $Na_2S_2O_4$, which is practically insoluble in ether, but which dissolves in the water coming out from the tissues. This powerful reducing agent kept the tissues perfectly white, but the effect it might have on the auxins themselves has not yet been investigated. The addition of methanol to ether improved the latter solvent so much that it was not necessary to look further into the matter. It was inferred, as a working hypothesis, that since either methanol alone or a mixture of ether and methanol would prevent browning, they would perhaps also stop the enzymatic activity of plant tissues which have caused in the past so many artefacts during auxin extraction. If enzymatic activity is prevented (at least by the 0°C temperature and the short duration of the extraction, such as 1–3 hours), then there should be no danger of other artefacts, such as those arising from an enzymatic esterification of indole-3-acetic acid (IAA) with methanol or ethanol. Such an esterification does not seem to proceed at an appreciable rate *in vitro*. We have left IAA in ethanol (1 mg/c.c.) for three months at 25°C in the dark, and after that time we have chromatographed it and detected only one spot on the paper, that of IAA.

Of course, we not only need a solvent which does not cause artefacts to develop, but also one which has a good extractive power. In order to determine how several organic solvents compare, as far as the actual extraction of auxins is concerned, we have performed with different solvents parallel extractions of aliquots of the same material. The extracts were chromatographed, so that not only the total quantity, but also the nature of the extracted substances would become apparent. Three examples of this study will be given. The first one (*Figure 1*) concerns tomato fruits, harvested 20 days after pollination, which have been immediately frozen, lyophilized, and ground to a fine powder. Aliquots of 100 mg (dry weight) of this powder were extracted for 3 hours at 0°C (ice-bath) with 20 c.c. of the chosen solvent, plus two rinsings. The extracts were filtered over cotton, concentrated under reduced pressure, and transferred to the paper strips by means of a tuberculin syringe, as previously described (Nitsch and Nitsch, 1955). The chromatograms were run in the dark and at room temperature in the *iso*propanol (80)+28 per cent ammonia (10)+H_2O (10) (v/v) solvent recommended by Stowe and Thimann (1954). When the solvent front had travelled 20 cm past the initial spot, the paper strips were taken out of the tubes, dried in a stream of air, and cut transversely into twenty segments 1 cm wide. Each of these segments was incubated with 0·5 c.c. of a buffer at pH 5·0 (see below) containing 2 per cent sucrose and with ten 4 mm oat coleoptile sections.

The diagrams of *Figure 1* show the location on the chromatograms and the activity in the coleoptile sections of the growth substances extracted with (1) anhydrous acetone, (2) ether, (3) ethyl acetate, and (4) absolute methanol. In all cases, two groups of active compounds are apparent, one around R_f 0·4, the other around R_f 0·7. The *size* of the growth peaks varies with the solvent, however. In addition, the *number* of the peaks also varies with the solvent. For example, acetone seems to extract substances which remain near the origin and which are not visible in the diagram corresponding to the ether extract. Indications of the presence of growth inhibitors can be seen, especially in the ether extract. When the amount of tissue extracted with ether is increased, the inhibitory regions around R_f 0·5 and R_f 0·9 become very marked. Thus, this first example shows that different extracting solvents may give different auxin pictures, both quantitatively and qualitatively. As far as quantities are concerned, with the tissue used in this

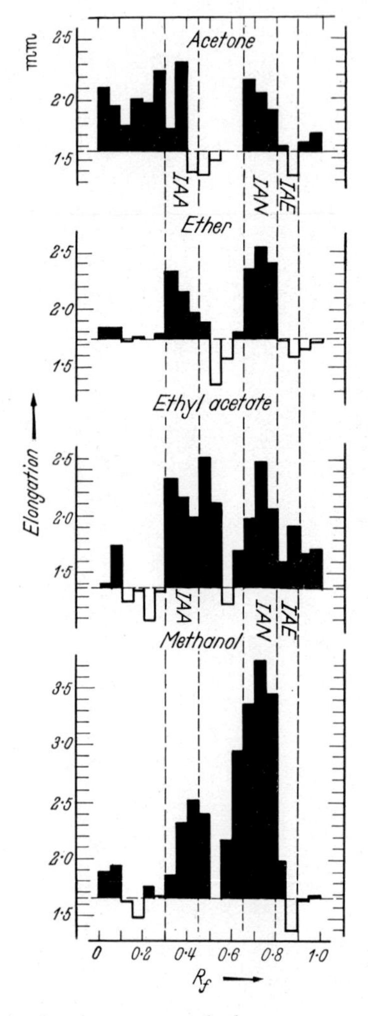

Figure 1. Histograms showing the biological activity of substances extracted with different solvents from tomato ovary tissues. The unripe tomato fruits (male sterile mutant of the var. John Baer) were harvested 20 *days after hand-pollination and lyophilized.* 100 *mg (dry weight) of the lyophilized powder were extracted for* 3 *hours at* 0°C *with the indicated solvent. The crude extracts were concentrated under reduced pressure and chromatographed in* isopropanol+28% *ammonia+water* (80; 10; 10) *(v/v). When the solvent front had travelled* 20 *cm past the initial spot, the paper strips (Whatman No.* 1 *paper) were air-dried and cut into twenty* 1 *cm segments. Each of these paper segments was incubated with* 0·5 *c.c. of solution and ten oat coleoptile sections. The elongation of these sections after about* 20 *hours is plotted along the ordinate axis of the diagrams. The position of the paper segment on the original chromatogram is plotted in R_f units along the other axis.*

particular instance, ethyl acetate and especially methanol were better than ether.

A second example is taken from another fruit, the bean. Lyophilized bean seeds, dissected out of the pods about 8 days after pollination, were extracted for 5 hours at 0°C in the dark with 10 c.c. each of absolute methanol, absolute ethanol, or anhydrous ethyl acetate. The aliquot extracted with ethyl acetate was washed at the end with absolute ethanol and the two extracts combined. The chromatograms were developed in the same solvent as above and assayed with oat coleoptile segments. The results shown in *Figure 2* were obtained.

It is clear from *Figure 2* that for bean seed tissue methanol seems to be a better solvent than ethanol, since the peaks of growth, especially the one in the indole-3-acetonitrile (IAN) region, are higher. It seems also that ethyl acetate extracts a still higher amount of auxins, although the peak in the IAN region is less marked; in addition, ethyl acetate appears to extract a substance having a R_f higher than IAA but lower than IAN.

To find out whether ethyl acetate was a better solvent than methanol, the following experiment was performed. Lyophilized immature bean seeds were first extracted for one and a half hours with absolute methanol at 0°C, then with anhydrous ethyl acetate for another one and a half hours, also at 0°C.

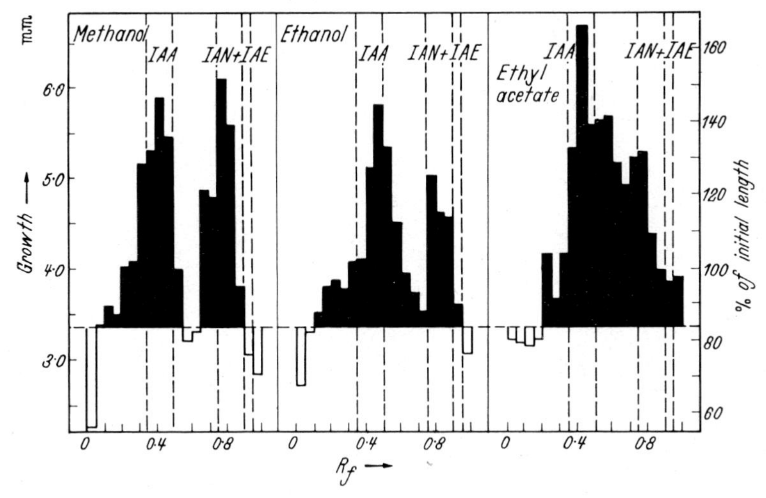

Figure 2. Histograms made under conditions similar to those of Figure 1, except that the three extracts are of 15 *mg (dry weight) each of lyophilized bean seeds (var. Dwarf Shell Red Kidney), dissected out of the immature pods about one week after flowering. The extractions were made at* 0°*C during* 5 *hours with absolute methanol, absolute ethanol, and ethyl acetate respectively. The material extracted with ethyl acetate was washed with absolute ethanol and the two extracts were combined.*

The two extracts were chromatographed separately in our new *iso*butanol (80)+methanol (5) +H_2O (15) (v/v) solvent which has been substituted for the previous one for reasons which will be discussed below. The results obtained when the chromatograms were assayed with oat coleoptile segments (see *Figure* 3) show clearly that after the methanol extraction, which yields large quantities of auxins, ethyl acetate extracts only very small amounts. In addition, no indication of auxins different from those extracted with methanol can be seen on the diagram corresponding to ethyl acetate, since the small peaks obtained correspond in general with those of the other diagram. It may be noted in passing that the chromatographic solvent used in the present instance reveals the existence of substances which were not found with the *iso*propanol–ammonia solvent (compare with *Figure 2*). These substances either are not separated or are transformed into other substances during chromatography in the latter solvent. As far as the identity of the growth peak found in the IAA region is concerned, it is most probably IAA since the characteristic colour reaction of IAA was obtained on the paper in the IAA position with both the Salkowski and the Ehrlich reagents.

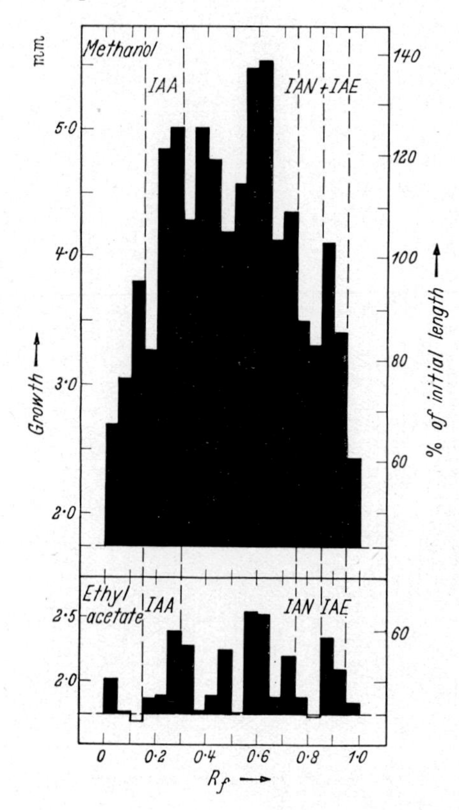

Figure 3. Histograms showing the growth-promoting activity of 1 *cm sections of chromatograms run in* isobutanol–methanol–water (80; 5; 15). *Lyophilized immature bean seeds (as in Figure 2, but* 30 *mg dry weight) were first extracted at* 0°C *for* 1·5 *hours with* 10+5+5 *c.c. of cold absolute methanol. This extract gave the upper histogram. The same bean material was then extracted for another* 1·5 *hours at* 0°C *with* 10+5+5 *c.c. of cold ethyl acetate and chromatographed in the same solvent (lower histogram).*

THE PURIFICATION OF THE EXTRACTS

To obtain a clean chromatogram with well-separated spots, one has generally to purify the crude plant extract. Such a purification can be achieved in several ways, among which we have used the following ones:

1. *Bicarbonate purification*—This well-known technique, already used by Boysen-Jensen (1941), purifies the acid auxins, especially IAA, very well. They enter the aqueous phase as salts, whereas most of the coloured impurities remain in the ether phase. Upon acidification of the aqueous fraction with dilute HCl (Larsen, 1955), it is possible to re-extract the acid auxins with fresh ether. Clean chromatograms of IAA which can be used for colour reactions are obtained in this way.

2. *Acetonitrile purification*—The bicarbonate technique, unfortunately, does not work for neutral auxins. Adapting a technique devised originally for insecticides by Jones and Riddick (1952), it was possible to eliminate at least the fatty substances and some of the carotenoids from the extract (Nitsch, 1955). The original extract is evaporated down to dryness, then shaken with

about equal parts of anhydrous acetonitrile and hexane or heptane. Under these conditions, IAA and IAN remain in the acetonitrile phase, as well as ethylindole acetate (IAE), although there might be, possibly, some losses of the latter compound.

3. *Chromatographic purification*—It was found that some of the coloured impurities of plant extracts are strongly absorbed on paper, so that when a chromatogram is eluted with ether, some of the coloured material remains on the paper. Two types of chromatographic purifications have been used:

(*a*) The crude extract was first chromatographed in distilled H_2O and dried. The initial spot was then cut off and thc rest of the paper eluted with ether or absolute ethanol.

(*b*) The crude extract was first chromatographed in *iso*propanol (80) +ammonia (10)+water (10) (v/v) and dried. Then the initial spot was cut off and discarded, and the rest of the paper cut transversely in the middle. The lower portion then contains mainly the acid auxins and the upper one the neutral auxins which can be eluted and rechromatographed separately.

During the purification procedure, there is always a possibility of loss of active material and alteration of labile compounds. It has been possible, however, to avoid any purification by using crude extracts of small quantities of plant material and a very sensitive bio-assay test. The procedure adopted will be described below.

THE CHROMATOGRAPHIC PROCEDURE

In order to obtain an initial spot as small as possible, the plant extract is applied on the starting line of the paper strip by means of a tuberculin syringe (*Figure 4*) in a stream of air to allow the rapid evaporation of the

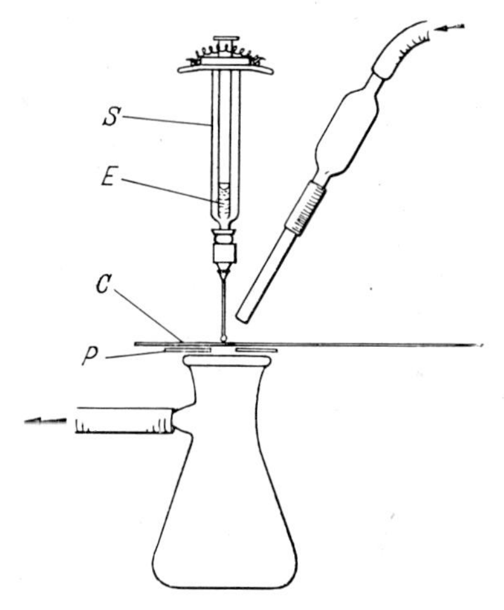

Figure 4. Technique used to obtain small initial spots on chromatograms. The extract (E) was taken up in a tuberculin syringe (S) and deposited on the starting point of a paper chromatogram (C) laid down on a perforated paper disk (P). A stream of air, filtered through cotton, was blown through the glass tubing at the right and was sucked into the suction flask connected with a vacuum pump, thus activating the evaporation of the extract on the paper strip (cf. Nitsch and Nitsch, 1955).

solvent (Nitsch and Nitsch, 1955). After complete drying, the paper strip is equilibrated overnight over the solvent in a large glass tube (*Figure 5*), a technique originally used by Stowe and Thimann (1954). All the experiments reported were performed at room temperature in a dark cabinet.

The finding of a suitable solvent is the key to successful chromatographic separation of a mixture of compounds. More or less empirically, many workers in different laboratories arrived at various recipes for solvent mixtures that would separate certain auxins, especially the acid ones. In general, a mixture of an alcohol, ammonia, and water has been adopted. Stowe and Thimann (1954) substantiated this through systematic studies

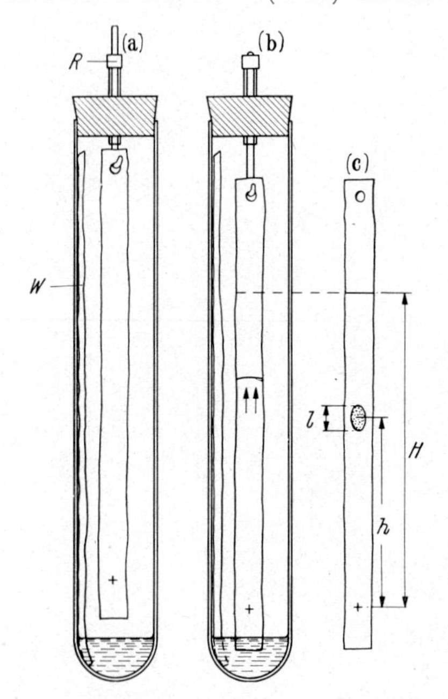

Figure 5. (a) The chromatogram is first equilibrated over the solvent overnight. A paper wick (W) keeps the upper part of the tube saturated with the vapour of the solvent. A ring of rubber tubing (R) supports the inner glass rod. (b) After equilibration, the inner glass rod is pushed down so that the lower 5 *mm of the paper strip will penetrate into the solvent. (c) When the solvent has travelled up a height (H) of* 20 *cm, the paper is air-dried, and sprayed with a suitable reagent. Both the position (h) and length (l) of the coloured spots are noted. The technique illustrated under (a) and (b) is essentially that of Stowe and Thimann,* 1954. *(After Nitsch and Nitsch,* 1955.)

and recommended a mixture of *iso*propanol (80)+28 per cent ammonia (10)+water (10) (v/v) which we have used on many occasions with good results. We have tried to go further in this investigation by asking this question: 'What is the simplest mixture which can separate auxins on paper?' The results of *Table 2* speak for themselves: first of all, the presence or the absence of ammonia does not appreciably affect the separation of the three auxins

Table 2

Search for the simplest chromatographic solvent

All paper strips were equilibrated overnight over the solvent.

Solvent	R_f†			
	IAA	*IBA*‡	*IAN*	*IAE*
*iso*Propanol (80%)+water (10%)+28% ammonia (10%)	0·35	0·48	0·76	0·83
*iso*Propanol (80%)+water (10%)	0·40	0·50	0·75	0·83
*iso*Propanol (100%)	0	0	lost?	0·83
Water (100%)	0·65	0·64	0·32	0·47

† The symbol R_f ('ratio front') designates the ratio of the movement of a given compound to the movement of the front of the solvent. $R_f = h/H$ (see *Figure 5*).
‡ IBA = indole-3-butyric acid.

considered, nor their R_f's (see also *Figure 6(a)*); secondly, the removal of *iso*propanol changes the R_f's but does not impair the separation of the compounds—in fact, it improves it; thirdly, the removal of water definitely ruins the value of the solvent. Thus, from all components of the mixture only one is really indispensable, namely water. This is true even in the case of water-insoluble compounds such as hexane, as demonstrated by Nitsch and Nitsch (1955). It is probable that water, at least in the vapour state, has to impregnate the paper fibres in order to give a good chromatogram. These investigations give support to the use of water alone previously reported by Bitancourt, Schwartz, and Dierberger (1954) and by Sen and Leopold (1954). These authors, however, did not equilibrate their paper strips over the water

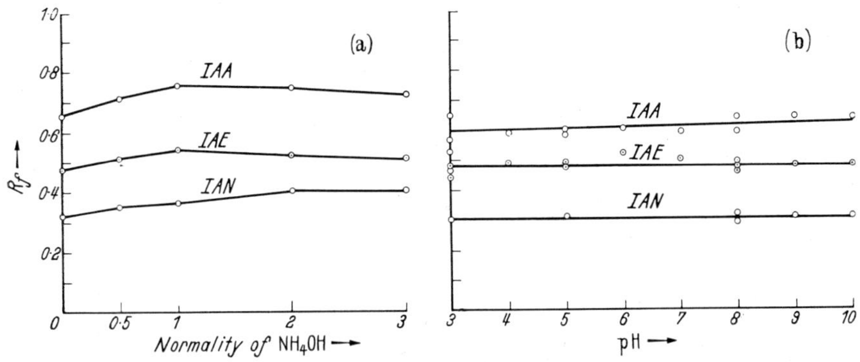

Figure 6. (a) R_f's of IAA, IAE, and IAN in water to which various concentrations of ammonia have been added. (b) The effect of pH *on the R_f's of IAA, IAE, and IAN in water.* pH 3·0 *has been obtained both with citrate–phosphate buffer (about* 0·03 M) *and* HCl (0·001 M); pH'*s* 4·0–7·0 *with citrate–phosphate buffers (about* 0·03 M); pH 8·0 *with citrate–phosphate buffer and with borate–*KCl *buffer (about* 0·05 M); pH'*s* 9·0–10·0 *with borate–*KCl *buffers (about* 0·05 M) *(cf. Nitsch and Nitsch,* 1955).

solvent before chromatography. It has been shown (Nitsch and Nitsch, 1955) that a preliminary equilibration improves markedly the quality of the chromatography in water by giving compact spots.

The use of water alone in the chromatographic separation of auxins has its limitations. First of all, it does not separate the acid auxins one from another (for example, IAA and indole-3-butyric acid (IBA) practically run together, as shown in *Table 2*). In the second place, when fatty material is present in the plant extract, the auxins, more soluble in fats than in water, may not move readily out of the initial spot, and streaking may occur. For these reasons, it was necessary to improve the water solvent. Changing the pH did not help at all (*Figure 6(b)*), but the addition of an organic solvent such as acetonitrile, or an alcohol, allowed a good separation of several acid auxins (*Figure 7*), whereas the neutral ones, such as IAN and IAE, ran together. It was then concluded that no one solvent could be ideal for compounds as widely different in their physico-chemical properties as acids, esters, and nitriles, and that it was better to look (*a*) for a solvent separating the acid compounds, (*b*) for another one separating the neutral substances.

For acid auxins there exists already an excellent solvent, the one developed by Stowe and Thimann (1954). The need for a different mixture was not felt until it was discovered, in the course of the search for a solvent applicable to neutral auxins, that ammonia, under certain circumstances, leads to the hydrolysis of IAE (*Table 3*). Such an hydrolysis was not apparent (using only a colorimetric detection of auxins) with the *iso*propanol solvent. However,

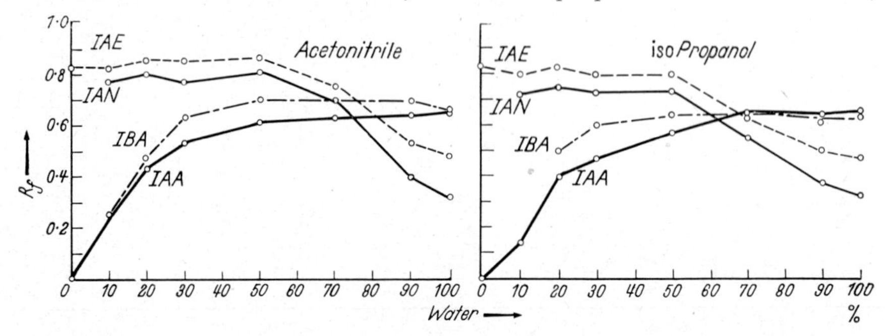

Figure 7. Effect on the R_f's of IAA, IBA, IAN, and IAE of various percentages of acetonitrile (left) and iso*propanol (right) in water.*

the possibility that ammonia might affect natural auxins more labile than IAE led us to start a new search for a good solvent to separate the acid auxins. Knowing that ammonia did not change the R_f's appreciably, we simply omitted it and used *iso*propanol+water (80;20) (Nitsch and Nitsch,

Table 3

Hydrolysis of ethylindole acetate by ammonia on paper chromatograms

All the chromatograms were equilibrated overnight, then run for about 8 hours at room temperature in the dark. Only ethylindole acetate (4 γ) was applied to each chromatogram initially. The spots were revealed with either the Gordon and Weber or the Ehrlich reagent.

Solvent mixture (Proportions in per cent v/v)			*Intensity of colour*	
			IAE spot	*IAA spot*
Hexane	H_2O	28% *ammonia*		
80	20	—	++++	—
80	18	2	+++	+
80	16	4	+++	++
80	10	10	++	+++
80	4	16	—	++++
80	—	20	+	+++
*iso*Propanol	H_2O	28% *ammonia*		
80	20	—	++++	—
80	10	10	++++	—
80	5	15	++++	—
80	—	20	++	—

1955). Later, however, with a new supply of *iso*propanol, we occasionally ran into two difficulties: (1) the IAA spot was somewhat larger than when ammonia was present, (2) the R_f of IAA was sometimes too high. Several different alcohols were then tried systematically (*Table 4*). In general,

Table 4

Effect of various alcohol isomers on the size of the IAA spot

The chromatograms were equilibrated overnight, then run for 8–10 hours at room temperature in the dark. 2 γ of the indole-3-acetic acid were applied to each strip. All proportions are v/v.

Solvent mixture	*Length of spot in mm*
Propanols	
n-propanol (86%)+H_2O (14%)	22
*iso*propanol (86%)+H_2O (14%)	24
Butanols	
n-butanol (86%)+H_2O (14%)	17
*iso*butanol (86%)+H_2O (14%)	15
sec.butanol (86%)+H_2O (14%)	27
tert.butanol (86%)+H_2O (14%)	20

compact IAA spots were obtained with *n*-butanol, but *iso*butanol was even better, yielding consistently small, rounded spots with IAA and indole-3-butyric acid (IBA). However, with *iso*butanol, the R_f of the IAA spot was too low. It is known (Stowe and Thimann, 1954; Nitsch and Nitsch, 1955) that increasing the percentage of water in an alcohol–water mixture brings the R_f of IAA up (*Figure 7*). Unfortunately, water is not very soluble in *iso*butanol, so that a one-phase mixture cannot be achieved with more than about 14 per cent water at room temperature. This difficulty was overcome by adding to the *iso*butanol–water mixture either *tertiary* butanol (in which water is soluble in all proportions) or methanol. Thus, the following solvents gave good results: (1) *iso*butanol (50%)+*tertiary* butanol (30%) +water (20%), and (2) *iso*butanol (80%)+methanol (5%)+water (15%). The latter solvent was preferred because it ascends somewhat faster than the first one, which moves very slowly. In conclusion, two good chromatographic solvents for auxins are as follows:

	R_f			
	IAA	*IBA*	*IAN*	*IAE*
Stowe and Thimann's *iso*propanol (80%)+28% ammonia (10%) +water (10%)	0·37 (18)	0·50 (17)	0·75 (17)	0·82 (24)
*iso*butanol (80%)+methanol (5%) +water (15%)	0·24 (16)	0·45 (18)	0·76 (25)	0·85 (16)

The numbers in parentheses give the length of the spots in mm for 2 γ of IAA, 1 γ of IBA, 10 γ of IAN, and 5 γ of IAE when the solvent front has moved 20 cm. It can be judged by comparing the diagrams of *Figures 2* and *3* that the *iso*butanol solvent proposed here separates a greater number of different compounds in bean extracts than does the *iso*propanol–ammonia–water solvent.

In attempting to separate the neutral auxins such as IAN and IAE, it was observed that they generally have high R_f's in the alcohol–water or acetonitrile–water mixtures. We looked, therefore, for solvents in which these substances would be very slightly soluble. Thus hexane and heptane were tried, together with carbon tetrachloride, benzene, carbon disulphide, toluene, etc. It was soon found that success or failure in these attempts depended on the presence of a very small amount of water, even though these solvents were water-insoluble. In the case of carbon tetrachloride and carbon disulphide, which are heavier than water, the paper strip was lowered in a beaker containing the organic solvent with water surrounding the beaker. When water was present, IAN and IAE were usually separated, except in the case of CCl_4, CS_2, and benzene, which are slightly soluble in water. The best results were obtained with hexane (*Table 5*) and the 'practical' grade

Table 5

The use of water-insoluble compounds in the chromatography of auxins

Solvents	R_f			*Comments*
	IAA	*IAN*	*IAE*	
Hexane (Eastman, practical) (90%)+water (10%)	0	0·50	0·98	Excellent separation
Hexane (100%)	0	0	0·57	
*cyclo*Hexane (90%)+water (10%)	0	0·39	0·97	
n-Heptane (90%)+water (10%)	0	0·26	0·99	
Trimethylpentane (90%)+ water (10%)	0	0·14	0·78	
Benzene (95%)+water (5%)	0	0·81	0·93	IAN and IAE spots touching
Benzene (100%)	0	lost	0·63	
Carbon tetrachloride (90%)+ water (10%)	0	0·89	0·93	IAN and IAE spots touching
Carbon disulphide (90%)+ water (10%)	0	0·80	0·87	IAN and IAE spots touching

(Eastman P 1135) was better than *n*-hexane. Although water is insoluble in hexane, it was noted that the amount of water in the tube modifies the position of the IAN spot on the chromatogram (Nitsch and Nitsch, 1955). This peculiarity seems to depend on how well the paper wick plunges into the water phase to provide enough water vapour above the solvent; indeed, when the paper wick does not touch the water, the chromatograms may behave as if they were run in anhydrous hexane.

The fact that two types of chromatographic solvents are now available, one for the acid auxins, the other for some neutral ones, does not, unfortunately, solve everybody's problems. Rather, it seems that each worker may have to devise his own solvent to fit his particular needs, though it is hoped, at least, that the principles studied above may be useful in this task.

THE BIO-ASSAY

Since the primary aim of our study is to separate and identify biologically active substances, it is important to have a sensitive, reliable, and easy-to-perform bio-assay. The results of a search for a suitable plant material† led us to conclude that the coleoptile and the first internode of the oat seedling were suitable test objects. The variety Brighton‡, a hulless oat, was used throughout these studies. When coleoptiles were wanted, the seeds were exposed to red light after soaking to prevent the growth of the first internode.

Figure 8. The physiological 'merry-go-round' used to rotate the oat first internodes. The 125 *c.c. Erlenmeyer flasks are ready to receive the* 13 × 100 *mm Pyrex tubes containing the sections plus* 0·5 *c.c. of solution. If the atmosphere of the room is dry, the tubes should be closed with vaccine stoppers. The machine rotates at* 1 *r.p.m.*

When first internodes were wanted, the seeds were grown in total darkness. All manipulations were performed under green light, at a wavelength (about 546 mμ) which has practically no inhibitory effect on the growth of first internodes.

A difficulty encountered early in this work was that the first internodes curved so much in the auxin solutions that they were difficult to measure. Rotating the sections around a horizontal axis solved this problem, and the sections coming out of the physiological 'merry-go-round' (*Figure 8*) grew straight. The coleoptiles, on the other hand, were gently shaken on a

† The details of this work can be found in a paper by Nitsch and Nitsch, to appear in *Plant Physiol.* **31** (1956).

‡ Kindly supplied by the Canadian Department of Agriculture, Central Experimental Farm, Ottawa, Canada.

Figure 9. Thimann's guillotine, which allows exact sectioning of coleoptiles and first internodes.

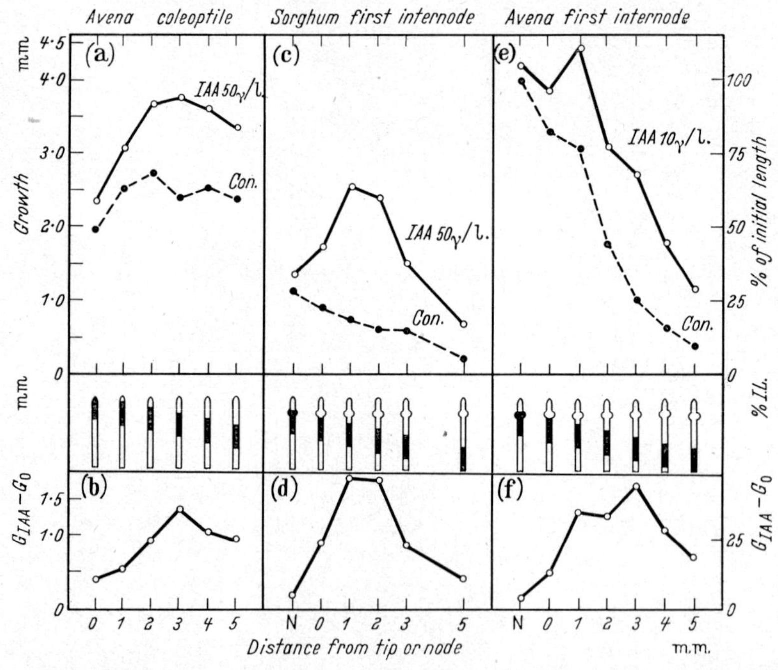

Figure 10. Effect of the location *of* 4 *mm section on the growth in sucrose + buffer without added IAA (black circles, dotted lines) and with IAA (white circles, solid lines), and on the difference of these two elongations (curves (b), (d), and (f)).* Left ordinate: *scale in mm.* Right ordinate: *scale in per cent of the original* 4 *mm length. On the abscissa of the curves (c), (d), (e), and (f), 'N' means that the section includes the coleoptilar node. Each point is the mean of ten replicates.*

horizontal shaker. To be able to section the coleoptiles and internodes accurately, we used Thimann's 'guillotine' (*Figure 9*), an improvement over the original Van der Weij's 'coleoptile microtome' (1932). The primary leaf was always left included in the coleoptile. This procedure simplifies the test without impairing its sensitivity or reliability.

The first question to be decided was: 'Where should we cut the sections?' A series of experiments in which 4 mm sections were cut, first including the tip or the node, then starting 1 mm, etc., below them, gave the results shown in *Figure 10*. It should be noted that what is important here is not so much

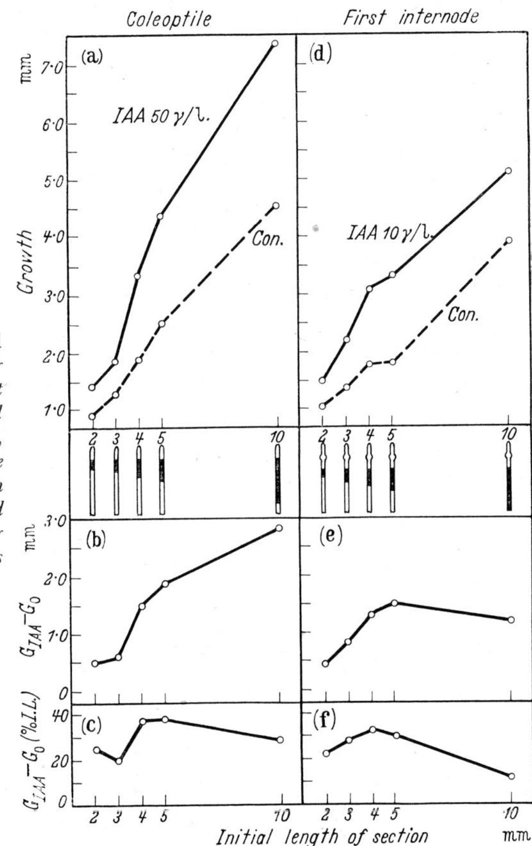

Figure 11. Effect of the initial length *of oat sections on their growth in buffer + sucrose without added IAA (white circles, dotted lines) and with IAA (white circles, solid lines): graphs (a) and (d). The other curves represent this effect on the difference* $G_{IAA}-G_0$ *expressed in mm (curves (b) and (e)) or in per cent of the original lengths (curves (c) and (f)).*

the maximum growth in IAA as the maximum differential growth between the IAA-treated sections and the controls. This difference, which we can represent by $G_{IAA}-G_0$ (growth in IAA minus growth without IAA), is maximum under our conditions when the 4 mm section is cut 3 mm below the tip or 3 mm below the node of the oat seedling. Since the growth of internode sections taken 3 mm below the node is very low without auxin (which makes it difficult to detect any inhibitor on chromatograms), we decided always to cut the internode sections only 2 mm below the node.

The second question was: 'What length should we cut the sections?' Some workers use 3 mm sections, others prefer them 10 mm long. An experiment designed to clear up this point gave the results shown in *Figure 11.* It was evident that, as the initial length of the section increased, the absolute amount of elongation increased. However, the growth of the controls also increased, so that the difference $G_{IAA}-G_0$ may not benefit from longer initial lengths. This is the case for internodes (*Figure 11*(*e*)) in which the zone which responds to the addition of IAA seems more restricted than in the case of coleoptiles. If one looks for maximum *absolute* response to IAA over that of controls, then a 10 mm coleoptile section or a 5 mm internode section is better than shorter ones. But if one considers this response expressed as percentage of the initial length, then a 4 mm section gives about the largest

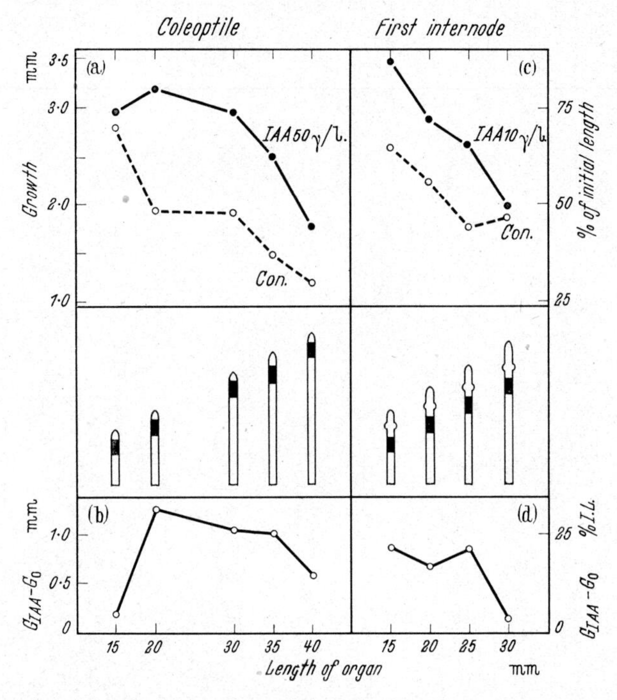

Figure 12. Effect of the physiological age *of the oat seedling* (*represented by the length of the coleoptile or of the first internode at the time of sectioning*) *on the growth of the sections in buffer + sucrose without IAA* (*white circles, dotted lines*) *and with IAA* (*black circles, solid lines*), *and on the difference between these growths* (*curves b and d*). *Scales at the left ordinate are in mm, on the right ordinate in per cent of the initial* 4 *mm length.*

differential response (*Figure 11*, curves *c* and *f*). To be able to use small volumes of solution and avoid the lack of straightness inherent to long sections, an initial 4 mm length was adopted for both coleoptile and internode sections.

An important factor in the sensitivity of oat plants is their age. In general, the younger they are, the more they grow, but they do so also without added auxin. The optimal size at the time of sectioning is when the coleoptile and the mesocotyl have reached about respectively 20 and 15 mm in length (*Figure 12*). Longer internodes rapidly lose their sensitivity, whereas coleoptiles up to 35 mm in length (in the variety Brighton) still respond relatively well to added IAA. In our experiments, the coleoptiles were sectioned when they had reached about 25 mm in length and the internodes about 20 mm.

If one wants to employ small volumes of test solutions, it is important to wash the sections before use. The length and the nature of this pretreatment was investigated. It was found that washing both coleoptiles and mesocotyls for one hour in glass-distilled water increased the IAA response and the reproducibility of the test results (*Table 6*). If the presoaking time is increased, the response to IAA decreases. It also decreases if the sections are immersed.

Table 6

Effect of various pretreatments on the response to IAA

Ten 4 mm sections were used in each case. The sections were always breaking the surface of the solutions unless otherwise indicated.

Plant part (oat)	*Pretreatment*	*Time (hrs)*	*Growth of controls (mm)*	*Growth in IAA (mm)*	$G_{IAA}-G_0$ *(mm)*
First internodes	None	–	1·27	10γ/l. : 2·95	1·68
	H_2O	1	1·09	10γ/l. : 3·34	2·25
First internodes	H_2O, floating	3	1·30	10γ/l. : 3·25	1·95
	H_2O, immersed	3	1·77†	10γ/l. : 2·28	0·51
	2% sucrose, floating	3	1·40	10γ/l. : 3·24	1·84
	2% sucrose, immersed	3	1·58	10γ/l. : 3·43	1·85
Coleoptiles	None	–	1·40	50γ/l. : 2·49	1·09
	H_2O	1	1·69	50γ/l.: 3·38	1·69
Coleoptiles	H_2O	5	1·88	50γ/l. : 2·72	0·84
	$H_2O + MnSO_4 \cdot H_2O$ at 0·1 mg/l.	5	3·00	50γ/l. : 3·98	0·98
	$H_2O + MnSO_4 \cdot H_2O$ at 1 mg/l.	5	2·54	50γ/l. : 4·64	2·10
	$H_2O + MnSO_4 \cdot H_2O$ at 10 mg/l.	5	1·93	50γ/l. : 3·46	1·53

† Immersion in water increases somewhat the length of the controls, but a close examination shows that the sections become more slender than when they are floated.

This decrease, however, can be prevented by the addition of sucrose (2 per cent). Immersion in the liquid presents no problem for coleoptiles which naturally float on the solutions, but, in the case of first internodes which are of solid stem tissue, it was necessary to lay them on stretched cheese-cloth to keep them breaking the surface of the solution. It was thought that the increase in response to IAA caused by presoaking in water might be due to the washing away of an IAA-destroying system. To test this idea, presoaking in reducing agents such as ascorbic acid, glutathione, $Na_2S_2O_4$ was tried, but with no significant results. Nor did presoaking in Ca pantothenate, folic acid, arginine, or cobalt chloride (10–1,000 γ/l) have any appreciable effect. On the contrary, manganese, which is well known to stimulate growth when used together with IAA, was found to increase the growth of coleoptiles but not of internodes when supplied in the pretreatment water at the concentration of $5{\cdot}9 \times 10^{-6}$ M. However, we did not add $MnSO_4$ to the solutions during the whole test period for fear that it might help to destroy labile substances present in the plant extracts. In summary, a 3-hour soaking period in $MnSO_4+H_2O$ (1 mg/l.) was adopted for coleoptile sections and a 1-hour presoaking period in glass-distilled water for the internode sections, the latter being maintained breaking the surface on stretched cheese-cloth.

In a given plant extract, the quantity of auxin is generally small. The problem is how to make the best use of it to get the maximum growth response. If we have, let us say, 0·01 γ of IAA, is it better to dissolve it in 1 c.c. of assay solution, or in 10 c.c.? It is known (cf. Schneider, 1938) that

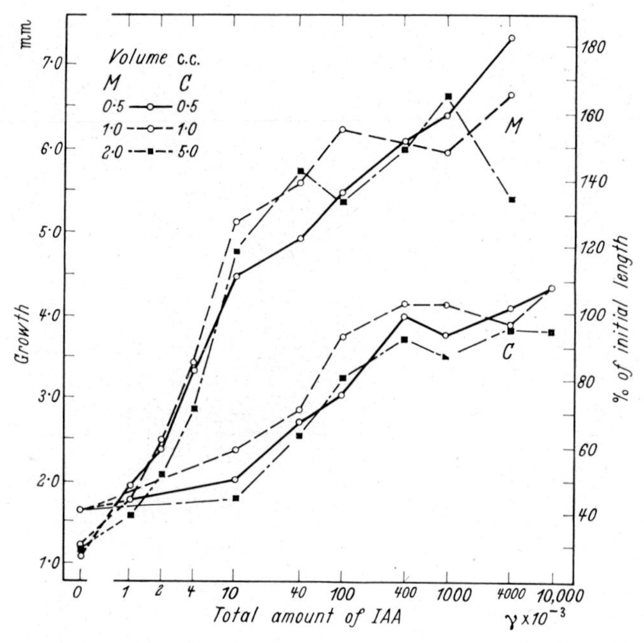

Figure 13. Effect of the volume of solution *on the growth of oat first internodes* (*M*) *and coleoptiles* (*C*). *The total amounts of IAA indicated on the abscissa* (*logarithmic scale*) *were dissolved in either* 0·5, 1·0, *or* 2·0 *c.c.* (*when using first internodes*) *or* 0·5, 1·0, *or* 5·0 *c.c.* (*when using coleoptiles*) *of the usual buffer solution plus* 2 *per cent sucrose and* 0·1 *per cent Tween* 80.

controls in distilled water tend to grow less in large than in small volumes, presumably because of the dilution of a food factor. This effect can be ruled out (1) by presoaking the sections in large volumes of solutions before the actual assay and (2) by adding a food factor, such as sucrose, to the assay solutions. Experiments in which these precautions were taken showed repeatedly that the growth of the controls is the same in 0·5 c.c. or 5 c.c., and that growth of both coleoptile and internode sections in IAA plus sucrose and buffer does not change appreciably according to the volumes used (*Figure 13*), provided, of course, that no evaporation takes place during the assay with 0·5 c.c. It should be mentioned that the coleoptile sections were incubated in special glass dishes having flat bottoms in order to ensure a uniform depth of the liquid with 0·5 c.c.

Many workers have found that the addition of a sugar, especially sucrose, markedly increases the response of oat coleoptile sections to IAA, though Schneider (1941) reported that first internodes were almost insensitive to sucrose. A study of this point, conducted with both coleoptiles and internodes, demonstrated beyond any doubt that the growth of first internodes as well as that of coleoptiles is strongly increased by sucrose in the presence of IAA and that the optimum sucrose concentration is 2 per cent (*Figure 14*).

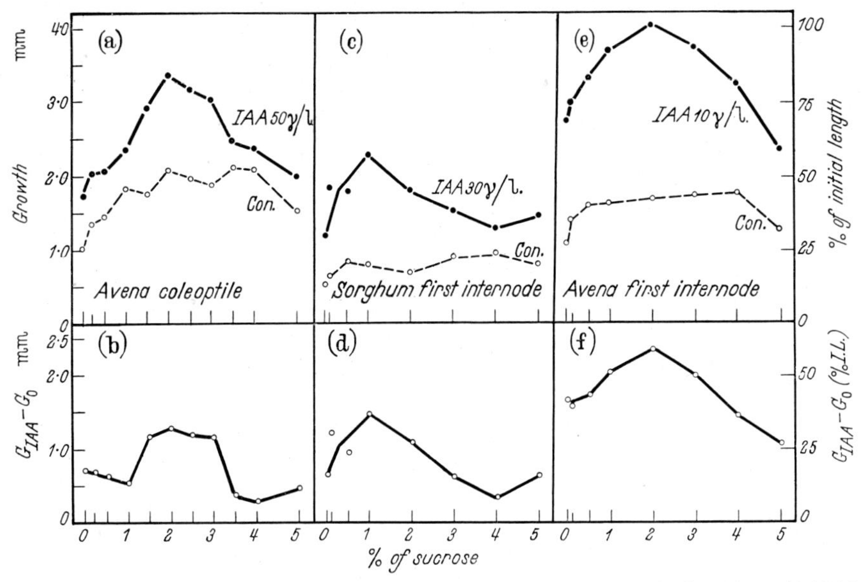

Figure 14. Effect of sucrose concentration *on the growth of sections in buffer without added IAA (white circles, dotted lines) and with IAA (black circles, solid lines), and on the difference between these growths (curves (b), (d), and (f)). Scales are in mm (left ordinate) and in per cent of the initial* 4 *mm length (right ordinate).*

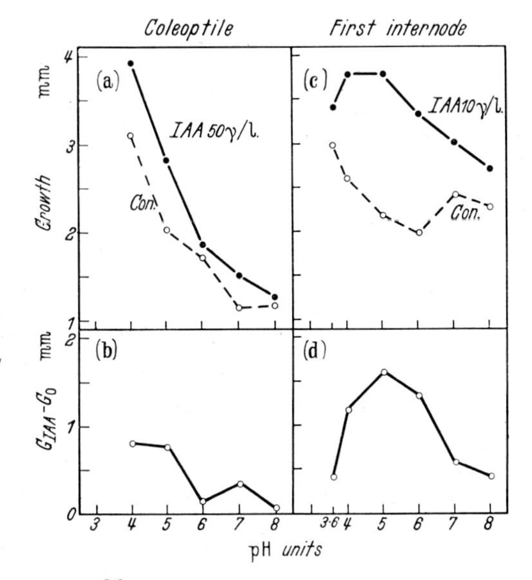

Figure 15. Effect of pH *on the growth of oat sections in buffer + sucrose without IAA (white circles, dotted lines) and with IAA (black circles, solid lines), and on the difference between the two (curves (b) and (d)).*

Similar investigations concerning the effect of pH and buffer concentration gave the results shown in *Figures 15* and *16*. Accordingly, a pH of 5·0 was used in all our experiments and a concentration of 10^{-2} M for K_2HPO_4 in the buffer was adopted. This is not the optimal concentration as far as the

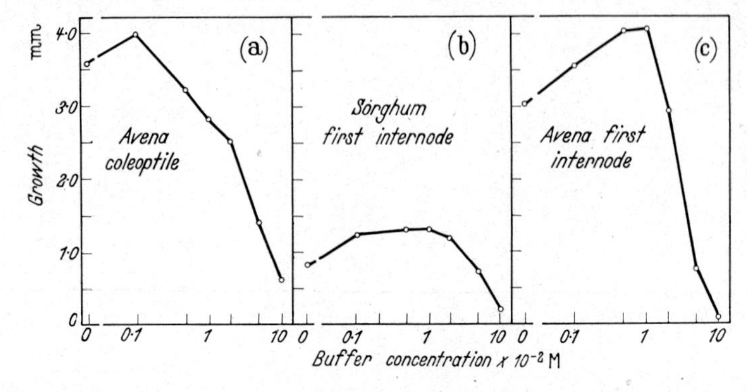

Figure 16. Effect of concentration *of citrate–K phosphate buffer at* pH 5·0 *in the presence of sucrose on the growth of* 4 *mm sections. The IAA concentration was* 50 *γ/l. in the case of oat coleoptiles and* 10 *γ/l. for sorghum and oat first internodes. The concentration given along the abscissa is that of the* K_2HPO_4 *component; the concentration of citric acid is one half of it.*

coleoptile sections are concerned, but it was feared that lowering the concentration would diminish the buffering capacity to such an extent that certain compounds separated on the chromatograms of plant extracts would change the pH considerably.

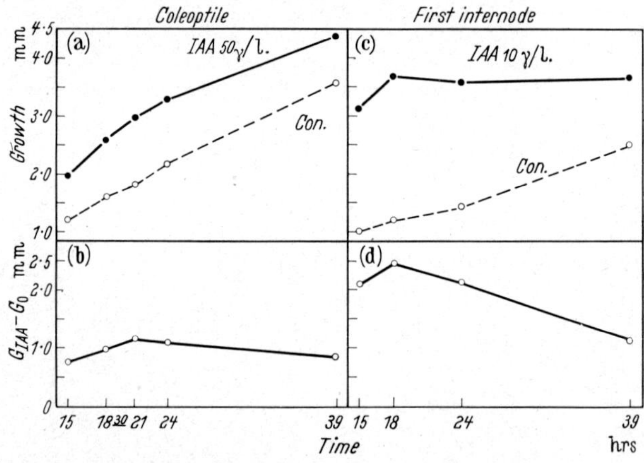

Figure 17. Effect of length of incubation *on growth of oat sections in buffer + sucrose without added IAA (white circles, dotted lines) and with IAA (black circles, solid lines), and on the difference between these growths (curves (b) and (d)). Before time* 0, *the coleoptile sections had been presoaked for* 3·5 *hours in* $MnSO_4 \cdot H_2O$ (1 *mg/l.) and the internode sections for* 1 *hour in glass-distilled water. To exclude the effect of light during the measurements,* 5 *replicates of* 10 *sections each were started at the same time; at each time interval, one of these dishes was measured and discarded.*

The relationship between elongation and time of growth in the solution was also investigated. By starting with a certain number of replicate dishes and measuring one of them at various time intervals, the curves of *Figure 17* were obtained. They show that coleoptiles in 50 γ/l. of IAA (plus buffer and sucrose) continue to grow for a long time after they have been put in the solution, whereas the first internodes in the auxin solution stop growing after 18 hours. A short incubation time has the great advantage of minimizing the danger of bacterial contamination in the solutions. Therefore, an incubation period of about 20 hours was adopted and was found adequate in subsequent work.

We can now attempt to obtain a comparison between the response of coleoptiles and that of internodes to increasing concentrations of IAA. As

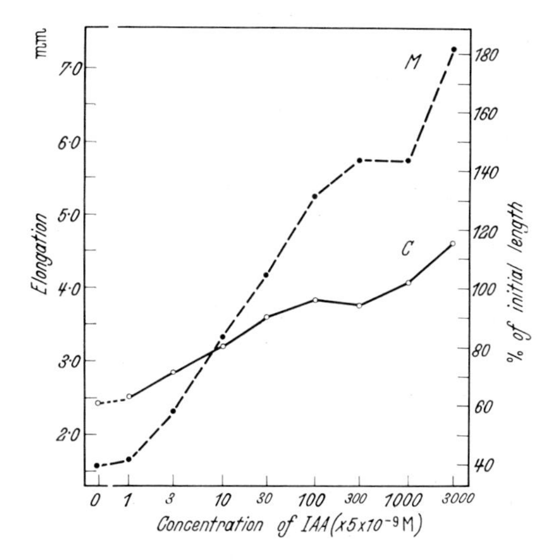

Figure 18. Growth curves of oat coleoptile (C) and first internode (M) sections in buffer + sucrose + Tween 80 (0·1 *per cent) with various concentrations of IAA. The scale on the left ordinate gives the growth in mm over the initial* 4 *mm; the scale on the right ordinate gives it in per cent of the original length. The scale giving the IAA concentration is logarithmic. The coleoptile sections had been floated* 5 *hours on* $MnSO_4 \cdot H_2O$ (1 *mg/l.) and the internode sections* 1 *hour on* H_2O *prior to being put in the auxin solutions.*

Figure 18 shows, the amplitude of the response is larger in internodes than in coleoptiles. A clearly detectable increase over the growth of the controls can be obtained with the first internodes at a concentration of 10^{-8} M IAA, or 1·75 γ/l. The lowest amount of IAA detectable is approximately 2 γ/l. in 0·5 c.c., or one thousandth of a gamma. The lowest amount of IAA detectable in the *Avena* curvature test, for which about 0·3 c.c. of agar has to be used in order to make 12 small blocks, is 10 γ/l. in 0·3 c.c., or 3×10^{-3} γ. The new internode test can thus be 3 times more sensitive than the *Avena* curvature test. Moreover, as shown on *Figure 18*, its proportionality range is wider than that of the curvature test (about a hundred fold, from 2 to 200 γ/l.), higher concentrations giving irregular results. The accuracy, however, is less than that obtained with the *Avena* test in which the curvature is directly proportional to the auxin concentration, whereas here, the elongation is proportional to the logarithm of this.

So far, we have studied the effect of IAA only. But, in extracts of plants there are other auxins, such as IAN or IAE. The effect of these substances on the growth of coleoptiles and internodes of Brighton oats under the conditions defined above (presoaking, buffer, 2 per cent sucrose, 0·5 c.c. volumes, etc., plus 0·1 per cent Tween 80 to help dissolve substances which are poorly soluble in water), can be seen in *Figures 19* and *20*. On the whole,

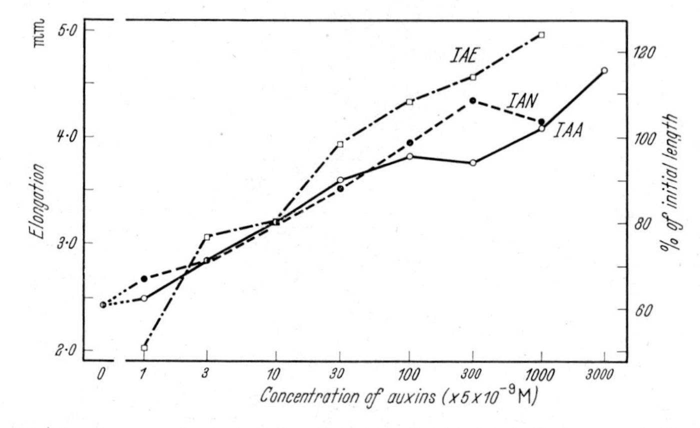

Figure 19. Growth curves of oat coleoptile sections (var. Brighton) in buffer + sucrose + Tween 80 (0·1 *per cent) and various molar concentrations of IAA, IAN, and IAE. Pretreatment of sections and scales are as in Figure 18.*

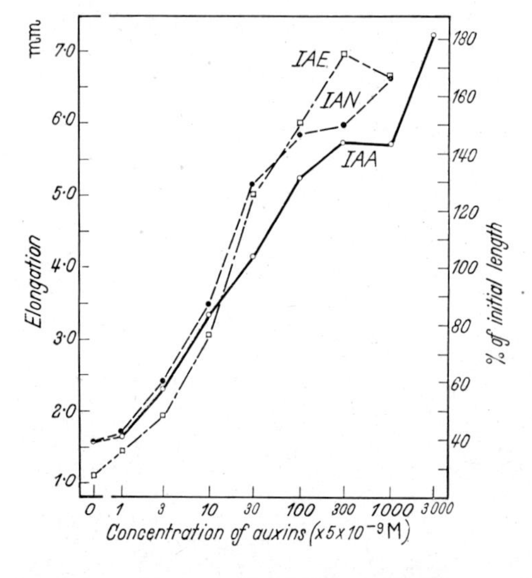

Figure 20. Growth curves of oat internode sections in conditions similar to those of Figure 19.

at equal molar concentrations, the three substances have about the same activity, especially at low concentrations. At higher concentrations, IAN and especially IAE tend to be more active than IAA, but the difference is not a ten-fold one such as can be obtained in the case of IAN with Victory oats under different experimental conditions.

The following examples show how this more sensitive first internode test can be used in the detection of auxins on paper chromatograms. The first example is taken from our work on fruits and concerns the auxins in the seeds of Tokay grapes. The ether extract (2 hours at 0°C) of 3 g (fresh weight) of the seeds of nearly ripe grapes was purified through hexane and

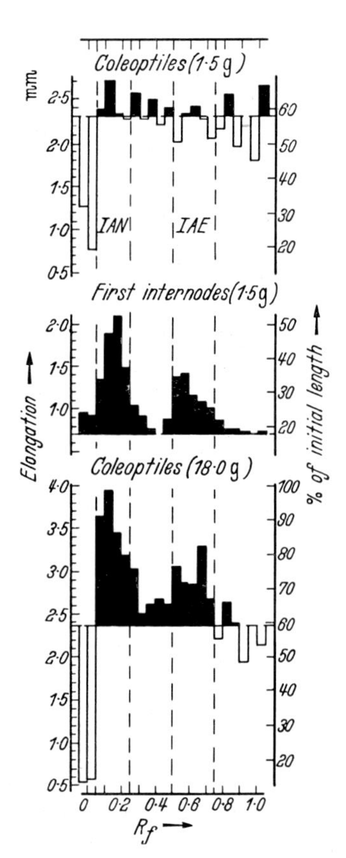

Figure 21. Histograms showing the biological activity of 1 *cm sections of chromatograms when incubated for about* 20 *hours at* 25°*C in the dark with* 0·5 *c.c. buffer+sucrose+Tween* 80 (0·1 *per cent*). *The* first *histogram shows the activity of an ether extract of* 1·5 *g (fresh weight) of seeds from nearly ripe Tokay grapes (after purification through hexane and acetonitrile) when assayed with coleoptiles. The* middle *histogram shows the activity of the same extract when assayed with first internodes. The* bottom *histogram shows the activity obtained with* 18·0 *g (fresh weight) of the same material when assayed with coleoptiles. The chromatograms were run in hexane+water.*

acetonitrile, and divided into two equal portions which were chromatographed in hexane (90)+water (10) (v/v). One chromatogram (corresponding to 1·5 g of grape seeds) was assayed with coleoptile sections, the other with first internodes. The results with coleoptiles (*Figure 21*, top diagram) were inconclusive, except that a marked inhibition was obtained at the initial spot. The first internodes, on the other hand, gave a clear-cut result (middle diagram) with the same amount of grape extract, with a growth peak in the IAN and another in the IAE position. No inhibitor was detected, for first internodes are less sensitive to inhibitors than coleoptiles, their endogenous growth being less. The growth peaks detected with internodes can, however, also be detected with coleoptiles, but it is necessary to extract ten times more material (bottom diagram). Thus, this first example shows that the use of internodes instead of coleoptiles allows one to obtain a good picture of the auxins present in an extract with at least ten times less plant material.

A second example of the use of the internode test can be found in the field of plant tissue cultures. It is well known that certain tissues can be grown *in vitro* if the medium contains an auxin, whereas others can grow on sugar and mineral salts alone (see Gautheret, 1954). It has also been shown that the extract of the tissues which can grow without added auxin in the medium are active in the *Avena* curvature test (Kulescha, 1951), but it is not very clear if the difference in the auxin requirement is due to an increased

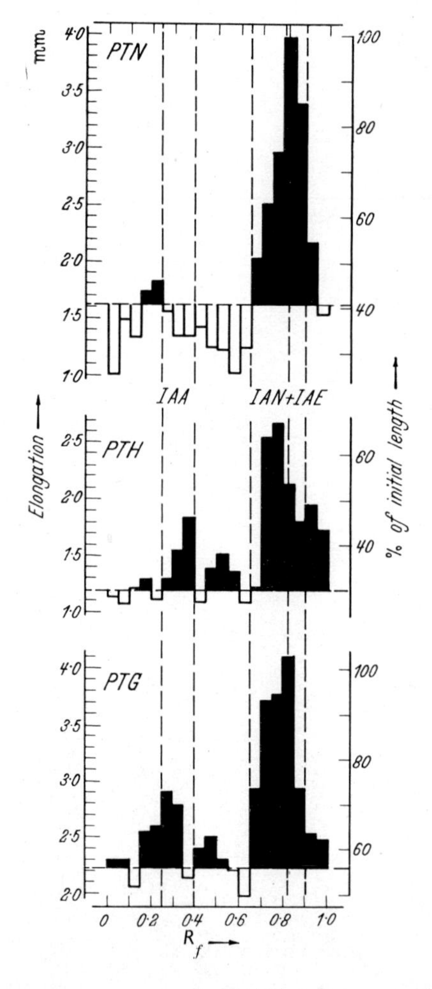

Figure 22. *Histograms showing the biological activity of chromatograms of tissue culture extracts run in* iso*propanol* + *water* (80;20) *and assayed with first internode sections. PTN* = *crude ether extract* (3 *hours at* 0°C) *of* 6 *g* (*fresh weight*) *of* Parthenocissus tricuspidata, *normal tissue, grown* in vitro *for* 4·5 *months on a medium containing sucrose, mineral salts, and IAA* (50 γ/*l.*). *After this length of time, the added IAA had been completely exhausted. PTH* = *crude ether extract* (2·5 *hours at* 0°C) *of* 4·5 *g* (*fresh weight*) *of* Parthenocissus tricuspidata *'habituated' tissue, grown for* 4·5 *months on a medium containing only sucrose and mineral salts. PTG* = *crude ether extract* (2 *hours at* 0°C) *of* 5 *mg* (*fresh weight*) *of* Parthenocissus tricuspidata *crown-gall tissue, grown for* 2·5 *months on a medium containing only sucrose and mineral salts.*

endogenous synthesis (Henderson and Bonner, 1952), or to a reduced destruction (Platt, 1954). Using three types of tissues from the same species, *Parthenocissus tricuspidata* (Sied. and Zucc.) Planch., namely the 'normal' tissue (requiring added auxin), the tissue 'habituated to auxin' (derived from the normal strain, but capable of growing without added auxin), and the crown-gall tissue (growing without added auxin) isolated by Morel (1948), we have studied the auxins which can be detected after a 3-hour ether extraction at 0°C. About 5 mg (fresh weight) of tissue were generally used and the extracts were not purified. The chromatograms were assayed with first internodes. When *iso*propanol (80)+water (20) was used as a solvent, a very interesting picture was obtained (*Figure 22*). The normal tissues, which require added IAA to grow, did not contain appreciable quantities of IAA, whereas a growth peak could be detected at the IAA position in the extracts of the two other types of tissues. On the other hand, a very large growth promotion was detected in the zone of neutral auxins such as IAN and IAE in all cases. Thus the hypothesis was formed, that perhaps the normal tissues manufacture appreciable amounts of a substance like IAN, but are unable to convert it into IAA, whereas the other tissues can.

Other tissues grown *in vitro*, such as the vascular parenchyma of the tuber of Jerusalem artichoke, are incapable of transforming IAN into IAA, as

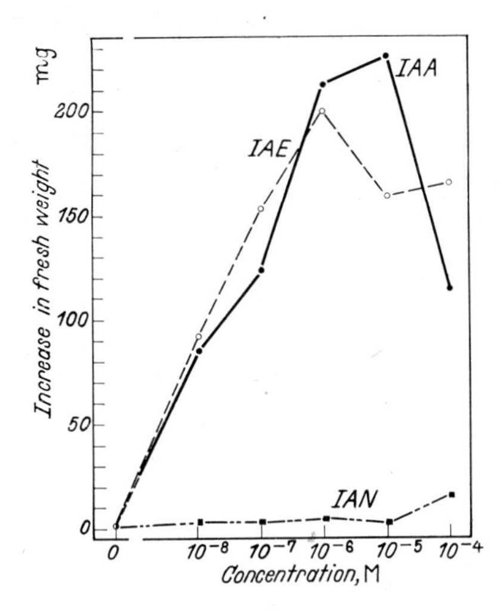

Figure 23. Effect of various concentrations of IAA, IAN, and IAE on the growth of small cylinders of the tuber of Jerusalem artichoke, var. Piédallu 17. *The initial explants each weighed* 22 *mg (fresh weight); they were harvested after* 21 *days of growth on media containing sucrose, mineral salts, and the added auxin (sterilized by filtration). Note that concentrations are given on a molar basis.*

shown in *Figure 23*. Nevertheless, from the results of *Figure 22* alone we cannot be certain that the growth peaks found in all cases in the IAN region are actually due to IAN, for the solvent used cannot separate IAN from other auxins such as IAE. Another set of chromatograms was developed, therefore, in the hexane–water solvent (*Figure 24*), but unfortunately from a different batch of cultures. In all three cases, a marked growth promotion was detected in the IAN region, but in addition, another growth peak in the IAE region was also apparent. Thus, at this point, it is difficult to say if the hypothesis presented above is correct, for IAE is roughly as active, on a molar basis, as IAA in tissue culture, at least in the case of Jerusalem artichoke tissues.

A last example will illustrate even better the usefulness of the first internode assay technique. It concerns the examination of a chromatogram obtained with the extract of about 150 apices of rhizomes of the fern *Adiantum pedatum* dissected under the binocular microscope by Professor Wetmore, so that only the top millimetre or less of tissue was cut off. Altogether, these meristems weighed about 300 mg (fresh weight). Upon dissection, each of them was immediately plunged into a mixture of 2/3 ether and 1/3 absolute ethanol (v/v) kept cold in brine. The total extract was chromatographed in *iso*propanol–ammonia–water (80;10;10) (v/v) and assayed with first

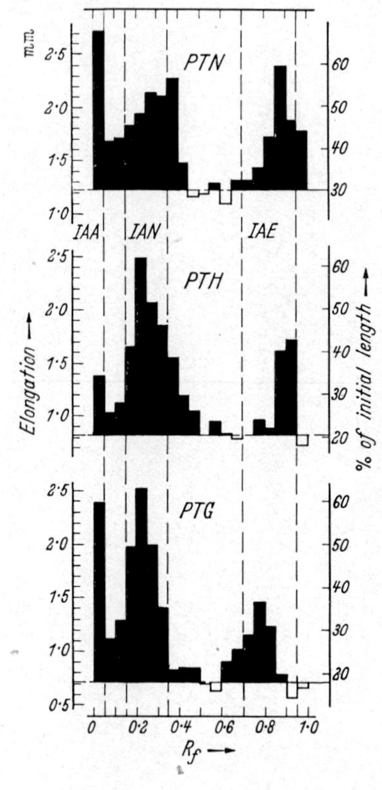

Figure 24. Histograms showing the biological activity of chromatograms of tissue culture extracts run in hexane+water and assayed with first internode sections. PTN = extract with 2/3 ether+1/3 ethanol (3·5 hours at 0°C) of 4·5 g (fresh weight) of Parthenocissus tricuspidata *normal tissue grown* in vitro *for 5 months on a medium containing sucrose, mineral salts, and IAA (50 γ/l.). PTH = extract with 2/3 ether+1/3 ethanol (2 hours at 0°C) of 4 g (fresh weight) of* Parthenocissus tricuspidata *'habituated' tissue, grown for 2 months on a medium containing only sucrose and mineral salts. PTG = extract with 2/3 ether+1/3 ethanol (2 hours at 0°C) of 3·75 g (fresh weight of* Parthenocissus tricuspidata *crown-gall tissue grown for three months on a medium containing only sucrose and mineral salts.*

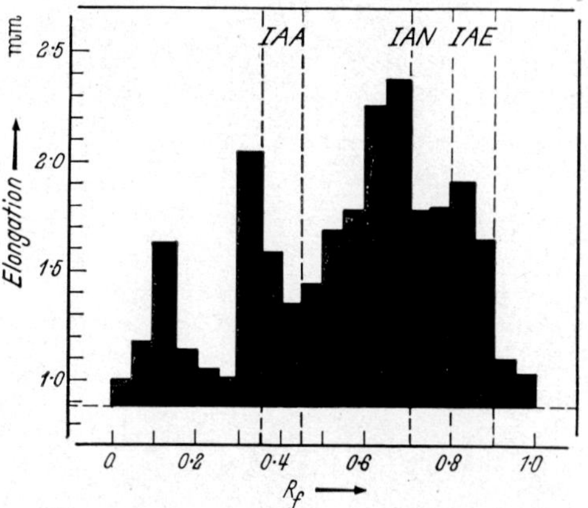

Figure 25. Histogram showing the biological activity of a chromatogram run in iso*propanol+ammonia+water* (80;10;10) *of an extract of* 300 *mg (fresh weight) of apical meristems of* Adiatum pedatum, *assayed with oat first internodes.*

internodes. *Figure 25* gives the results which demonstrate well that a good picture of the auxins present in plant tissues can be obtained with a crude extract, and with as little as 300 mg fresh weight of material.

THE CHEMICAL IDENTIFICATION OF AUXINS ON THE CHROMATOGRAMS

From the results presented so far, it is clear that one can detect numerous biologically active substances on the chromatograms of plant extracts. This, however, does not conclude our task. We want to know also the chemical identity of these substances. This is much more difficult because, for analytical investigations, the chemist generally needs larger quantities of material than the biologist. However, if we have a set of synthetic auxins, we can try to see if some of the natural compounds are identical with them. For example, we always run control chromatograms with synthetic IAA, IAN, and IAE. If a given substance in an extract runs at the exact location of, let us say, synthetic IAN, we have a first presumption that it could be IAN. If the same substance, chromatographed in a totally different solvent, runs again at the location of synthetic IAN, then the presumption is strengthened. This is not enough to identify a compound, however. We have attempted to identify compounds on the paper by determining their absorption spectra.

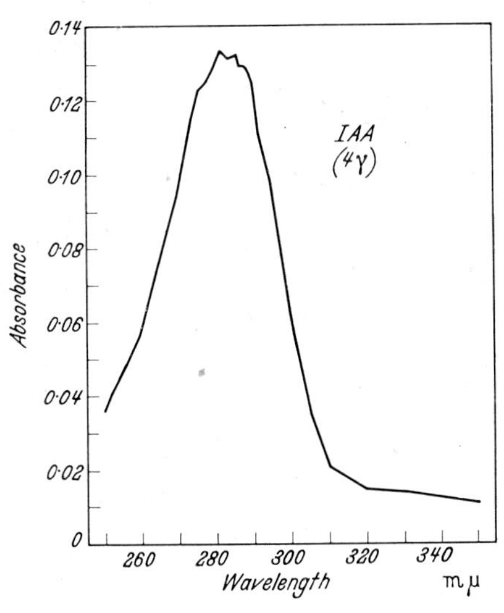

Figure 26. Absorption spectrum in ultra-violet light of 4 γ *of IAA on unwashed Whatman No.* 1 *paper observed in a Beckman spectrophotometer. The determination was made* 20 *minutes after spraying the chromatogram with paraffin oil.*

This can be done in two ways. First, if we know the location of the compound on the paper, we can try to obtain its absorption spectrum in the u.v. This cannot be done readily because the paper absorbs the ultra-violet light. To render the paper translucent, we have simply sprayed it with paraffin oil. The readings, taken 20 minutes after spraying, in a Beckman spectrophotometer, Model DU, gave the absorption curve of *Figure 26* with 4 γ of IAA. The fine details of the IAA absorption curve are lost, of course, owing to the paper (unwashed Whatman No. 1), but the general shape and the region of maximum absorption fit reasonably well with those given by IAA in solution. On the other hand, if we do not know where the substance is, but if it appears as a coloured spot upon spraying with a suitable reagent, then we can determine the absorption spectrum of the coloured product (in visible light, this time) and compare it with that of a synthetic auxin. The curves of *Figure 27* have been obtained in this manner. The coloured product obtained after spraying 1 γ of IAA with the ferric–perchloric acid reagent of Gordon and Weber (1951) (100 c.c. of 35 per cent perchloric acid+270 mg of $FeCl_3 \cdot 6H_2O$+100 c.c. of 95 per cent ethanol) had, on the paper, an absorption maximum at 550 mμ 45 minutes after spraying, while the maximum was at 580 mμ in the case of IAN and around 460 mμ for

IAE. In the latter case, a 'bump' in the curve around 550 mμ probably indicated the presence of IAA, liberated by hydrolysis under the influence of perchloric acid.

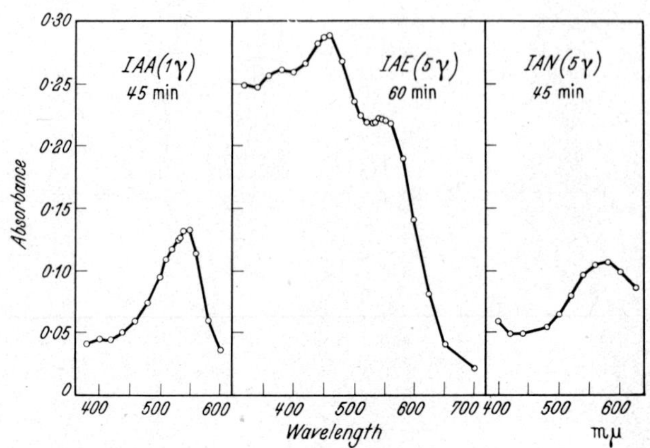

Figure 27. Absorption spectra, in visible light, of the coloured products formed on unwashed Whatman No. 1 paper after spraying the spots of synthetic IAA, IAE, and IAN with the ferric–perchloride reagent described in the text. These spectra change with time.

The absorption maxima can be used to determine quantitatively, and directly on the paper, amounts of IAA, IAN, and IAE as low as 0·5 γ (*Figure 28*). This procedure avoids the losses which occur when one tries to

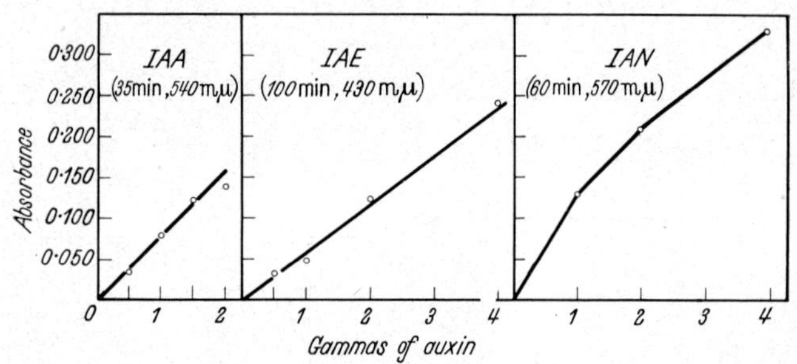

Figure 28. Quantitative relationships between absorbency and amounts of IAA, IAE, and IAN when measured directly on the paper after spraying with the ferric–perchloride reagent.

eluate a substance from the paper. It requires that the spot be kept small and that no interfering substances be present. Crude as these techniques may still be, they nevertheless can assist in the difficult task of identifying chemically the biologically active growth substances.

In conclusion, it is hoped that this study of the extraction, chromatography, bio-assay, and chemical identification techniques may be a help to those engaged in the auxin field.

REFERENCES

Bitancourt, A. A., Schwartz, K., and Dierberger, R. (1954). La Nature des auxines des tumeurs végétales. *C. R. Soc. Biol., Paris,* **148,** 822.

Boysen-Jensen, P. (1941). Quantitative Bestimmung der beschleunigenden Streckungswuchsstoffe in der sauren Fraktion der Ätherextrakte aus höheren Pflanzen. *Planta,* **31,** 653.

BRIGGS, W. R., MOREL, G., STEEVES, T. A., SUSSEX, I. M., and WETMORE, R. H. (1955a). Enzymatic auxin inactivation by extracts of the fern, *Osmunda cinnamomea L. Plant Physiol.* **30,** 143.

BRIGGS, W. R., STEEVES, T. A., SUSSEX, I. M., and WETMORE, R. H. (1955b). Comparison of auxin destruction by tissue extracts and intact tissues of the fern, *Osmunda cinnamomea L. Plant Physiol.* **30,** 148.

GAUTHERET, R. J. (1954). Catalogue des cultures de tissus végétaux. *Rev. gén. Bot.* **61,** 672.

GORDON, S. A., and WEBER, R. P. (1951). Colorimetric estimation of indoleacetic acid. *Plant Physiol.* **26,** 192.

GUSTAFSON, F. (1941). The extraction of growth hormones from plants. *Amer. J. Bot.* **28,** 947.

HENDERSON, J. H. M., and BONNER, J. (1952). Auxin metabolism in normal and crown gall tissue of sunflower. *Amer. J. Bot.* **39,** 444.

JONES, L. R., and RIDDICK, J. A. (1952). Separation of organic insecticides from plant and animal tissues. *Analyt. Chem.* **24,** 569.

KULESCHA, Z. (1951). Recherches sur l'élaboration de substance de croissance par les tissus végétaux. Thesis, Paris.

LARSEN, P. (1955). On the separation of acidic and non-acidic auxins. *Physiol. Plant.* **8,** 343.

MOREL, G. (1948). Recherches sur la culture associée de parasites obligatoires et de tissus végétaux. *Ann. Épiphyt. Sér. Path. Vég.* **14** (N.S.), 123.

NITSCH, J. P. (1955). Free auxins and free tryptophane in the strawberry. *Plant Physiol.* **30,** 33.

NITSCH, J. P., and NITSCH, C. (1955). The separation of natural plant growth substances by paper chromatography. *Beitr. Biol. Pfl.* **31,** 387.

OVERBEEK, J. VAN, VAZQUEZ, E. S. DE, and GORDON, S. A. (1947). Free and bound auxin in the vegetative pineapple plant. *Amer. J. Bot.* **34,** 266.

PLATT, R. S., Jr. (1954). The inactivation of auxin in normal and tumorous tissues. *Année biol.* **30,** 349.

SCHNEIDER, C. L. (1938). The interdependence of auxin and sugar for growth. *Amer. J. Bot.* **25,** 258.

SCHNEIDER, C. L. (1941). The effect of red light on growth of the *Avena* seedling with special reference to the first internode. *Amer. J. Bot.* **28,** 878.

SEN, S. P., and LEOPOLD, A. C. (1954). Paper chromatography of plant growth regulators and allied compounds. *Physiol. Plant.* **7,** 98.

STEEVES, T. A., MOREL, G., and WETMORE, R. H. (1953). A technique for preventing inactivation at the cut surface in auxin diffusion studies. *Amer. J. Bot.* **40,** 534.

STOWE, B. B., and THIMANN, K. V. (1954). The paper chromatography of indole compounds and some indole containing auxins of plant tissues. *Arch. Biochem. Biophys.* **51,** 499.

TANG, Y. W., and BONNER, J. (1947). The enzymatic inactivation of indoleacetic acid. I. Some characteristics of the enzyme contained in pea seedlings. *Arch. Biochem.* **13,** 11.

THIMANN, K. V., and SKOOG, F. (1940). The extraction of auxin from plant tissues. *Amer. J. Bot.* **27,** 951.

THIMANN, K. V., SKOOG, F., and BYER, A. C. (1942). The extraction of auxin from plant tissues. II. *Amer. J. Bot.* **29,** 598.

WAGENKNECHT, A. C., and BURRIS, R. H. (1950). Indoleacetic acid inactivating enzymes from bean roots and pea seedlings. *Arch. Biochem.* **25,** 30.

WEIJ, H. G. VAN DER (1932). Der Mechanismus des Wuchsstofftransportes. *Rec. Trav. bot. néerl.* **29,** 379.

WILDMAN, S. G., and MUIR, R. M. (1949). Observations on the mechanism of auxin formation in plant tissues. *Plant Physiol.* **24,** 84.

THE DISTRIBUTION OF NATURAL HORMONES IN GERMINATING SEEDS AND SEEDLING PLANTS†

PHYLLIS M. CARTWRIGHT‡, J. T. SYKES, and R. L. WAIN
Wye College, University of London

MANY investigators have reported on the occurrence of auxins and inhibitors in seeds. Germination inhibitors or 'blastocholines' are of widespread occurrence in fruits and seeds, and seem to be important in those which require special environmental conditions for germination.

The purpose of the present investigation was to identify the natural auxins and inhibitors in maize and pea seeds and to follow their changes in concentration and distribution during germination and subsequent seedling growth. It was hoped that by using paper chromatography all the active components could be isolated and their concentrations estimated by biological and perhaps by chemical methods. Ether extracts were made from seeds at different stages of germination and these extracts were separated into acid and non-acid fractions by a method developed from that of Boysen-Jensen (1941). The components of the acid fraction were isolated by paper chromatography and identified by biological assay and chemical colour reactions. The non-acid fractions, prepared by a variety of methods, always contained large amounts of oily substances which interfered with the chromatography. Those examined gave unsatisfactory results and little biological activity was found, though in each case all regions of the paper were assayed.

The importance of obtaining a comprehensive picture of hormone and inhibitor status in plant tissues is, of course, recognized, and has been stressed by a number of workers. However, the quantitative estimation of such activity in the neutral fraction of tissue extracts has not been successfully accomplished here or elsewhere. Because of these limitations, only the results from acid fractions will be considered in this paper, and in adopting this procedure the work is in line with similar investigations on natural auxins carried out by other workers. It will be realized that any hormones of a non-acidic nature, such as indolylacetonitrile, would be present mainly in the non-acid fractions.

In carrying out the experiments, large numbers of seeds were germinated under uniform conditions, samples taken at suitable intervals of time, and their auxin and inhibitor content estimated. For the extraction procedure, the seeds were cut into slices and extracted at 2°C with 3 changes of wet peroxide-free ether for a total period of 24 hours. It is agreed with other workers that this does not give a maximum yield of auxin, and with maize, for example, further small amounts have been obtained by prolonged extractions for 2 weeks. However, since the largest part of the auxin is extracted in the first 24 hours, it was decided to limit the analysis to this fraction in the first instance. For separation of acidic and non-acidic fractions, a technique

† This paper was read at the conference by Phyllis M. Cartwright.

‡ Present address: Department of Agricultural Botany, University of Reading.

developed from that of Boysen-Jensen (1941) and similar to that of Bennet-Clark and Kefford (1953) was used. The acidic components were taken out from the ether extract by shaking repeatedly with 1 per cent sodium bicarbonate solution. The combined aqueous layers were titrated to pH 4 with N sulphuric acid and re-extracted with ether. This ether extract was dried over sodium sulphate in a refrigerator overnight and then concentrated to small bulk in a water bath not exceeding 45°C. The concentrated acid fraction so obtained was spotted on to the starting line of a Whatman No. 1 chromatogram paper, usually in 3 small spots about half an inch apart.

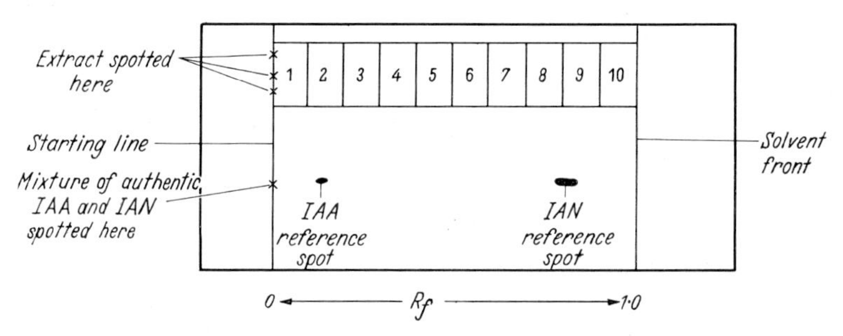

Figure. 1. Division of chromatogram for biological assay (see text).

The chromatograms were developed in the descending manner in aqueous butanol/ammonia solvent (200 ml *n*-butanol : 6 ml 0·880 ammonia : 36 ml water) at a controlled temperature of 20°C for about 14 hours, by which time the solvent front had travelled about 10 inches. The paper was then removed from the tank and quickly dried by hanging in a fume cupboard. It was then cut transversely into 10 strips of equal size, representing R_f values of 0–0·1, 0·1–0·2, etc. These will be referred to as strip 1, strip 2, etc. (see *Figure 1*).

The biological activity of these strips was determined by a special modification of the wheat cylinder test of Smith, Wain, and Wightman (1952). Each chromatogram strip was immersed in 3 ml 1 per cent sucrose solution in a small glass dish. Ten 5 mm segments from wheat coleoptiles, threaded on glass capillaries, were floated on top of the solution and the dishes placed in a water-saturated atmosphere at 25°C. The lengths of the coleoptile segments were measured after incubation for 24 hours.

In all experiments a mixture of known indole compounds was run simultaneously as authentic spots and their positions were detected by spraying with Ehrlich reagent. Under these conditions IAA has R_f 0·17 and runs in strip 2 of the chromatogram, and IAN has R_f 0·82 and runs mainly in strips 8 and 9.

EXPERIMENTAL RESULTS

The results from an experiment in which a solution containing 1 mg IAA and 1 mg IAN was separated into acid and non-acid fractions, both of which were assayed by the methods described above, are shown in *Figure 2*. All the IAA activity is in strip 2 of the chromatogram. The IAN activity is divided between the fractions, the larger part being in the non-acid fraction. Since equal amounts were taken, it is clear that IAN is several times as active as IAA in this particular test.

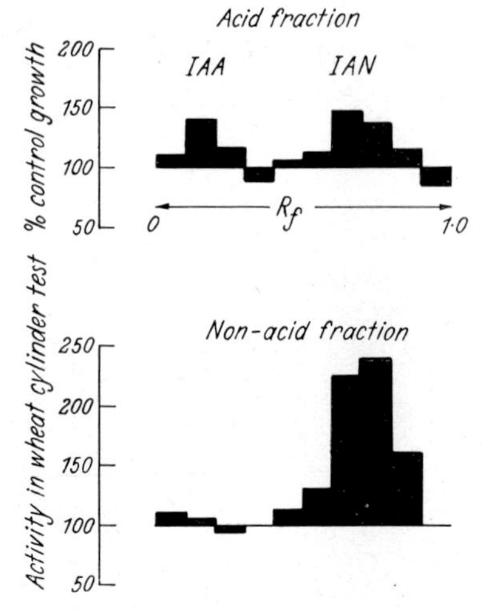

Figure 2. Biological assay of chromatograms of acid and non-acid fractions from a solution containing 1 μg IAA and 1 μg IAN.

Experiments with maize

A preliminary experiment was carried out with maize, variety 'White Horse Tooth.' Samples of 200 seeds were extracted and assayed at intervals of 12 hours during 60 hours germination at 25°C in the dark. The results are presented in *Figure 3.* It can be seen that most of the auxin extracted by this

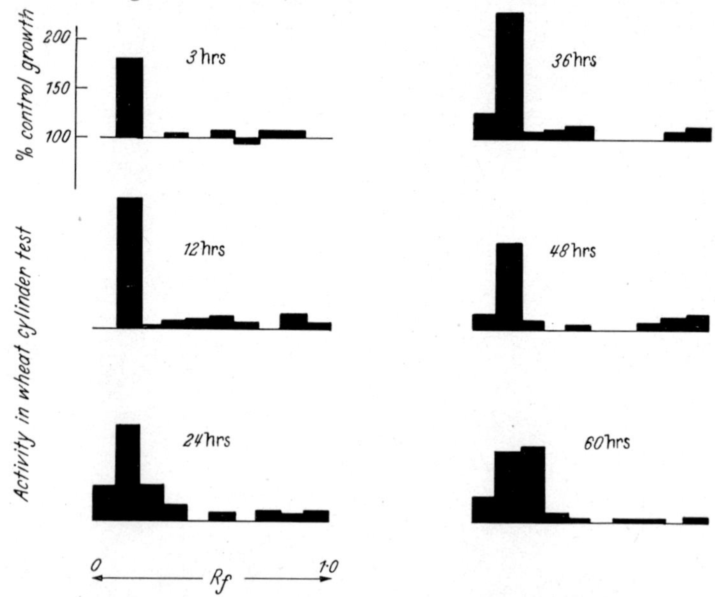

Figure 3. 'White Horse Tooth' maize. Preliminary experiment.

procedure is in strip 2 of the chromatogram and it has been confirmed that this is indolylacetic acid by colour reactions and by measurements of R_f in different solvents. It seems that the amount of IAA extracted by this procedure increases rapidly in the early stages of germination, reaches a maximum after about 24 hours, and then begins to decrease.

Further experiments were carried out in order to relate biological activity of IAA to the actual amounts present in the extracts. Although this auxin is concentrated mainly in strip 2 of the chromatogram, it occasionally spreads into strip 1 and strip 3. In these experiments, therefore, the chromatograms were divided up in a different manner. The zone of R_f 0–0·3 was cut longitudinally into 3 similar strips, which were assayed separately, and the IAA content of the sample was calculated from their mean value. By using known amounts of IAA it was possible to construct a calibration graph in which the wheat cylinder extension growth, expressed as a percentage of the control growth, was shown to give a linear relationship with the log of the IAA concentration.

Samples of germinating maize grains were taken at intervals of 12 hours as in the preliminary experiment and biological assays of IAA were carried out on extracts from different numbers of seeds at each sampling time. The results of these experiments are presented in *Table 1* and *Figure 4*. These show

Table 1

Extracts from whole seeds

Time of germination, hours	*Independent estimates of IAA content per* 100 *seeds,* γ	*Mean*	*Standard error*	95% *confidence limits of real mean*
3	18, 10, 30, 48, 32	27	6·5	27±17·9
12	75, 45, 32, 49, 63	53	7·4	53±19·8
24	233, 122, 352, 228, 159, 154	223	33·6	223±76·9
36	221, 185, 339, 336, 333, 300, 345	294	27·6	294±59·1
48	238, 107, 96, 128	142	33·8	142±110·7

Changes in IAA content of seeds during germination

Time interval, hours	*Change in IAA content,* γ *per* 100 *seeds*	*Least significant difference, to* 5%
3–12	+26	22·9
12–24	+170	77·5
24–36	+71†	127·0
36–48	−151	100·1

† Not significant.

a rapid increase in the IAA content of the seed during the first 24 hours of germination. The mean values obtained for 24 and 36 hour extracts are not significantly different but a significant decrease is indicated between 36 and 48 hours.

The results so far reported deal with total changes in the whole seed. An experiment was next carried out in order to follow changes in the embryo and endosperm separately. At each sampling time, the seeds were separated into

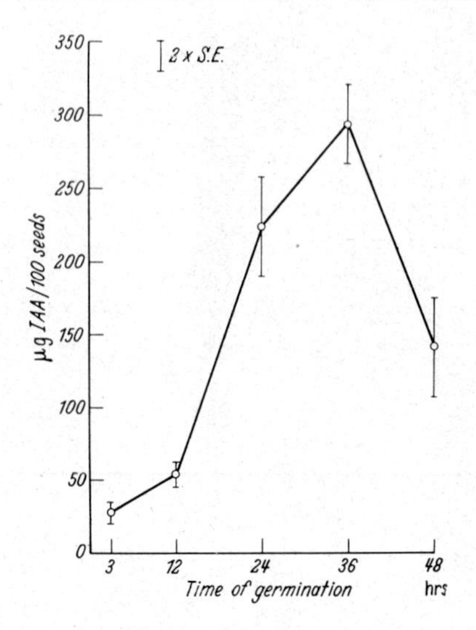

Figure 4. IAA content of maize grains at different stages of germination.

embryo (including scutellum) and endosperm and the IAA contents determined independently. The results are summarized in *Table 2.* It is clear that the estimated IAA contents of the endosperm extracts are of the same order as those of the whole seed extracts, and there is practically no IAA in the endosperm and scutellum at any stage of germination.

Table 2

Extracts from separated endosperms and embryos

(*a*) *Endosperms*

Time of germination, hours	*Independent estimates of IAA content, γ per* 100 *endosperms*	*Mean*
12	18, 22	
15	95, 232, 58, 49	108
24	342, 657, 377, 197, 308, 123	334
36	143, 285, 462, 624, 300	363
48	84, 154, 50, 52, 360	140

(*b*) *Embryos + scutellums*

Time of germination, hours	*Independent estimates of IAA content, γ per* 100 *embryos + scutellums*
0	10, 2, 0, 0
12	0, 13
15	0, 24, 7, 4
24	22, 7
36	0, 5, 0, 6
48	0, 5, 7, 0

In chromatograms sprayed with Ehrlich reagent, an intense blue spot due to IAA always developed in strip 2. Immediately behind this there were often two more faint and diffuse spots, a pinkish region of R_f approx. 0·14 and a greenish blue one of R_f 0·10. It was difficult to separate these completely from the IAA but our results would suggest that they were either inactive or only weakly active in the wheat cylinder test.

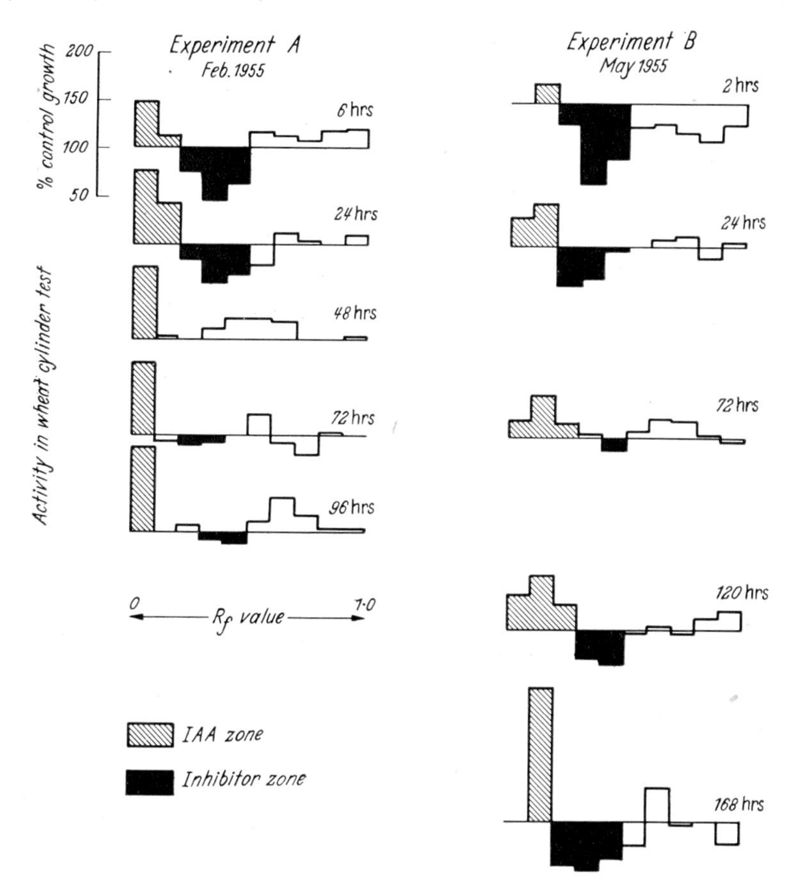

Figure 5. Biological assay of hormones and inhibitors in extracts from germinating peas, var. Alaska. (Acid fractions.)

Experiments with peas

Similar experiments have been carried out with pea seeds—a typical non-endospermic dicotyledon. In these experiments the variety 'Alaska' was used and the methods were similar to those described for maize. The results of two experiments with peas are presented in *Figure 5.*

From the results the following observations can be made:

(*a*) At all stages the IAA content is much lower than in maize. In the early stages of germination it is extremely low and it increases slowly as germination proceeds.

(*b*) There is at the earlier sampling times an inhibitor, an acidic substance with R_f 0·3–0·4, whose concentration decreases during the first 3 days of germination. None was detected in the 72- and 96-hour extracts. In the next few days of seedling growth, however, this inhibitor re-appears.

(*c*) In the 7-day-old etiolated pea seedling an appreciable amount of IAA has been built up, and there is also a significant concentration of inhibitor.

(*d*) In many instances, there is some stimulatory activity in strips 7 and 8 of the chromatogram. This, however, does not appear consistently and it cannot with certainty be attributed to any known hormone.

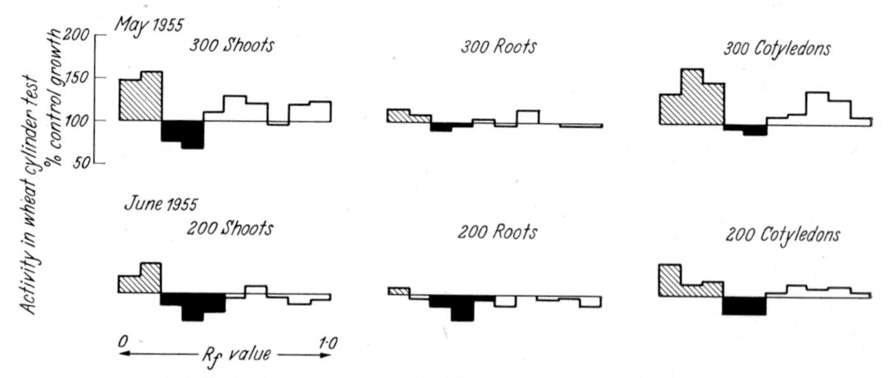

Figure 6. Distribution of hormones and inhibitors in 8-day-old etiolated pea seedlings.

A series of six experiments with peas indicated similar changes in auxin and inhibitor content during germination. There was, however, a considerable variability in the amounts of activity on different occasions and no attempt has been made to relate the results to absolute amounts of IAA present at each sampling time.

The results of two experiments carried out to show the distribution of auxin and inhibitor in 8-day-old etiolated seedlings are presented in *Figure 6*. The shoots contain inhibitor and a relatively large amount of IAA. In the root extracts there is a lower auxin and inhibitor activity. Again, calculation of the absolute amounts of IAA in the tissues has not been attempted, but the histograms suggest that in these etiolated seedlings the shoot contains of the order of 10 times as much IAA as the root system. Since the fresh weight of the shoot is only about 25 per cent greater than that of the root, a higher internal IAA concentration is indicated. In the cotyledons there is stimulatory activity in the 'IAA zone' and in strips 7 and 8 of the chromatogram.

Chromatograms similar to those used for biological assay were sprayed with Ehrlich reagent and besides the blue spot due to IAA a pink spot of R_f 0·1 developed which has the same R_f and colour reactions as indole-3-carboxylic acid. The possible significance of this is discussed in other papers of this Symposium (Seeley *et al.*, 1956; Fawcett *et al.*, 1956).

From these investigations on germinating peas it would seem that the disappearance of an inhibitor during the early stages of germination may be of physiological significance. This inhibitor has completely disappeared after 48 hours when the radicles have emerged. The auxin content, however, increases very slowly during germination proper and only builds up to an appreciable concentration in the shoot of the young seedling. It might therefore be tentatively suggested that auxin has little physiological significance during the actual germination process but may be important in the subsequent growth of the seedling shoot.

In maize, the auxin content of the seed is considerably higher, and there is a rapid increase in extractable auxin during the first 12 hours of germination. After about 48 hours when the radicles emerge, the auxin content is decreasing. Our results, however, show that these changes are in the endosperm only and that there is practically no IAA in the embryo and scutellum at any stage of germination. The maize experiments provide no evidence of a growth inhibitor, although such a substance may be present in the non-acid fraction. Voss (1939) and Pohl and Tegethoff (1949) reported the presence of an 'auxin inactivator' in the scutellum of maize, and since in this investigation little auxin was found in the scutellum and embryo, it is possible that indolylacetic acid moving out of the endosperm into the scutellum is immediately inactivated by the scutellum 'Hemmstoff.' Skoog (1937) and Voss (1939) obtained evidence that auxin precursor or inactivated auxin was translocated to the coleoptile tip and was there re-converted to the auxin which controls extension growth in the coleoptile.

On the basis of all results reported in this paper, it would seem justified to suggest, as a general hypothesis, that auxin extracted from seeds by the procedure we have adopted is not of physiological importance during germination. The growth of the seedling shoot, however, is clearly associated with auxin production.

REFERENCES

Bennet-Clark, T. A., and Kefford, N. P. (1953). Chromatography of the growth substances in plant extracts. *Nature*, **171,** 645.

Boysen-Jensen, P. (1941). Quantitative Bestimmung der beschleunigenden Streckungswuchsstoffe in der sauren Fraktion der Ätherextrakte aus höheren Pflanzen. *Planta*, **31,** 653.

Fawcett, C. H., Taylor, H. F., Wain, R. L., and Wightman, F. (1956). The degradation of certain phenoxy acids, amides, and nitriles within plant tissues. This volume, p. 187.

Pohl, R., and Tegethoff, B. (1949). Der Hemmstoff des Maisscutellums—ein Wuchsstoffinaktivator. *Naturwissenschaften*, **36,** 319.

Seeley, R. C., Fawcett, C. H., Wain, R. L., and Wightman, F. (1956). Chromatographic investigations on the metabolism of certain indole derivatives in plant tissues. This volume, p. 234.

Skoog, F. (1937). A deseeded *Avena* test method for small amounts of auxin and auxin precursors. *J. gen. Physiol.* **20,** 311.

Smith, M. S., Wain, R. L., and Wightman, F. (1952). Studies on plant growth regulating substances. V. Steric factors in relation to mode of action of certain aryloxyalkylcarboxylic acids. *Ann. appl. Biol.* **39,** 295.

Voss, H. (1939). Nachweis des inaktiven Wuchsstoffes, eines Wuchsstoffantagoniste und deren Wachsumsregulatorische. *Planta*, **30,** 261.

HORMONES AND HORMONE PRECURSORS IN LEAVES, ROOTS, AND SEEDS†

JOYCE A. BENTLEY,‡ S. HOUSLEY, and G. BRITTON
Department of Botany, Manchester University

THIS work is concerned with the naturally occurring hormones and their precursors in several plant tissues. The substances studied have been located in the main by paper chromatography of plant extracts and bio-assay of the separated fractions for physiological activity. So far, workers have concerned themselves almost entirely with the acid ether-soluble constituents of plant extracts, and evidence has accumulated that there are several active substances in this fraction. 3-Indolylacetic acid (IAA), 3-indolylacetonitrile (IAN), 3-indolylpyruvic acid (IPyA), accelerator-α, and an inhibitor have all been demonstrated or postulated by various workers on the evidence of zones of activity obtained at various R_f's on paper chromatograms run under specified conditions.

In this paper other fractions of plant extracts, in particular the aqueous, non-ether-soluble fraction, have been examined and have led to evidence of other active substances and hormone precursors. The presence of IAN in an acid ether fraction, reported in particular by Bennet-Clark and Kefford (1953) in their extracts of *Aegopodium* rhizomes and potato tubers, was of interest to us, since we have obtained evidence of a neutral, ether-soluble substance with R_f and chromogenic reactions of the nitrile being released from a water-soluble precursor. An acidic water-soluble precursor of a neutral growth substance in cabbage has already been reported by Bonde (1953). In view of these reports it was decided to examine the aqueous fractions of our extracts.

In addition, work on synthetic IPyA led us to reorganize our views on the role of this substance as a plant hormone and the possibility of its being identical with Bennet-Clark's accelerator-α.

TECHNIQUES

All commercially-supplied chemicals were of the purest grade obtainable. Anaesthetic ether was rendered and maintained peroxide-free by standing over sodium wire in darkness at 0°C. Glass-distilled water was used for preparing all solutions. Oats (var. Victory) of the 1951 harvest were used in the bio-assays.

Extraction techniques

(*a*) *Cabbage*—A single plant was collected in early October 1953, the inner etiolated leaves frozen and ground, and extracted with 95 per cent ethyl alcohol acidified to pH 3·2 with sulphuric acid for 40 hours at −10°C. The pH of the tissue-free extract was raised to 5 with barium hydroxide, the extract filtered, and the alcohol removed at 35°C by distillation under

† This paper was read at the conference by Joyce A. Bentley.
‡ Present address: Marine Laboratory, Torry, Aberdeen.

reduced pressure. The aqueous extract remaining was extracted with ether and the ethereal solution separated into acid and neutral fractions with sodium bicarbonate. Some of the aqueous fraction was distilled under reduced pressure until a thick syrup remained.

(*b*) *Excised and seedling roots of tomato* (*var. Best-of-All*)—Excised roots were obtained by growth of 10 mm clonal tips, derived from clonal sector cultures, in a modified White's medium for 10–12 days at 27°C. The method of culture has been described by Street (1954). The average yield of material was 18 g fresh weight per 100 roots.

Seedling roots were grown in sand in a greenhouse, watered daily with the culture medium (less sucrose, vitamins, and $Fe_2(SO_4)_3$), and harvested after 4–5 weeks. Harvested roots were stored at −15°C until sufficient quantities had been collected.

The extraction technique was essentially the same as for the cabbage, except that sometimes, where stated, ether was used for extraction instead of alcohol.

(*c*) *Maize roots and seeds*—Seed of maize (var. Great White Horse Tooth) was germinated in sand and the roots and seeds collected when the coleoptiles were approximately 2 cm long. The material was well washed, frozen, and extracted with ether.

Paper chromatography technique

The descending method was used with Whatman No. 1 papers. Loading was usually in the form of a strip, and controls of IAA and IAN (approx. 40 μg) were run simultaneously with each extract. Chromatograms were developed in the dark at room temperature without prior equilibration, in either 4 vol. *iso*propanol : 1 vol. 0·15 N ammonia, or *n*-butanol saturated with 1·5 N ammonia. They were developed for about 20 hours, by which time the solvent front normally reached a distance of 20–30 cm, dried in a current of air at room temperature for 20 min and examined in filtered u.v. light (2537 Å transmitted) for fluorescence. Chromatograms were usually divided for bio-assay according to the fluorescence pattern. Each division was eluted in 12 ml water. Chromatographic solvents were removed *in vacuo* with air drawn through the solution at a bath temperature of 35–40°C.

Spray reagents

Chromogenic reactions were developed by drying the papers at 35°C, and then heating at 50–60°C for 1–5 min. The following sprays were used: ferric chloride/perchloric acid, 2 ml 0·05M $FeCl_3$ plus 100 ml 5 per cent $HClO_4$; nitrous/nitric acid, 1 g KNO_2 in 200 ml HNO_3 (sp. gr. 1·42 diluted ×10); *p*-dimethylaminobenzaldehyde, 2 g in a mixture of 20 ml HCl (sp. gr. 1·18) and 80 ml absolute ethanol.

Bio-assay techniques

The method of *Avena* straight-growth assay has been reported (Bentley, 1950), and the technique described in detail (Bentley and Housley, 1954). 10 mm sections were cut from coleoptiles of either 1·4–1·6 cm, 1·6–1·8 cm, or 1·8–2·0 cm, floated on 10 ml test solution in 2 in. Petri dishes, and their length measured after approximately 17 hours. Ten replicates per treatment were used except when otherwise stated.

The cress assay method was a modification of that used by Moewus (1949a and b). Seeds, placed 1 cm apart, were germinated in Petri dishes lined with wet filter paper. 24–28 hours later, 6 seedlings with roots of 5 mm length were placed into a 2 in. Petri dish containing 10 ml 1·5 per cent agar into which the test solution had been previously incorporated. Approximately 17 hours later the root lengths were determined to the nearest mm by measuring on graph paper after removal from the agar medium. The assay was carried out at 27°C in phototropically-inactive light, and subsequent root growth was at 25°C in the dark.

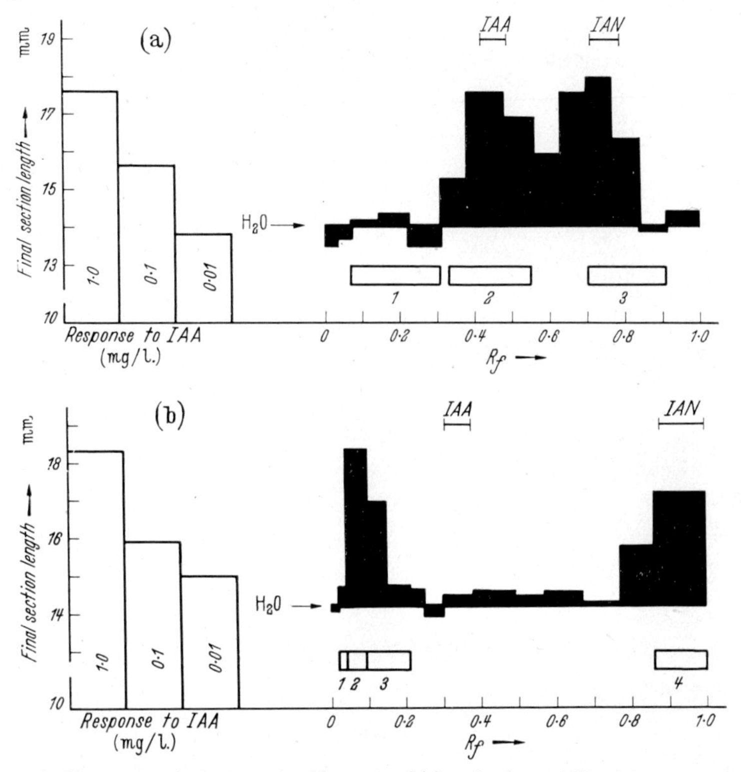

Figure 1. Chromatography in ammoniacal iso*propanol (a) and* n-*butanol (b) of the aqueous fraction of an extract of cabbage leaves. U.v. fluorescence on the chromatograms is shown below. (a) Zone* 1 *yellow pigment on blue background,* 2 *blue with faint purple,* 3 *bluish-purple. (b) Zone* 1 *light blue,* 2 *purple,* 3 *bluish-purple,* 4 *bluish-purple.*

RESULTS

Aqueous fraction of cabbage

Chromatography of the syrup (approximately 50 mg) obtained from distillation of the aqueous fraction was carried out initially in *iso*propanol/ammonia; a typical result is shown in *Figure 1(a)*. Peaks of growth promotion were obtained at the IAA and IAN zones; chromogenic sprays gave shades of yellow with ferric chloride/perchloric acid and with nitrous/nitric acid between R_f 0·1 and 0·5. Near the IAN region nitrous/nitric acid produced a pale mauve colour resembling that of IAN at low concentration.

The demonstration of a growth promoter in the IAA zone but not giving a red chromogenic reaction typical of IAA, prompted the examination of the syrup in another solvent system, *n*-butanol/ammonia. The result (*Figure 1*(*b*)) differed from that shown in *Figure 1*(*a*) in that the first peak of activity no longer corresponded to IAA though activity again occurred in the IAN zone. Results with chromogenic sprays gave yellow at R_f 0–0·2 and mauve at IAN.

These results, in which the pattern of growth promotion varied with the solvent system used, suggested that the growth-active zones at IAA (*Figure 1*(*a*)) and at the starting line (*Figure 1*(*b*)) should be examined further to see whether they are identical.

Two 28 cm chromatograms were each loaded with 200 mg syrup and chromatographed in *iso*propanol/ammonia. U.v.-fluorescent zones corresponding to 1 and 2 in *Figure 1*(*a*) were removed and eluted at 5°C with 4 ml water. 0·75 ml of this eluate was pipetted on each of two papers, and chromatographed in ammoniacal *iso*propanol or *n*-butanol (*Figures* 2(*a*) and (*b*)). The histogram of the *iso*propanol chromatogram is essentially the same as that of *Figure 1*(*a*), while that in *n*-butanol differs but slightly from that of *Figure 1*(*b*). In *Figure 2*(*b*), the chromatogram division at R_f 0–0·08 was according to u.v. fluoresence, but it was too uneven to warrant the conclusion that two growth promoters had been separated. Before discussing this experiment further, data of the complementary experiment are presented.

Two chromatogram papers were prepared as in the preceding experiment and chromatographed in *n*-butanol/ammonia. Two zones were removed, viz., the area of initial loading and the following zone to R_f 0·18 (corresponding to u.v.-fluorescent zones 1–3 in *Figure 1*(*b*)). These were eluted with 1 ml and 2 ml water respectively. 0·4 ml of each eluate was rechromatographed in ammoniacal *iso*propanol or *n*-butanol. The histogram of the starting line eluate run in *iso*propanol/ammonia (*Figure 2*(*c*)) resembles *Figure 1*(*a*), except for differences in relative position of IAN and the growth promoter near the solvent front. In *n*-butanol/ammonia (*Figure 2*(*d*)) the histogram is basically similar to *Figure 1*(*b*), but there is an ill-defined peak at R_f 0·8 and continuous tailing behind it. It is probable that growth promotion at R_f 0·06–0·19 does not actually overlap the IAA control and that division of the chromatogram has caused this effect.

Histograms of the remaining eluate differ slightly from those described above. Chromatography in *iso*propanol/ammonia (*Figure 2*(*e*)) gave an active region at R_f 0·12–0·25, which may correspond with the R_f 0–0·02 zone on the *n*-butanol chromatogram (*Figure 2*(*f*)). Uneven chromatogram division, however, prevents one from stating this with certainty.

The results shown in *Figures 2*(*a*)–(*f*) indicate that the substance at the IAA zone on *iso*propanol chromatograms is identical with that near the starting line on *n*-butanol chromatograms. Thus, differences in relative position of this substance and IAA result from chromatographic factors, and not from molecular change under the influence of these different solvent systems. From *Figures 1*(*a*) and (*b*), it is clear that chromatography in *n*-butanol gives better separation of active zones, which in this solvent may be complete. One may deduce from *Figures 2*(*c*)–(*f*) that promotion at the IAN zone originates from a precursor on and near the starting line of *n*-butanol chromatograms; in *iso*propanol this precursor occurs at the IAA zone and/or in a zone of smaller R_f range (see *Figures 2*(*a*) and (*b*)).

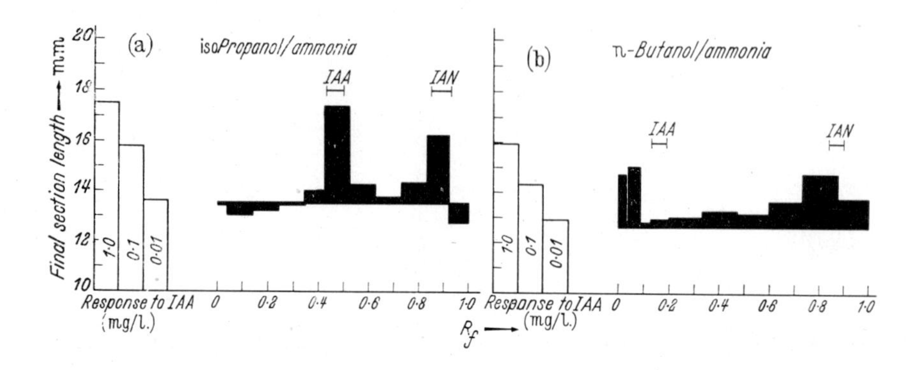

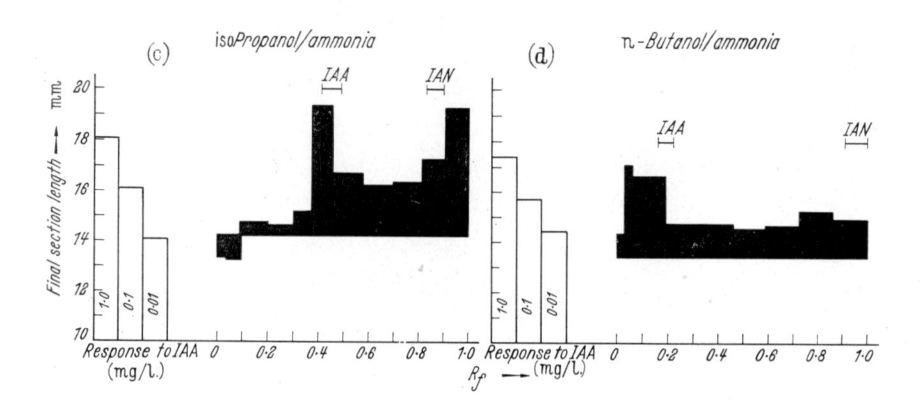

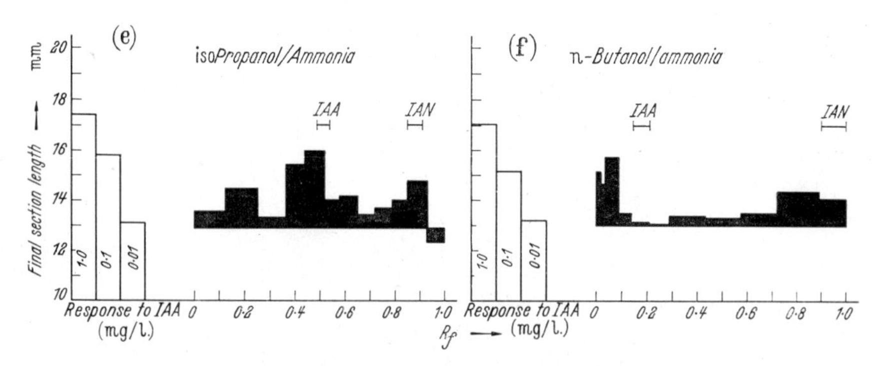

Figure 2. Chromatography of the aqueous fraction of an extract of cabbage leaves. (a), (b) Chromatography was first carried out in ammoniacal iso*propanol. The u.v.-fluorescent zones corresponding to* 1 *and* 2 *in Figure* 1(*a*) *were eluted with water and rechromatographed in ammoniacal* iso*propanol (a) and* n-*butanol (b). (c)–(f) Chromatography was first carried out in ammoniacal* n-*butanol. The starting line was eluted in water and rechromatographed in ammoniacal* iso*propanol (c) and* n-*butanol (d). Following this zone, u.v.-fluorescent zones corresponding to* 2 *and* 3 *in Figure 1(b) were treated in a similar manner ((e) and (f) respectively).*

Comparison of *Figures 2(c)*, *2(e)*, and *1(a)* suggests that there is a growth promoter at R_f 0·1–0·2, which is probably being formed from another substance, and the lack of the peak in *Figure 2(a)* is in agreement with this. It is also possible that unstable compounds are involved, and small differences in technique are influencing their reactions.

Aqueous fraction of tomato roots

The hormone content of ethereal extracts of excised and seedling roots is low. Attention was therefore turned to the aqueous fraction, which, like that of cabbage, showed high activity.

130 g fresh weight of excised roots were extracted with ether and the aqueous fraction prepared as in the cabbage experiments. Approximately

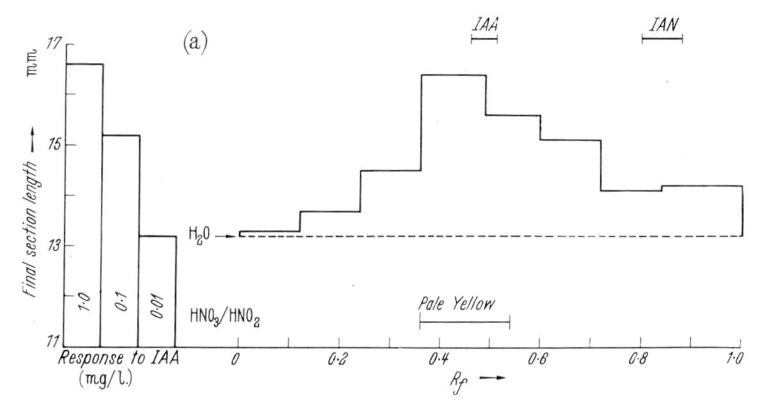

Figure 3(a). Aqueous fraction of approximately 13 *g excised tomato roots developed in ammoniacal* iso*propanol.*

one-tenth of the aqueous fraction was chromatographed in *iso*propanol/ammonia. On initial chromatography separation was poor, so the chromatogram was eluted and redeveloped, when good separation was obtained. The results show (*Figure 3(a)*) that there is considerable activity in the aqueous fraction, with optimum stimulation at R_f 0·36 to 0·48 almost as great as the 1 mg/l. IAA control. The u.v. fluorescence at the position of optimum stimulation was deep purple tailing to pale blue. With HNO_2/HNO_3 a pale yellow colour was obtained at R_f 0·36–0·54, but no colour appeared with $FeCl_3/HClO_4$ or with *p*-dimethylaminobenzaldehyde (MeAB).

A further one-tenth of the aqueous fraction was chromatographed and gave the same fluorescence as in the previous experiment. The zones of R_f 0·32 to 0·76, corresponding to the stimulatory zone of the previous experiment, were isolated, and re-eluted in a small quantity of water, which was then reduced to 2 ml by distillation under reduced pressure. This extract was chromatographed in *iso*propanol/ammonia, examined in u.v. light and cut into 2·5 cm strips for bio-assay. The results are shown in *Figure 3(b)*. The greatest activity, in the region R_f 0·72 to 0·84, was almost equal to that of 1·0 mg/l. IAA and corresponded in position with the IAN control, though it could not be associated with any fluorescence. Clearly, these experiments show that an active substance which runs at R_f 0·4–0·5 in *iso*propanol/ammonia liberates a further active substance which runs at the same R_f as IAN on further chromatography. The re-chromatography involves heating to about 60°C and further treatment with weak alkali.

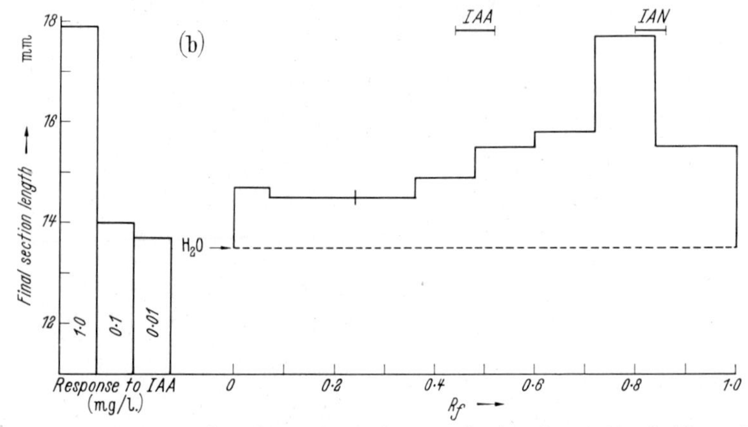

Figure 3(b). Active area from chromatogram of aqueous fraction of approximately 13 *g excised roots re-chromatographed in ammoniacal* iso*propanol.*

The experiment was repeated to examine the chromatogram with colour sprays. No colour reactions could be obtained in the IAN region with HNO_2/HNO_3, $FeCl_3/HClO_4$, or with MeAB. There is thus no evidence, apart from R_f value, that the activity near the solvent front is due to IAN.

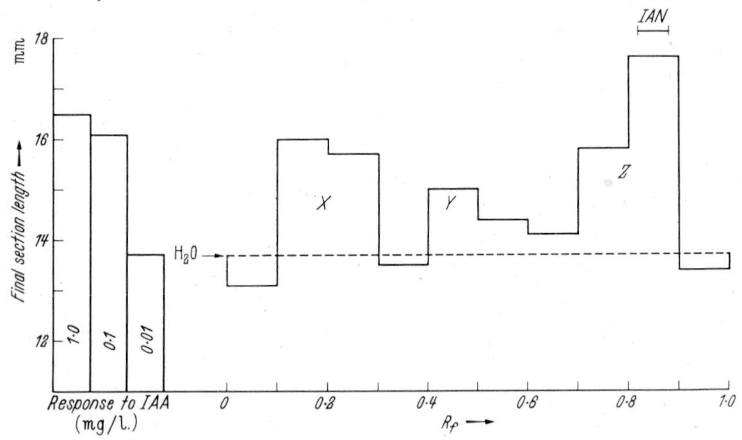

Figure 4. Aqueous fraction of approximately 13 *g excised tomato roots developed in ammoniacal* n-*butanol.*

On spraying with bromo-cresol green, a yellow area in the zone of activity corresponding to the IAA region was obtained, suggesting that the second active substance near the solvent front comes from an acidic precursor.

Because of the poor separation in *iso*propanol/ammonia, the experiment was repeated using *n*-butanol/ammonia (*Figure 4*). Again separation was poor, so the chromatogram was eluted and re-developed, when a good separation was achieved. Peaks of activity were obtained at R_f 0·1–0·3 (zone *X*), R_f 0·4–0·6 (zone *Y*), and R_f 0·7–0·9 (zone *Z*). Stimulation at *Z* was greater than with 1·0 mg/l. IAA. Stimulation at *X*, which closely followed the IAA control, could be associated with a pale blue and purple fluorescence. Zone *Y* had a pale pink fluorescence and zone *Z* no fluorescence. With the colour sprays no reactions similar to those of IAA and IAN could be obtained.

This experiment was repeated several times, with the same results. It was decided to try to isolate these three peaks to study their behaviour and to determine any relationships between them.

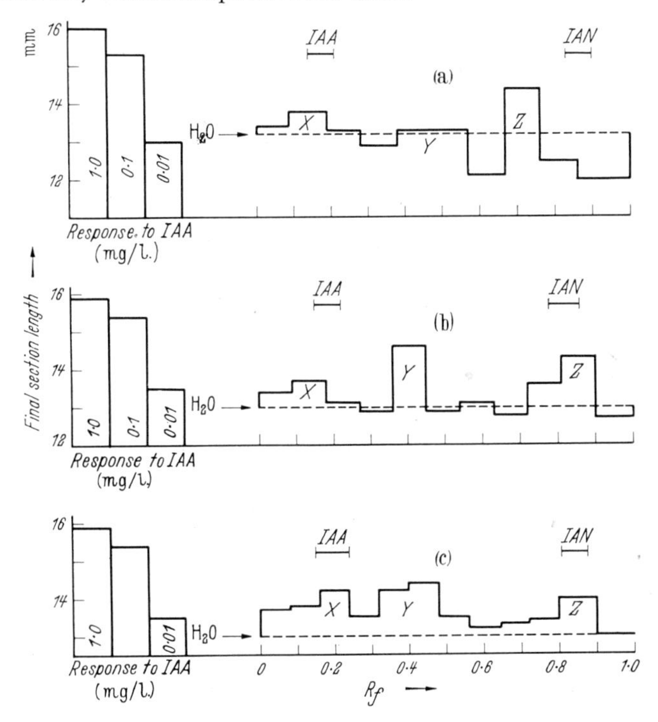

Figure 5. (a) Aqueous fraction of excised roots developed in ammoniacal n-*butanol. (b) Zone X of aqueous fraction developed in ammoniacal* n-*butanol. (c) Zone Y of aqueous fraction developed in ammoniacal* n-*butanol.*

Two further chromatograms, each loaded with one-tenth of the aqueous fraction, were developed in the same tank. One chromatogram was bioassayed to locate zones *X*, *Y*, and *Z* (*Figure 5(a)*). The zones of the second chromatogram corresponding to *X* and *Y* were re-chromatographed in *n*-butanol/ammonia (*Figures 5(b)* and *(c)* respectively).

In each case the running of zone *X* or zone *Y* had produced three peaks. A pale purple fluorescence was obtained at zone *Z* in each chromatogram. It is possible that separation of *X* and *Y* may not have been complete before re-chromatography. However, it is clear that *Z* was formed from either *X* or *Y*, though it is not possible to state which of the two zones was responsible. It would appear that *X* and *Y* are interconvertible, behaving like tautomers of a substance which is the precursor of Z. This precursor is either active itself or is converted to an active substance by the action of the coleoptile tissues during bio-assay.

Zone Z was eluted from *Figure 5(a)* and attempts were made to extract it with ether. It remained almost entirely in the aqueous fraction, however, and this result, together with the lack of reaction with the colour sprays, is evidence against Z being IAN.

Further experiments similar to the ones reported above were carried out with seedling roots, and essentially the same results were obtained, with two peaks of activity in *iso*propanol/ammonia and three peaks, X, Y, and Z, in

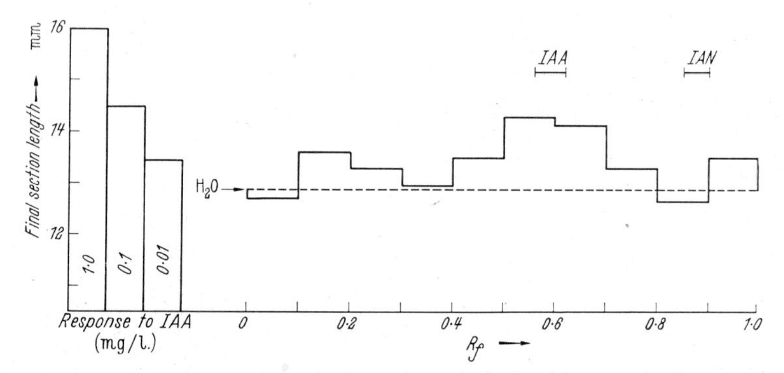

Figure 6. Aqueous fraction of germinating maize seeds developed in ammoniacal iso*propanol.*

n-butanol/ammonia. This fact is important, in view of the large amount of work now performed on excised tissues, and in particular on excised roots. If the results of work on excised tissues are to be of any real value in plant physiology, then we must have a comparison between excised and intact tissues.

Aqueous fraction of maize roots and seeds

In these experiments there was again considerable activity in the aqueous fractions, just as was found in both cabbage and tomato. The maize roots showed a pattern of hormone activity similar in many respects to that obtained with tomato roots, in both ammoniacal *iso*propanol and ammoniacal n-butanol. Full details of these results will be presented elsewhere as they do not contribute anything further to the present discussion. Chromatography of the aqueous extract from maize seeds, however, is worth considering in detail at this stage as it led to an investigation of 3-indolylpyruvic acid (IPyA), a hormone reported to be present in maize seeds (Stowe and Thimann, 1953). The results of chromatography of an aqueous extract are shown in *Figure 6.*

Again there is considerable activity in the IAA region and some near the solvent front, but the region we wish to consider in particular is the zone of activity approximately half-way between the starting line and the IAA zone. This corresponds to the zone of activity found by Stowe and Thimann in extracts of dormant maize seeds, and identified by them as IPyA. Slight activity in a similar position was found in cabbage extracts in the aqueous fraction (e.g. *Figures 1(a), 2(c), 2(e)*) and also in the acid and neutral ethereal fractions (results of these fractions are published in detail elsewhere). It was therefore decided to examine synthetic IPyA to determine whether, in fact, it could be responsible for the activity in this region.

3-Indolylpyruvic acid

IPyA has been synthesized and fully characterized by Dr. G. F. Smith, Dr. K. R. Farrar, and Mr. W. Taylor of the Chemistry Department, Manchester University. Its behaviour under the conditions of chromatography used by Stowe and Thimann to demonstrate its presence in maize endosperms, and also its growth-promoting activity, have been investigated.

In order to permit a detailed account of this work to appear elsewhere (Bentley, Farrar, Housley, Smith, and Taylor, 1956), the remainder of the lecture which dealt with the results of these investigations is not reported here. It may be briefly stated, however, that work on synthetic IPyA has shown that it breaks down completely to form IAA, together with other substances, under the conditions of ammoniacal chromotography used in the studies of Stowe and Thimann. The presence of IPyA itself cannot be demonstrated using the solvent system employed by these authors.

Chromogenic studies of chromatograms of the aqueous extract of maize (*Figure 6*) have shown that IAA is not present on these chromatograms. It appears improbable, therefore, that the activity near the starting line in *Figure 6* is due to IPyA, suggesting that there is yet another unknown auxin in this region.

It has also been suggested by Stowe and Thimann that the ether-soluble acidic substance called accelerator-α (Bennet-Clark and Kefford, 1953) which runs between IAA and the starting line under conditions of ammoniacal chromatography is probably IPyA. Bennet-Clark and Kefford have demonstrated that accelerator-α promotes root-growth, whereas we find that synthetic IPyA causes only inhibition of root-growth (cress assay method), with an activity approximately one-tenth that of IAA. The zone of activity between the starting line and IAA in *Figure 6* has not yet been tested for its effect on root growth.

DISCUSSION

Examination of the aqueous, ether-insoluble portion of cabbage, tomato, and maize extracts has shown that this fraction has auxin activity which is usually considerably greater than that obtained in ether extracts. Only low activity is obtained in acid ether extracts, and this largely follows the same pattern as the aqueous extracts. Two clear-cut peaks are obtained in cabbage with both ammoniacal *iso*propanol and *n*-butanol; in tomato, there are three clear-cut peaks with ammoniacal *n*-butanol.

The growth promoter near the solvent front in cabbage is neutral, ether-soluble, and has the R_f, fluorescence, and chromogenic reactions of IAN, with which it is believed to be identical. On the other hand, the hormone near the solvent front in tomato has been similarly examined, and, apart from R_f value, no convincing evidence has been obtained that this zone is due to the nitrile. It has not been possible to obtain even a transient reaction with HNO_2/HNO_3 at this position.

Clearly, both these zones arise from precursors which travel on the chromatograms nearer to the starting line. In tomato there is evidence of two precursors which are interconvertible (*Figure 5*). It is not possible to say from the evidence so far obtained whether these precursors are themselves physiologically active or whether they are converted to an active substance or substances during bio-assay. The first step to answering this question is obviously chemical identification.

Earlier workers have constructed theories (e.g. the Cholodny–Went theory) to explain the growth of roots in terms of IAA. It is evident that the hormone situation in roots is far more complex than had hitherto been suspected. Obviously, more work needs to be done on the inter-relationships between the water-soluble hormones and hormone precursors demonstrated in the present work, and on their chemical identity, before it is possible to construct satisfactory theories of hormone-controlled root growth.

Yet another zone of activity nearer to the starting line than IAA has been demonstrated in maize seeds, both in the aqueous fraction in the present work, and in the ethereal fraction by earlier workers. It has been suggested that activity in this region of the chromatogram is due to IPyA. Work on synthetic IPyA has shown that it breaks down to form IAA, together with other substances, under the conditions of chromatography used in these studies. On chromatograms of maize extracts, $FeCl_3/HClO_4$ gives a yellow colour at the position of IAA while other chromogenic reagents clearly show that physiological activity at this position cannot be due to IAA. Therefore, quite apart from the fact that IPyA does not survive under conditions of ammoniacal chromatography, it cannot be responsible for the activity near the starting line in the maize extracts, as there is no production of IAA. This zone is therefore due to yet another unidentified auxin.

We regard the presence of IPyA in plants as yet unproved, but even if it does exist, it cannot be identical with the accelerator-α of Bennet-Clark and Kefford (1953) as postulated by Stowe and Thimann (1953): the former authors have shown that α promotes root growth, whereas the present work shows that IPyA causes only inhibition.

SUMMARY

1. A report in the literature indicates that an acidic precursor of a neutral growth substance exists in cabbage. An alcoholic extract of mature cabbage has been prepared, and from this an aqueous, ether-insoluble fraction has been obtained. This fraction has been examined by chromatography in *iso*propanol/ammonia and *n*-butanol/ammonia. It contains a substance which is physiologically active on bio-assay with *Avena* coleoptiles. This substance runs differently relative to 3-indolylacetic acid (IAA) controls in the two solvent systems used, and gives a yellow colour with ferric chloride/perchloric acid and nitrous/nitric acid sprays. It gives rise to a further substance by the action of mild alkali, including ammoniacal chromatography, and heat. This second substance is believed to be 3-indolylacetonitrile (IAN).

2. Aqueous fractions of seedling and excised tomato roots and of maize roots gave a similar result, except that no evidence could be obtained that the substance liberated from the precursor was IAN. The precursor could

be resolved into two zones of activity when chromatographed in *n*-butanol/ammonia. These zones appear to be interconvertible.

3. A further zone of activity was obtained between the starting line and IAA controls in aqueous fractions of maize seeds. Synthetic 3-indolyl-pyruvic acid (IPyA) was examined to determine whether it could be responsible for this activity, but results showed that it appears to be destroyed under conditions of ammoniacal chromatography and cannot therefore be demonstrated in plant extracts by this technique. From an examination of its effect on root growth, IPyA cannot be identical with the accelerator-α of Bennet-Clark and Kefford.

ACKNOWLEDGEMENTS

The authors wish to thank Professor S. C. Harland, F.R.S., and Professor E. R. H. Jones, F.R.S., for facilities for this work in the Departments of Botany and Chemistry, the Agricultural Research Council for grants which have assisted the botanical work, and Mrs. V. Shaw for technical assistance. The work described in this lecture will be reported in greater detail in the Journal of Experimental Botany (cabbage and tomato) and the Biochemical Journal (IPyA).

We are indebted to Professor H. E. Street for suggesting the examination of hormones in excised roots and for providing help and facilities for growing this material.

REFERENCES

BENNET-CLARK, T. A., and KEFFORD, N. P. (1953). Chromatography of the growth substances in plant extracts. *Nature*, **171,** 645.

BENTLEY, J. A. (1950). An examination of a method of auxin assay using the growth of isolated sections of *Avena* coleoptiles in test solutions. *J. exp. Bot.* **1,** 201.

BENTLEY, J. A., FARRAR, K.R., HOUSLEY, S., SMITH, G. F., and TAYLOR, W. (1956). Some chemical and physiological properties of indole-3-pyruvic acid. Biochem. J. (in the press).

BENTLEY, J. A., and HOUSLEY, S. (1954). Bio-assay of plant growth hormones. *Physiol. Plant.* **7,** 405.

BONDE, E. K. (1953). Auxins and auxin precursors in acid and nonacidic fractions of plant extracts. *Bot. Gaz.* **115,** 1.

MOEWUS, F. (1949a). Die Wirkung von Wuchs- und Hemmstoffen auf die Kresse-wurzel. *Biol. Zbl.* **68,** 58.

MOEWUS, F. (1949b). Der Kressewurzeltest, ein neuer quantitativer Wuchsstofftest. *Biol. Zbl.* **68,** 118.

STREET, H. E. (1954). Growing roots without plants. *Discovery*, **15,** 7.

STOWE, B. B., and THIMANN, K. V. (1953). Indolepyruvic acid in maize. *Nature*, **172,** 764.

STOWE, B. B., and THIMANN, K. V. (1954). The paper chromatography of indole compounds and some indole-containing auxins of plant tissues. *Arch. Biochem. Biophys.* **51,** 499.

CHROMATOGRAPHISCHE UNTERSUCHUNGEN ÜBER DIE WUCHSSTOFFE UND HEMMSTOFFE DER HAFERKOLEOPTILE†

H. Söding und Edith Raadts

Staatsinstitut für Allgemeine Botanik, Hamburg

Die chemische Natur des Wuchsstoffes der Haferkoleoptile ist noch nicht restlos klar. Als sicher erscheint, daß es sich um einen indolartigen Wuchsstoff handelt, Indolessigsäure (IES) oder einen nahe verwandten Stoff.

Wildman und Bonner (1948) konnten mit der Salkowskireaktion den extrahierbaren Wuchsstoff der Koleoptile quantitativ bestimmen und hielten ihn für IES. Zum selben Ergebnis kommt Reinert (1950) auf Grund der übereinstimmenden Wirkungskurven und der Empfindlichkeit gegen Erbsenenzym. In eigenen Untersuchungen erwies sich der aus der Spitze der Koleoptile *diffundierende* Wuchsstoff als säureempfindlich und laugenstabil in Übereinstimmung mit IES. Aus weiteren Befunden schlossen wir aber, daß es sich jedenfalls nicht um reine und freie IES handeln könne.

Im Maisendosperm konnten außer der IES verschiedene andere Indolderivate gefunden werden. Stowe und Thimann (1954) trennten chromatographisch vier Stoffe, IES, Indolbrenztraubensäure, und zwei weitere noch nicht identifizierte Wuchsstoffe, während Yamaki und Nakamura (1952) im Maisendosperm IES und Indolacetaldehyd fanden. Es scheint jedoch, daß ein Unterschied im Gehalt an Wuchsstoffen bei den einzelnen Maissorten besteht. IES konnte in *allen* Extrakten als einziger gemeinsamer Wuchsstoff festgestellt werden.

Bei der Chromatographie des Haferkoleoptilenwuchsstoffes fand Terpstra (1953) nur IES. Bei Extrakten von zerriebenen und gefrorenen Spitzen treten aber im Chromatogramm Schwänze auf. Diese sollen durch einen Komplex entstehen, der auf dem Papier langsam IES freigibt. Im *Diffusat* aus intakten Koleoptilenspitzen war nur freie IES enthalten ohne Schwanzbildung im Chromatogramm.

Unsere eigenen Versuche wurden ausschließlich mit Diffusionswuchsstoff gemacht. Im Gegensatz zu Terpstra (1953) erhielten wir aber bei der Chromatographie zwei Wuchsstoffe (Haferkrümmungstest, Zylindertest). Der eine stets anzutreffende Wuchsstoff ist IES, der zweite Wuchsstoff ist eine sehr labile Substanz, die nicht in allen Fällen nachweisbar war; alle Versuche, durch Änderung der Methodik die Ausbeute zu erhöhen, waren vergeblich (Diffusion oder Extraktion mit Alkohol oder heißem Wasser, Abfangen in gepufferter Lösung, Einengen des Wuchsstoffes oder Abdampfen bei 100°C oder niedriger, verschiedene Chromatographierflüssigkeiten, Anzucht der Pflanzen bei Licht oder Dunkelheit). Dieser Wuchsstoff konnte noch nicht identifiziert werden. Er ist aber nach dem R_f-Wert in 70 prozent. Äthanol nicht identisch mit Indolbrenztraubensäure.

Wenn dieser zweite Wuchsstoff fehlte, so konnte meist durch Auswaschen

† This paper was read at the Conference by H. Söding.

der betreffenden Stelle ein Eluat gewonnen werden, das nach Stehen über Nacht bei pH 3 einen Wuchsstoff enthielt, der mit Chloroform ausgeschüttelt werden konnte und im Haferkrümmungstest wirksam war. Wenn das Eluat aber selbst eine geringe Wirksamkeit hatte, wurde diese durch Säurebehandlung und Ausschütteln mit Chloroform verstärkt. (In diesen Versuchen war 70 prozent. Äthanol als Chromatographierflüssigkeit benutzt worden.)

Nach diesen Ergebnissen ist also in der Pflanze eine inaktive Wuchsstoffvorstufe vorhanden, die bei Säurebehandlung leicht in einen aktiven Wuchsstoff übergeht. Wie es aber kommt, daß dieser Übergang in der Pflanze im Zylindertest, selbst bei 20-stündiger Testzeit, nicht geschieht, können wir nicht sagen. Vielleicht handelt es sich hier um einen ähnlichen Vorgang, wie ihn Larsen (1944) bei seinem neutralen Wuchsstoff aus Erbsen beschreibt, der teils in einer sofort wirksamen, teils in einer inaktiven Form extrahiert wurde. Auch Bonde (1953) gibt an, daß in der neutralen Fraktion von Erbsenstengeln und im Erbsensaft eine inaktive Vorstufe erst durch Behandeln mit Koleoptilensaft aktiviert und im Hafertest nachweisbar wird.

Es ist also außer der IES noch ein zweiter aktiver Wuchsstoff oder wenigstens seine Vorstufe im Spitzendiffusat vorhanden.

Ein weiterer Hinweis auf einen inaktiven Wuchsstoff im Spitzendiffusat ergibt sich aus folgenden Versuchen. Nach Alkalisieren (pH 8) läßt sich aus dem Diffusat kein im Hafertest wirksamer Wuchsstoff ausschütteln. Chromatographiert man aber diese ausgeschüttelte Substanz, so erhält man wieder IES und den zweiten Wuchsstoff. Im Spitzendiffusat muß also ein nichtsaurer inaktiver Wuchsstoff vorhanden sein, der beim Chromatographieren aktiviert wird.

Ob diese nichtsaure Vorstufe identisch ist mit dem inaktiven Wuchsstoff, der durch Säurebehandlung aktiviert wird, konnten wir noch nicht feststellen. Es gelang uns jedenfalls nicht, den aus der alkalischen Lösung ausgeschüttelten Stoff durch Säure zu aktivieren. Auch konnten wir nach Säurebehandlung keine größere Aktivität im Gesamtdiffusionswuchsstoff feststellen. Allerdings müssen diese Versuche noch wiederholt werden.

Wir finden also in unseren Versuchen folgende Stoffe:

1. IES,
2. den „2. Wuchsstoff",
3. eine inaktive Vorstufe, die durch Säurebehandlung leicht aktivierbar ist, aber mit dem Zylindertest auch bei langer Reaktionszeit nicht nachweisbar ist,
4. eine nichtsaure Vorstufe, die aus alkalischer Lösung ausgeschüttelt werden kann und beim Chromatographieren die beiden aktiven Wuchsstoffe liefert,†
5. zwei Hemmstoffe.

Es ist noch nicht restlos klar, ob die beiden inaktiven Wuchstoffe vielleicht doch identisch sind, und wie die genetischen Beziehungen zwischen diesen Stoffen sind.

Alle papierchromatographischen Ergebnisse sind also mit grosser Vorsicht

† Weitere Versuche machen es zweifelhaft, ob der 2. Wuchsstoff des Rohdiffusates und der 2. Wuchsstoff der alkalischen Ausschüttelung identisch sind.

zu beurteilen. Noch klarer zeigt das die Papierchromatographie des aus *dekapitierten Stümpfen* abzufangenden *aufsteigenden* Wuchsstoffstromes.

Nach zahlreichen älteren Versuchen handelt es sich bei diesem Wuchsstoff um einen im Haferkrümmungstest unwirksamen inaktiven Stoff (precursor oder Wuchsstoffvorstufe), der in der Koleoptilenspitze in den absteigenden Wuchsstoff umgewandelt wird.

Der inaktive Wuchsstoff läßt sich aus saurer und aus alkalischer Lösung ausschütteln. Er muß also eine neutrale Substanz sein (Raadts, 1952). Von Koleoptilzylindern wird er im Gegensatz zu dem durch Säurebehandlung aktivierbaren inaktiven Spitzenwuchsstoff leicht aktiviert (Zylindertest); beides müssen also verschiedene inaktive Wuchsstoffe sein. Auch ist es sehr zweifelhaft, ob er mit der nichtsauren Vorstufe identisch ist, die bei alkalischer Reaktion aus Spitzendiffusat ausgeschüttelt werden kann.

Die Papierchromatographie ergab, mit oder ohne vorhergehendes Ausschütteln (mit Chloroform), bishev nur IES als Wuchsstoff. Durch die Manipulationen muß sich also der aufsteigende inaktive Wuchsstoff in IES umgewandelt haben. Weiter findet man noch einen Hemmstoff, der vielleicht mit dem 1. Hemmstoff des Spitzendiffusates identisch ist.

Der aufsteigende Wuchsstoff enthält also:

1. einen neutralen inaktiven Wuchsstoff, der *in vitro* und *in vivo* sehr leicht in IES umgewandelt werden kann;
2. einen Hemmstoff.

Der Deutschen Forschungsgemeinschaft und der Joachim-Junguis-Gesellschaft in Hamburg danken wir für die Unterstützung dieser Untersuchungen.

SUMMARY

1. The growth substances occurring in *Avena* coleoptiles were studied, using a chromatographic technique. *Table 1* summarizes the experiments carried out and the results obtained.

Table 1

Part of coleoptile studied	*Method of extraction*	*Substances found to occur on paper chromatogram prepared from extract (Assay Methods,* Avena *Curvature Test,* Avena *Section Test)*
Apices	1. Diffusion into water	1. IAA 2. A second growth-promoting substance 3. Two growth-inhibiting substances 4. One inactive precursor (becomes active when treated with acid)
	2. Diffusion into water, shaken with chloroform at pH 8	1. IAA 2. A second growth-promoting substance (other substances not tested)
Coleoptile bases+seeds	1. Diffusion from base into water	1. IAA 2. One growth-inhibiting substance

2. The water diffusate from the apices contained the active substance indoleacetic acid, a second growth-promoting substance and two growth-inhibiting substances. *Table 2* shows the R_f-values of these substances (descending method). An inactive precursor was also found in this diffusate. This became active when treated with acid.

Table 2

Solvent mixtures	*IAA*	*Second growth-promoting substance*	*First growth-inhibiting substance*	*Second growth-inhibiting substance*
Water-saturated butyl alcohol+ammonia	0·36	0·56	0·82	—
*iso*Propyl alcohol+water+ammonia, 80:15:5	0·47	0·25	~0·90	~0·07
Ethyl alcohol+water+ammonia, 70:30(25):(5)	0·74	0·14	0·94	—
Water+ammonia, 95:5	~0·86	~0·50	—	—

Proportions: v/v. Ammonia = 25 per cent NH_3.

3. The diffusate, when made alkaline and shaken with chloroform, yielded a possibly different inactive precursor. During the development of the chromatogram this gave rise to the same two growth-promoting substances as were obtained in the water diffusate.†

4. The chromatogram developed from the inactive growth substances moving from the seed to the apex of the coleoptile showed two active substances: indoleacetic acid and a growth-inhibiting substance. The IAA must be formed during the chromatographic preparations.

LITERATUR

Bonde, E. K. (1953). Auxin and auxin precursors in acid and nonacid fractions of plant extracts. *Bot. Gaz.* **115,** 1.

Larsen, P. (1944). 3-indole acetaldehyde as a growth hormone in higher plants. *Dansk bot. Ark.* **11,** 1.

Raadts, E. (1952). Über den inaktiven Wuchsstoff der Haferkoleoptile. *Planta,* **40,** 419.

Reinert, J. (1950). Über den Wuchstoffgehalt der Avena-Koleoptilen-Spitze und die chemischen Natur des extrahierbaren Auxins. *Z. Naturf.* **5B,** 374.

Söding, H., and Raadts, E. (1953). Über das Verhalten des Wuchstoffes der Koleoptilenspitze gegen Säure und Lauge. *Planta,* **43,** 25.

Stowe, B. B., and Thimann, K. V. (1954). The paper chromatography of indole compounds and some indole-containing auxins of plant tissues. *Arch. Biochem. Biophys.* **51,** 499.

† From the results of further experiments, it is doubtful whether the second growth substance of the raw diffusate and the second growth substance of the alkaline shaking are identical.

TERPSTRA, W. (1953). Chromatographic identification of the growth substance extracted from *Avena* coleoptile tips. *Proc. K. Ned. Akad. Wetensch.* Ser. C, **56,** 206.
WILDMAN, S. G., and BONNER, J. (1948). Observations on the chemical nature and formation of auxin in the *Avena* coleoptile. *Amer. J. Bot.* **35,** 740.
YAMAKI, T., and NAKAMURA, K. (1952). Formation of indoleacetic acid in maize embryo. *Sci. Pap. Coll. gen. Education, Univ. Tokyo*, **2,** 81.

INDOLE COMPOUNDS IN PHOTOINDUCED PLANTS

A. J. VLITOS†

Boyce Thompson Institute for Plant Research, Yonkers, New York

INTRODUCTION

INDOLE compounds are known to regulate vegetative growth of plants but their influence on flowering has not been extensively studied. There is considerable evidence that the response to photoperiodic treatment can be modified by 3-indoleacetic acid (IAA). Application to short-day plants may inhibit flowering (Bonner and Liverman, 1953; Fisher and Loomis, 1954); an effect which can be counteracted by subsequent treatment with antiauxin.

Treatment of long-day plants with auxin may reverse the photoperiodic response since it prevents their flowering when held under long-day conditions and induces floral initiation under short-day conditions. Because of these observations Fisher and Loomis (1954) have postulated that flowering of Lincoln soybeans may depend upon a proper balance between auxin and a flowering hormone.

Further evidence in support of this hypothesis might be obtained by determining effects of photoinduction on the auxin content of plants. Studies were undertaken, therefore, to determine whether there was a decrease in the amount of indole compounds present in typical short-day plants such as Maryland Mammoth tobacco and Biloxi and Lincoln soybeans when they were photoinduced. The methods of extracting, identifying, and measuring quantitatively the various indole compounds before and after photoinduction are described in this paper.

PAPER CHROMATOGRAPHY OF INDOLE DERIVATIVES

Most of the work with quantitative auxin assays has been based upon nonspecific, biological assays (i.e. *Avena* coleoptile curvatures or *Avena* straight growth tests). Therefore, the precursors of IAA in plant tissues, examined by means of biological assays, have not been adequately considered in photoperiodic studies. With the advent of paper chromatography, a technique is now available to study, individually, the role of free IAA, IAA bound to proteins, and various precursors which can be converted into IAA in flowering. In addition, paper chromatography permits a direct study of the effect of naturally-occurring inhibitors on an auxin of known chemical composition.

In 1953 we described a method for the quantitative determination of IAA and other indole compounds in plant tissues (Vlitos and Meudt, 1953). The technique is based upon paper chromatographic methods and upon the measurement of the maximum density of spots developed with *p*-dimethylaminobenzaldehyde. A typical standard curve for IAA is reproduced in

† Holder of the Carbide and Carbon Chemicals Company Fellowship at the Boyce Thompson Institute.

Figure 1. If the concentration of IAA applied to the chromatogram is plotted against per cent of light transmissions, a straight-line relationship exists over the range 0·1 and 10 micrograms of IAA.

The calculated error inherent in the quantitative paper chromatography of IAA is within 3 per cent. This value is considerably below the values given by Block, LeStrange, and Zweig (1952) for the determination of amino acids by the maximum density method.

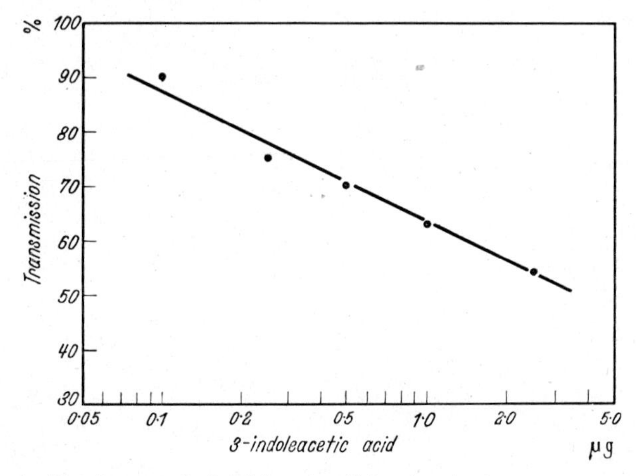

Figure 1. A calibration curve for 3-*indoleacetic acid based on densitometer readings of spots developed with* p-*dimethylaminobenzaldehyde on paper chromatographs.*

EXTRACTION OF INDOLE COMPOUNDS FROM PLANT TISSUES

It became apparent early in our study that a suitable extraction method for IAA and other indole compounds from plant tissues was necessary before quantitative paper chromatography could be utilized effectively (Vlitos and Meudt, 1954a). An extraction method was needed which would (1) preclude the conversion of tryptophan and other IAA precursors to IAA during extraction, and (2) extract free IAA with a single extraction over a short period of time.

While our work (Vlitos and Meudt, 1954a) was still in progress, a paper appeared by Terpstra (1953) which adequately reviewed the problems involved in the extraction or diffusion of auxins from plant tissues. Terpstra has described a method for extracting auxin from *Avena* coleoptiles, and from some green plant tissues, based on the water extraction of frozen material and subsequent dissociation of the extracted auxin-complex with ethyl ether. Kefford (1953) at about the same time described a method for the extraction of free indole compounds from plant tissues using absolute alcohol as the solvent. He found that all of the free auxin was obtained with one extraction at —12°C. We proceeded to evaluate the methods of Terpstra and Kefford. Absolute ethanol was found to be a more efficient solvent than water for the extraction of IAA and tryptophan from tomato or spinach tissue (*Tables 1, 2,* and *3*).

The extraction of IAA from frozen plant tissue with absolute ethanol at —10°C was found to fulfil the requirements for an extraction method set

Table 1

Percentage recovery of added IAA and tryptophan from control and treated tomato tissue with water at −10°C on paper partition chromatograms. Results of two experiments (A and B)

Treatment	*IAA*		*Tryptophan*†		*Other indole compounds*	
	A %	*B* %	*A* %	*B* %	*A* %	*B* %
Tissue + 80 mg IAA	67	75	0	0	0	0
Tissue + 80 mg tryptophan	0	0	80	71	6‡	10‡
Tissue (control)	0	0	0	0	0	0
80 mg IAA	62	75	0	0	0	0
80 mg tryptophan	0	0	85	100	0	0

† Tryptophan was recovered from the aqueous fractions.
‡ The R_f value of this compound corresponds to that for 3-indole-pyruvic acid and agrees with that reported by Stowe and Thimann (1954).

Table 2

Percentage recovery of IAA and tryptophan from treated tomato tissue with absolute ethanol and with mixtures of ethanol and water at −10°C

Treatment	*Percent of IAA recovered with*	
	Absolute ethanol	*Ethanol–water* (4:1)
Tissue + 80 mg IAA	100	100
Tissue + 80 mg tryptophan	0	0
Tissue (control)	0	2·1†
80 mg IAA	100	100
80 mg tryptophan	0	13

† Micrograms of IAA recovered from control tissue.

Table 3

Percentage recovery of IAA and tryptophan from spinach tissue with water and with absolute ethanol at −10°C

Treatment	*Percent recovered with*			
	Water	*Ethanol*	*Water*	*Ethanol*
	IAA		*Tryptophan*	
Tissue + 80 mg IAA	10	90	0	0
Tissue + 80 mg tryptophan	—	—	10	85
Tissue (control)	0	0	0	0
80 mg IAA	25	80	0	0
80 mg tryptophan	0	0	40	95

forth above (i.e. the free IAA was extracted with a single extraction and tryptophan was not converted to IAA during extraction). Therefore, the following extraction and chromatographic method was adopted for routine use in determining indole compounds in photoinduced tissues:

I. Extraction

1. 300 g plant tissue harvested and frozen instantly.
2. Frozen tissue ground to fine powder without thawing.
3. Frozen ground tissue extracted with absolute ethanol for 12 to 24 hours at −10°C.
4. Ethanol evaporated off *in vacuo* leaving aqueous fraction.
5. Aqueous fraction acidified to pH 4·0 with 0·1 N H_3PO_4.
6. Acidified aqueous fraction saturated with glucose and extracted three times with ethyl ether.
7. Ether extract concentrated to 2·5 ml or less.

II. Quantitative Paper Chromatography

8. 2·5 μl of extract were removed and applied to Whatman No. 1 paper as described previously (Vlitos and Meudt, 1953).
9. 0·1, 0·25, 0·5, 1·0, 2·5, and 5·0 micrograms of IAA (or any other indole compound) were applied to Whatman No. 1 paper.
10. After development of papers, density measurements of spots were used to construct standard calibration curve (Vlitos and Meudt, 1953).
11. The amount of indole compound in extract was calculated by referring to a standard calibration curve.

All the operations pertaining to extraction were performed in a cold room (−10°C). The standard calibration curve is based on five replicate paper chromatographs run simultaneously.

If smaller quantities of tissue are extracted it is of course possible to rely upon qualitative paper chromatography followed by elution of the substance from the paper and subsequent biological assays (*Avena* coleoptile tests, root-growth measurements, etc.). The latter procedure introduces additional steps in the method and, no doubt, reduces the quantitative precision of the technique. Therefore it is desirable to use at least 300 g of tissue per extraction and maintain the quantitative aspect of the method.

INFLUENCE OF ENVIRONMENTAL VARIABLES ENCOUNTERED DURING EXTRACTION ON THE STABILITY OF IAA

In addition to avoiding the conversion of precursors to IAA during extraction, it was necessary to assay the influence of the environmental variables which might affect the recovery of free IAA from plant tissues. The effects of pH, light, and temperature on the stability of IAA were evaluated only in so far as they might influence the recovery of IAA for the short periods of time encountered during extraction and chromatography of the extracts.

The influence of pH on the stability of IAA in a series of phthalate buffers adjusted to pH 1·5 to 9·0 with HCl and NaOH is recorded in *Table 4*.

If an extraction of free IAA from plant tissues is not completed within a few hours there is a possibility of inactivation of the compound at low pH values. However, in experiments of this type an acidified extract is usually

Table 4

Stability of IAA in a series of buffers ranging from pH 1·5 *to* 9·0†

Buffer+*IAA* 10 μg	pH	*Incubation (hours)* 1	3	76
		Amount	*IAA recovered*	(μg)
Phthalate–HCl	1·5	10	10	<1
Phthalate–HCl	2·5	10	10	<3
Phthalate–HCl	3·0	10	10	>3
Phthalate–NaOH	4·0	10	10	>8
Phthalate–NaOH	6·0	10	10	>8
Phosphate–NaOH	9·0	10	10	>8

† Similar results were obtained when the experiments were done in the presence of plant tissue extracts in the buffers.

not kept for more than a few hours so that changes in the structure of IAA would not be expected to occur.

The influence of infra-red and fluorescent radiation on the stability of IAA both in the presence and absence of plant brei is recorded in *Table 5.*

Table 5

Influence of infra-red and fluorescent radiation on the stability of IAA in the presence and absence of soybean leaf tissue

Incubation period (minutes)	*Soybean leaf tissue*	*Optical density of spots developed with* p-*dimethylaminobenzaldehyde on paper chromatographs*†	
		Fluorescent 0·2 *g cal/cm²/min*	*Infra-red* 1·15 *g cal/cm²/min*
5	Present	0·28	0·26
5	Absent	0·28	0·28
10	Present	0·23	0·26
10	Absent	0·29	0·28
30	Present	0·20	0·30
30	Absent	0·30	0·26
60	Present	0·24	0·18
60	Absent	0·27	0·26
180	Present	0·23	0·16
180	Absent	0·24	0·32

† Theoretical value for total recovery of IAA is 0·28 to 0·30.

The results indicate that there is little or no inactivation of IAA as a result of short-term exposures to either infra-red or fluorescent lighting. The intensities used in these experiments are much higher than those which are usually encountered under laboratory conditions.

It is often necessary to inactivate the enzyme systems which are responsible for catalysing the synthesis of IAA from tryptophan. Heating plant tissue to destroy these enzymes was first proposed by Gustafson (1941), but later discarded by other workers who found that boiling water released inhibitors of auxin from the tissue (Terpstra, 1953). Since the *Avena* coleoptile test was used for auxin determinations, the inhibitors may have had no direct effect on auxin but instead may have been inhibitory in themselves to the growth of *Avena* sections. Paper chromatography, however, permits a study of the effect of boiling directly on the stability of IAA. The results of experiments involving boiling tissue and added IAA are given in *Table 6*.

Table 6

Stability of IAA to heat in the presence and absence of plant tissue as determined by paper chromatography

Treatment	*Optical density*†
Tissue boiled 2 minutes; IAA added to boiled extract	0·34
Tissue+IAA boiled 2 minutes	0·32
IAA—no tissue—boiled 1 minute	0·30
IAA—no tissue—boiled 2 minutes	0·29
IAA—no tissue—boiled 10 minutes	0·30
IAA—no tissue—boiled 30 minutes	0·32

† Theoretical value for total recovery of IAA is 0·33.

There is no discernible release of inhibitors of IAA from plant tissue which is boiled. The results suggest that boiling plant tissue for short periods may be used to inactivate the enzymes which catalyse the conversion of tryptophan to IAA, providing that IAA content is determined chemically and not by means of biological assays.

FREE INDOLE ACIDS IN SHORT-DAY PLANTS GROWN UNDER PHOTOINDUCTIVE AND NON-PHOTOINDUCTIVE DAYLENGTHS

The development of the extraction procedure and the quantitative paper chromatographic technique was a pre-requisite to assays of indole compounds in photoperiodically sensitive plants (Vlitos and Meudt, 1954b). The above techniques were applied to answer the question: are free IAA levels decreased in short-day plants as a result of photoinduction? Such information is essential if plant physiologists are to examine the validity of the hypotheses which have been proposed to account for the influence of auxin in the flowering process (Bonner and Liverman, 1953; Fisher and Loomis, 1954).

Soybean (*Glycine max* Mer. varieties Biloxi and Lincoln) and tobacco (*Nicotiana tabacum* L. var. Maryland Mammoth) were the short-day plants used in the study. One group of plants was grown under greenhouse conditions in an environment providing a total of 18 hours light in a 24-hour cycle. The prevailing natural daylength was extended by light emanating from 500-watt Mazda tungsten lamps. The second group of plants was grown under short-day conditions (8-hour daylengths) attained by covering the plants with light-proof, aluminium-foil shields. The number of photo-inductive cycles necessary for floral initiation was determined from previous experiments under similar conditions. In every case the plants which were harvested for extraction were photoinduced or were completely vegetative. Photoinduced plants were harvested before macroscopic flower parts had formed. Vegetative plants were of the same age as photoinduced ones at harvest. Employing the extraction method and quantitative paper chromatography as described above the types and amounts of indole compounds recovered from extracts were recorded. Results of a typical experiment appear in *Table 7.*

Table 7

Amounts of 3-*indoleacetic acid (IAA),* 3-*indolepyruvic acid (IPA), and tryptophan (Tryp) in short-day plants grown under* 8- *and* 18-*hour photoperiods as determined by quantitative paper chromatography*

Tissue	*Photoperiod (hr)*	*µg/300 g of tissue*		
		IAA (R_f 0·51)	*IPA* (R_f 0·21)†	*Tryp*‡ (R_f 0·46)
Biloxi soybean	8	125·0	+++	Not determined
Biloxi soybean	18	<0·1	+	Not determined
Lincoln soybean	8	0·1–0·25	+++	Not determined
Lincoln soybean	18	<0·1	0	Not determined
Maryland Mammoth tobacco leaves	8	<0·1	++	++
Maryland Mammoth tobacco leaves	18	<0·1	0	++
Maryland Mammoth tobacco apices	8	<0·1	0	0
Maryland Mammoth tobacco apices	18	<0·1	0	++

† It was not possible to express the amounts of 3-indolepyruvic acid quantitatively since synthetic samples of the compound were too unstable to chromatograph quantitatively.
‡ Tryptophan was contained in the aqueous fractions of tobacco extracts. Soybean extracts were not assayed for tryptophan content.

A compound possessing an R_f value identical to 3-indolepyruvic acid (IPA) was detected in the three short-day plants which were studied. Strongly coloured spots were obtained on chromatograms for this compound in extracts from tissues grown under photoinductive cycles. Free IAA was present in highest concentration in extracts of tissues of Biloxi soybean plants grown under short-day conditions. Lincoln soybeans which were grown under these short-day conditions also contained more IAA than comparable plants grown under long-day cycles.

The results of this study indicate that free IAA and IPA levels are increased under light conditions which favour the flowering of short-day plants, Biloxi and Lincoln soybean. IPA levels in Maryland Mammoth tobacco leaves are highest in photoinduced tissue. These results are at variance with the hypothesis that photoinduction and reduction in endogenous IAA levels are related processes.

The recent work of Cooke (1954) substantiates most of the findings outlined above. Cooke found changes in auxin content in vegetative Maryland Mammoth tobacco (*Nicotiana tabacum* L.) and Biloxi soybean to be correlated with the daylength in which the plants were growing. In contrast to our work he found more auxin in plants growing under long-day than in plants growing under short-day conditions. Plants which were suddenly shifted from long-day to short-day conditions showed a rise in auxin content for the next few days. Similar increases in auxin content have been noted in plants which are transferred to total darkness (Gustafson, 1946). According to Cooke (1954) increased auxin concentration occurs during the period of floral induction and it is not until several days later that the concentration of auxin begins to decrease. A decrease in auxin is not the cause of flowering as this decrease does not occur until after the induction period. Cooke in his study measured auxin concentrations using the standard *Avena* method; therefore it is difficult to make direct comparison of IAA or IPA content which might have influenced the curvature of the *Avena* sections.

In summary, the evidence (Cooke, 1954; Vlitos and Meudt, 1954b) to date does not support the hypotheses advanced for the role of auxin or of indole derivatives in floral initiation. In the studies mentioned above where a thorough attempt has been made to follow the levels of either indole derivatives or unidentified auxins using two distinct techniques, the levels of indole compounds in photoinduced plants appear to be related with length of day rather than with floral induction. It is possible that the inhibition of flowering by exogenously applied auxins may be due to a general inhibition of growth rather than any direct effect on floral tissue. In any event, as newer experimental techniques become available workers in this field will be in a better position to evaluate critically the many observational and arbitrary hypotheses which have been advanced to account for photoperiodism in plants, particularly those hypotheses which require a quantitative interpretation.

REFERENCES

BLOCK, R. J., LESTRANGE, R., and ZWEIG, G. (1952). *Paper Chromatography*, Academic Press, New York, p. 195.

BONNER, J., and LIVERMAN, J. (1953). Hormonal control of flower initiation, *Growth and differentiation in plants*, Iowa State College Press, p. 283.

COOKE, A. R. (1954). Auxin content during the photoinduction of short-day plants. *Plant Physiol.* **29,** 440.

FISHER, J. E., and LOOMIS, W. E. (1954). Auxin-florigen balance in flowering of soybean. *Science*, **119,** 71.

GUSTAFSON, F. G. (1941). The extraction of growth hormones from plants. *Amer. J. Bot.* **28,** 947.

GUSTAFSON, F. G. (1946). Influence of external and internal factors on growth hormone in green plants. *Plant Physiol.* **21,** 49.

KEFFORD, N. P. (1953). Properties of growth substances separated from plants by chromatography. Thesis, University of London.

OVERBEEK, J. VAN, OLIVO, G. D., and VAZQUEZ, E. S. DE (1945). A rapid extraction method for free auxin and its application in geotropic reactions of bean seedlings and sugar cane nodes. *Bot. Gaz.* **106,** 440.

STOWE, B. B., and THIMANN, K. V. (1954). The paper chromatography of indole compounds and some indole containing auxins of plant tissues. *Arch. Biochem. Biophys.* **51,** 499.

TERPSTRA, W. (1953). Extraction and identification of growth substances. *Meded. bot. Lab. Rijksuniv., Gent,* **4,** 64.

VLITOS, A. J., and MEUDT, W. (1953). The role of auxin in plant flowering. I. A quantitative method based on paper chromatography for the determination of indole compounds and of 3-indoleacetic acid in plant tissues. *Contr. Boyce Thompson Inst.* **17,** 197.

VLITOS, A. J., and MEUDT, W. (1954a). The role of auxin in plant flowering. II. Methods for the extraction and quantitative chemical determination of free 3-indoleacetic acid and other indole compounds from plant tissues. *Contr. Boyce Thompson Inst.* **17,** 401.

VLITOS, A. J., and MEUDT, W. (1954b). The role of auxin in plant flowering. III. Free indole acids in short-day plants grown under photoinductive and non-photoinductive daylengths. *Contr. Boyce Thompson Inst.* **17,** 413.

THE BIOGENESIS OF NATURAL AUXINS

S. A. Gordon

Division of Biological and Medical Research, Argonne National Laboratory, Lemont, Illinois

In attempting to organize material for this symposium, I realised that extremely little is known about how auxin is synthesized in the plant. Biochemical pathways and intermediates are easily formulated, and, unfortunately, much too easily accepted. It is indeed fitting to bring to an institution such as Wye College, whose tradition verges into the mythological past, a topic so rich in mythology. In this paper I will attempt to summarize current ideas of auxin biosynthesis and point out a few of the uncertainties.

Most of us accept the pragmatic definition of auxins: growth substances that, though of multiple effect, have the specific ability to stimulate cell enlargement in shoots. Essentially it is a definition resting ultimately on bio-assay. With this biological criterion, what is the native auxin of higher plants?

Two decades ago this question could be readily answered—auxins *a* and *b*. Since then a number of attempts to repeat the original classical work have not succeeded, and many experiments indicated that the auxin in plant extracts and diffusates was indoleacetic acid (IAA). Several workers then took the position that IAA was the only auxin of higher plants. This position was equally unwarranted, since it was based almost entirely on indirect tests of doubtful validity: stability of activity in acid and alkali, molecular weight by diffusion velocity, dose-response curves, biological responses elicited by natural extracts as compared to pure auxins, colour tests, and destruction by 'IAA oxidase'.

Auxin is not a chemically specific term; it encompasses a large number of compounds having certain structural similarities. In the past few years less equivocal techniques have identified chemically, or indicated chromatographically, the presence in plants of ethyl indoleacetate, indoleacetonitrile, indoleacetaldehyde, and indolepyruvic acid. These compounds are all biologically active and may be classified as auxins since at low concentrations they stimulate cell elongation. I believe it is profitable, however, to consider that they are inactive *per se*, and exhibit activity only after being converted to IAA. Though this generalization cannot be rigorously defended, it seems particularly appropriate to the identified indolyl substances. Many of the responses these substances elicit are concomitantly accompanied by the formation of IAA. Indeed, indoleacetonitrile appears active only in those plant species or organs possessing an active mechanism for hydrolysing this nitrile to the acid. Thus, it does not seem unreasonable, at the moment, to assume that the native auxin of hormonal function in the plant is IAA. Pure IAA has the characteristics of polar transport, correlative action, and histogenicity as the native auxin formed at production loci. On this basis, our title of natural auxin biogenesis may be altered to the more specific topic of IAA biosynthesis.

Schematic pathways of IAA biogenesis are familiar to most of you. *Figure 1* indicates a recent version.

The concept that tryptophan was the primary precursor of IAA in plants arose from the works of Dolk, Nielson, and Thimann in the early nineteen-thirties, culminating in the isolation and characterization of IAA from *Rhizopus* cultures by Thimann (1935). Since the yield of auxin in cultures of

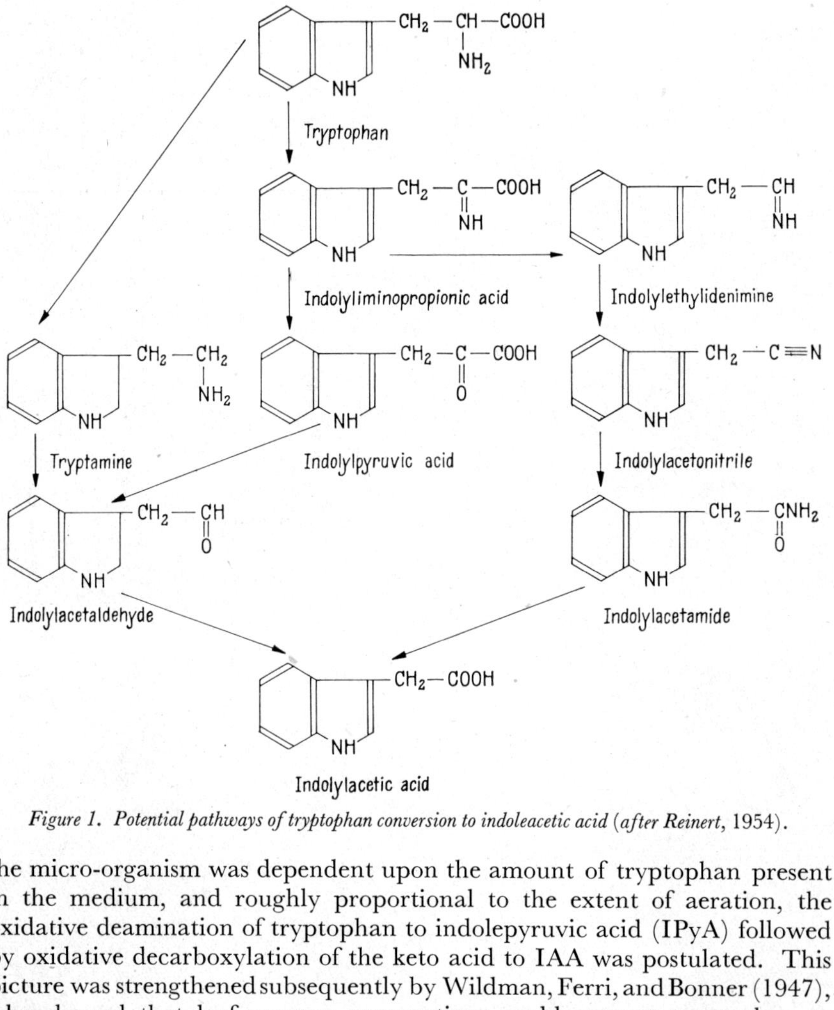

Figure 1. Potential pathways of tryptophan conversion to indoleacetic acid (after Reinert, 1954).

the micro-organism was dependent upon the amount of tryptophan present in the medium, and roughly proportional to the extent of aeration, the oxidative deamination of tryptophan to indolepyruvic acid (IPyA) followed by oxidative decarboxylation of the keto acid to IAA was postulated. This picture was strengthened subsequently by Wildman, Ferri, and Bonner (1947), who showed that leaf enzyme preparations could convert tryptophan to auxin or IAA, and that IPyA could also function as a source of auxin. Since Skoog (1937) found that tryptamine as well as tryptophan was converted slowly to auxin when applied to coleoptiles, the alternative pathway of tryptamine oxidation to IAA via indoleacetaldehyde was proposed. The existence of this dual pathway was also suggested by the results with whole tissue and enzyme preparations of the pineapple leaf. With these materials, the tryptophan to indoleacetaldehyde to IAA reactions apparently took place; either the amine or keto-acid could act as potential precursors of the aldehyde and auxin.

Many experimental results indirectly support the concept of tryptophan as the primary precursor. There is the almost ubiquitous occurrence of the tryptophan–IAA enzyme system in metabolically active tissues. There is also a parallelism in the relative enzyme activity and substrate concentration with known auxin production loci, and a parallelism between endogenous auxin level and tryptophan availability.

Further support for the thesis that native auxin or IAA is formed from tryptophan can be adduced from experiments dealing with the responses of

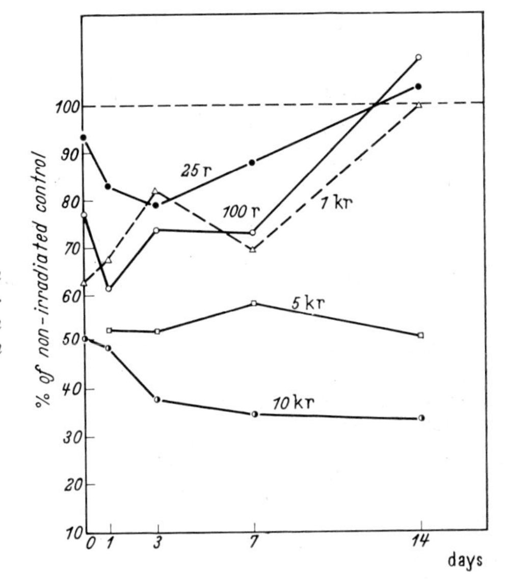

Figure 2. Relative free auxin levels in kidney bean plants following X-irradiation. The values shown were derived from the μg free auxin found per plant (bio-assay).

plants to ionizing radiation (Gordon, 1955). Low doses of ionizing radiation cause an immediate depression of free auxin levels in various plant species. For example, *Figure 2* indicates the relative auxin levels in kidney bean plants at various intervals after exposure to X-radiation. It may be observed that all the dosages employed, beginning at 25 r, caused an immediate depression of free auxin level. With the lower radiation dosages apparent recovery to control level was attained within one or two weeks. Inhibition and no recovery resulted after irradiations of 5 and 10 kr. The assumption that the lowering of auxin levels was caused by reduced rates of auxin production was substantiated by a number of studies on the effect of radiation on morphological phenomena known to depend on continued auxin production.

This sensitivity to irradiation and the pattern of temporary inhibition and recovery is closely paralleled by the effect of radiation on the enzymes converting tryptophan to IAA. *Figures 3, 4,* and *5* indicate that the enzyme system in mung bean seedlings may be examined under conditions where the conversion of tryptophan to auxin as a function of time is approximately linear. Substrate saturation and linear conversion may be attained *in vivo* by

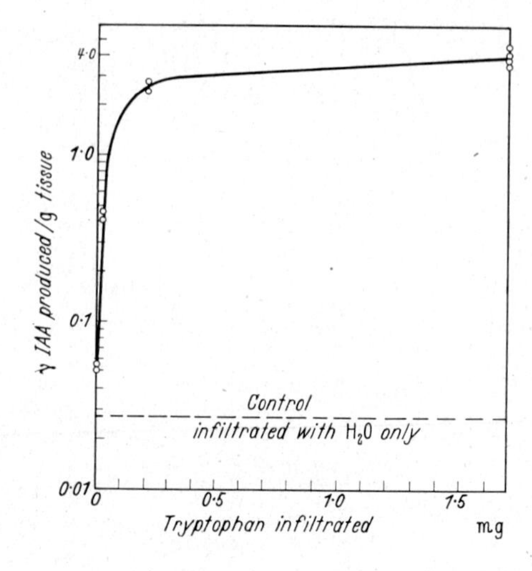

Figure 3. Auxin production in mung bean seedlings as a function of the weight of tryptophan incorporated into 5 plants by vacuum infiltration.

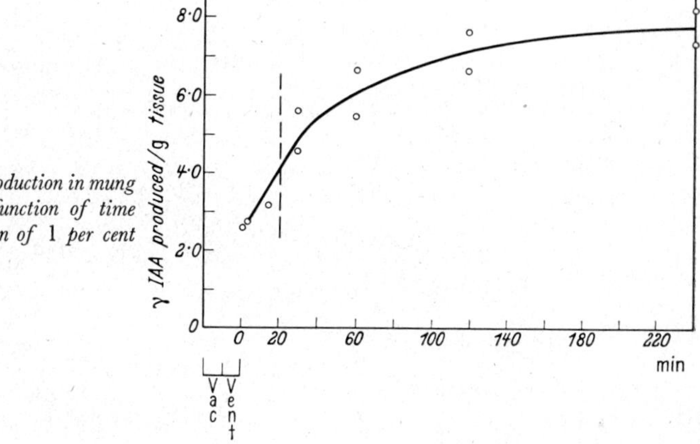

Figure 4. Auxin production in mung bean seedlings as a function of time after vacuum infiltration of 1 *per cent tryptophan.*

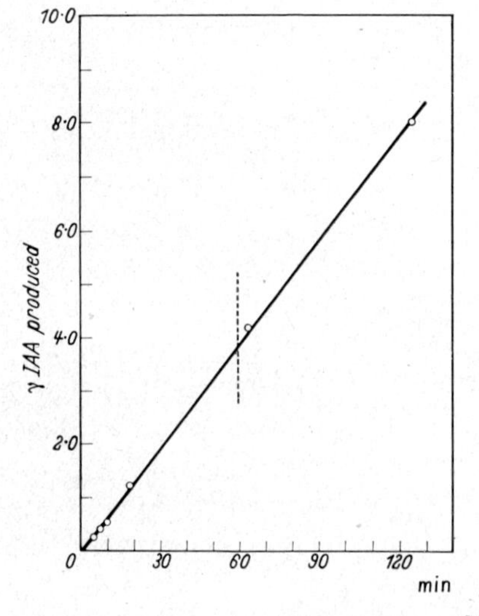

Figure 5. The in vitro *conversion of tryptophan to auxin (cell-free homogenates of mung bean seedlings).*

vacuum infiltration of tryptophan (*Figures 3* and *4*) or *in vitro* by the use of cell-free enzyme preparations (*Figure 5*). The vertical broken lines indicate the incubation times used in examining the effect of X-radiation on the activity of the tryptophan to IAA enzyme system.

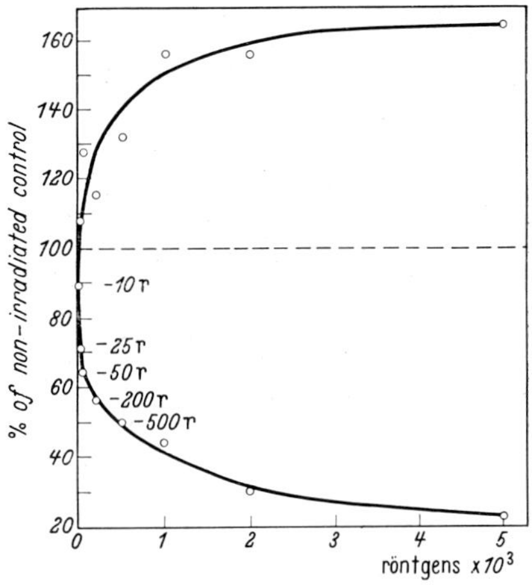

Figure 6. The in vitro *conversion of tryptophan to auxin by cell-free homogenates made from mung bean seedlings immediately after X-irradiation. The lower curve gives the relative amounts of IAA formed, the upper curve indoleacetaldehyde.*

The radiation sensitivity *in vivo* of the tryptophan–IAA enzyme is shown in *Figure 6*. Unusually low doses of X-rays inhibited the conversion of tryptophan to IAA. An almost identical response to irradiation was shown using the

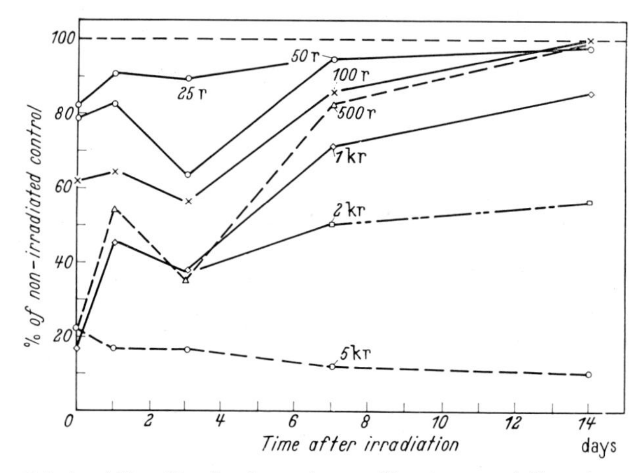

Figure 7. Relative ability of irradiated mung bean seedlings to convert infiltrated tryptophan to auxin at various times after irradiation.

vacuum-infiltration technique. The order of dosage required for inhibition of enzyme activity is similar to that shown in *Figure 2* for the reduction *in vivo* of free auxin level by X-radiation.

Figure 7 describes the post-irradiation responses of the enzyme system. Represented are the inhibitions and recoveries in the rates of tryptophan conversion relative to non-irradiated controls. It can be seen that the extent of inhibition following irradiation increases as the dose becomes larger. A recovery of biosynthetic ability is manifest up to about 1 kr. Recovery is virtually complete at either one or two weeks with the lowest dosages; partial recovery has been attained in two weeks by the plants receiving 1 kr; an inhibition with no recovery is shown by the seedlings receiving 5 kr. Again the similarity to *Figure 2* is clear. The parallel effects of radiation on auxin production (as indicated by free auxin assays and morphological studies) and on tryptophan conversion to IAA offers strong supporting evidence that the two processes are synonymous.

The effect of ionizing radiation on auxin formation may be tied a little closer, albeit less rigorously, to the accepted pathway of indoleacetate formation. *Figure 6* indicates that the presumed immediate precursor of IAA,

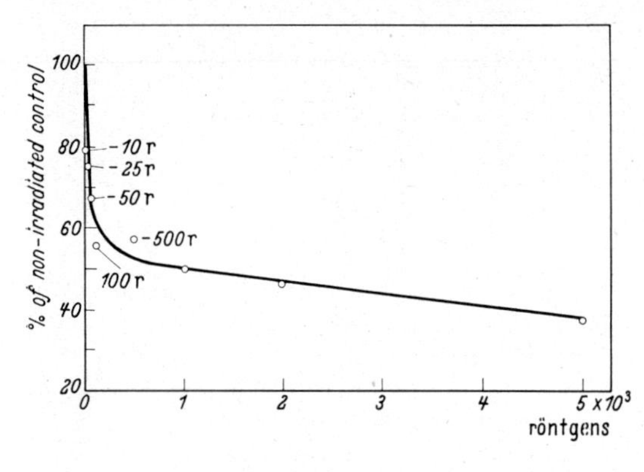

Figure 8. The relative conversion of crude indoleacetaldehyde to auxin by cell-free homogenates of X-irradiated mung bean seedlings.

indoleacetaldehyde, piles up during the conversion of tryptophan to IAA by homogenates of irradiated tissues. The same phenomenon was observed in the conversion of infiltrated tryptophan by irradiated plants. The evidence that we are really dealing with indoleacetaldehyde in these experiments is not unequivocal. The substance is neutral, possesses no or little activity in the *Avena* curvature test when tested directly, but is converted to IAA by coleoptile preparations and forms adducts with dimedone and bisulphite.

We assumed that this substance was indoleacetaldehyde. Its accumulation suggested that the radiation block occurred at the enzyme which oxidizes the aldehyde to the acid, analogous to the biochemical blocks in *Neurospera* mutants. It appeared desirable, therefore, to examine more directly the effect of irradiation on the activity of the terminal enzyme. *Figure 8* shows the relative conversion of crude preparations of indoleacetaldehyde to IAA by homogenates of irradiated tissues. Here again there is apparent the unusual *in vivo* sensitivity and dose response to ionizing radiation. It may be concluded that the radiation damage to IAA biosynthesis from tryptophan occurs at the oxidation of indoleacetaldehyde to IAA. If this is true, these experiments support the view that the aldehyde is an intermediate in auxin biogenesis.

We might at this point begin to examine more critically certain portions of the pathways of indoleacetate formation represented in *Figure 1.* We mentioned that the coleoptile can convert tryptamine to auxin and that leaves and leaf preparations of the pineapple plant form both the aldehyde and IAA from the amine. Even though active amine oxidases which could produce the corresponding aldehyde have been shown to occur in plants and animals, certain plants cannot utilize tryptamine in the formation of auxin or IAA. No auxin is formed from tryptamine by the spinach leaf. Neither mung bean seedlings nor cultures of *U. zea* will produce IAA from tryptamine. Perhaps more conclusive evidence for the non-participation of the amine is available from recent experiments with amine–oxidase inhibitors by Dr. R. Moss in our laboratory. In *Table 1* are shown the effects of both enzyme inhibitors and

Table 1
Amine–oxidase inhibitors and auxin formation

Inhibitor	*% Inhibition*		
	Tryptamine oxidation (O_2 *uptake*)	*Tryptamine to IAA*	*Tryptophan to IAA*
Marsalid 10^{-2} M	70	100	0
αα-Dipyridyl 10^{-3} M	100	90	0
n-Butylamine 10^{-2} M	+	31	0
Spermine 10^{-2} M	+	24	0
1:3-Diaminopropane 10^{-2} M	+	13	0

In all experiments, tryptamine and tryptophan $2{\cdot}5 \times 10^{-2}$ M.

competitive substrates on tryptamine oxidation and auxin formation. It may be seen that the first two compounds, marsalid and dipyridyl, inhibited almost completely the oxidation of tryptamine and the conversion of tryptamine to IAA. However, these compounds had no observable effect on the enzymatic conversion of tryptophan to IAA. Similarly, the monoamines and the diamine inhibited both tryptamine oxidation and conversion, but had no effect on the tryptophan reaction. If one may extrapolate to other plant materials from these experiments, it appears highly unlikely that tryptamine functions as an intermediate in the formation of IAA from tryptophan.

On the basis of comparative biochemistry, one might anticipate that indolepyruvate would be the more probable intermediate. Here again a scepticism is warranted on the basis of the experimental evidence available. Experiments with the keto-acid are complicated by its high degree of spontaneous breakdown to both IAA and the aldehyde as well as to other indole compounds. If corrections are made for spontaneous breakdown, or if enzymatic examination is facilitated by removal of the unreacted keto-acid as the phenylhydrazone after incubation, certain generalizations may be made. Several plant species can accelerate enzymatically the conversion of indolepyruvate to IAA. In this conversion, it has been shown with a number of plant tissues or plant preparations that no significant rise occurs in the level of the neutral component possessing the characteristics of the aldehyde. On the other hand, a similar treatment of tryptophan results in quite significant rises in level of the neutral component considered to be indoleacetaldehyde. At first glance this would suggest that the keto-acid is not an intermediate in the conversion of tryptophan to IAA.

This inference tends to be supported by the studies with ionizing radiation. The enzymatic conversion of indolepyruvate to IAA is not appreciably affected by ionizing radiation. It will be recalled from *Figures 2*, *6*, and *7* that low X-ray dosages will result in the inhibition of both native auxin formation and the formation of IAA from tryptophan. Conversely, the enzymatic transformation of indolepyruvate to IAA is not significantly affected by irradiation of mung bean plants with more than 10 kr X-ray doses. Thus, if we accept the view that indoleacetaldehyde is the immediate precursor of IAA in tryptophan conversion, a view supported by the radiation studies, the lack of inhibition of IPyA conversion to IAA by radiation makes it difficult to accept the function of IPyA in the sequence.

The conversion of IPyA to IAA without apparent formation of free aldehyde in most plant materials or preparations raises the interesting question of how the keto-acid is oxidized. By-pass of the aldehyde suggests the *ad hoc* explanation of 'simultaneous oxidative decarboxylation'. A mechanism whereby this may be accomplished was suggested by Krebs (1936) from his work on amino-acid oxidases. For example, kidney preparations will catalyse *in vitro* the oxidation of α-amino acids to yield the corresponding keto-acid and hydrogen peroxide. In the presence of catalase or a coupled peroxidative action to reduce the peroxide, the keto-acid accumulates. In the absence of a mechanism for peroxide utilization, the keto-acid undergoes further non-enzymatic oxidative decarboxylation to yield the next lower saturated acid. In terms of tryptophan conversion to IAA, this sequence can be represented as follows:

$$\mathrm{R{-}\overset{|}{\underset{|}{C}}{-}\overset{|}{\underset{\underset{NH_2}{|}}{C}}{-}COOH+O_2 \xrightarrow{\mathit{enz.}} R{-}\overset{|}{\underset{|}{C}}{-}\underset{\underset{NH}{\|}}{C}{-}COOH+H_2O_2} \qquad \ldots.(1)$$

$$\mathrm{R{-}\overset{|}{\underset{|}{C}}{-}\underset{\underset{NH}{\|}}{C}{-}COOH+H_2O \xrightarrow{\mathit{spont.}} R{-}\overset{|}{\underset{|}{C}}{-}\underset{\underset{O}{\|}}{C}{-}COOH+NH_3} \qquad \ldots.(2)$$

$$\mathrm{R{-}\overset{|}{\underset{|}{C}}{-}\underset{\underset{O}{\|}}{C}{-}COOH+H_2O_2 \longrightarrow R{-}\overset{|}{\underset{|}{C}}{-}COOH+CO_2+H_2O} \qquad \ldots.(3)$$

While it appears likely that reactions (2) and (3) may occur in the plant, evidence so far is against the occurrence of reaction (1). Plant amino-acid oxidases active on tryptophan are notable by their absence, or, if indicated, are of so low activity as to be of questionable significance. Of course, the low concentration of IAA in tissues and the low yields of IAA obtained from tryptophan might be considered evidence for the function of an enzyme in low concentration. At the moment, however, I would tend to discount the idea of an active tryptophan oxidase participating in IPyA synthesis.

If IPyA does function in IAA formation from tryptophan, a *trans*aminase active on tryptophan might be considered as a mechanism whereby the keto-acid is formed. This seems plausible, since IPyA will replace tryptophan as an essential amino acid in animals. It is of interest in this connection that no enhancement whatsoever of tryptophan conversion to IAA is obtained when α-keto-glutarate is added to suitable enzyme preparations, even with the amino acid in relatively high concentration. Hence one would also tend to discount a *trans*aminase reaction on tryptophan as a primary reaction in the biogenesis of auxin. Verification that IPyA occurs as such in plants is needed. If we accept the chromatographic evidence that it does occur, there appears to be no experimental basis for assuming that it is formed from tryptophan.

I would like to consider at this point a mechanism of pyruvate dehydrogenase action that may tie together a number of observations. Let us assume

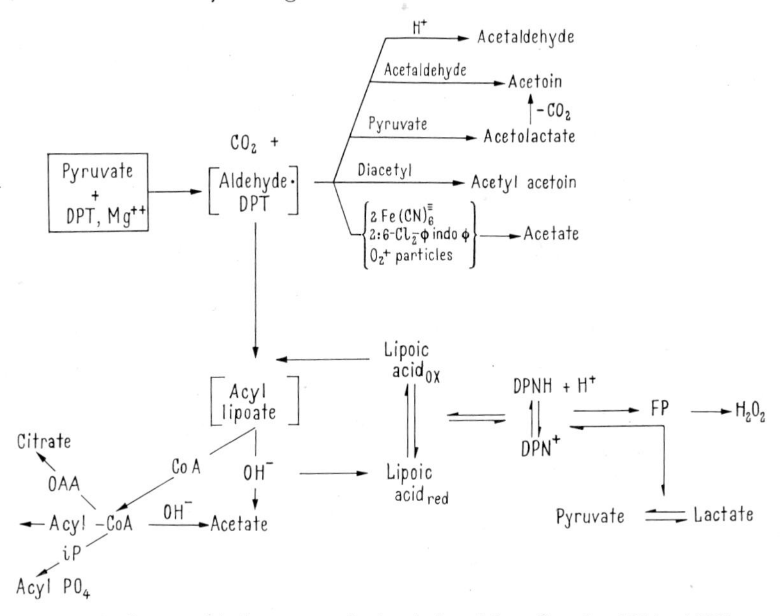

Figure 9. Pyruvate dehydrogenase mechanism (adapted from Gunsalus, 1954; 1955).

that IPyA occurs in plants and that it is derived from tryptophan. It may be suggested that the subsequent steps of auxin formation proceed by a sequence analogous to the dehydrogenase mechanism proposed for pyruvic acid oxidation (*Figure 9*). The 'core' of these reactions is the formation of an intermediate 'aldehyde-diphosphothiamine' or 'aldehyde-DPT-enzyme' compound, followed by donor reactions for the aldehyde. Oxidation to the acyl-CoA would occur via reduction of lipoic acid without the liberation of free aldehyde or acetate. Hydrolysis of the CoA ester would then yield the free acid. Alternatively, the free acid may arise directly from the aldehyde-DPT either enzymatically or non-enzymatically in the presence of suitable electron acceptors.

The above sequence would account for the conversion of IPyA to IAA by some tissues and tissue preparations either with or without the concomitant formation of free aldehyde. It is pertinent that free aldehyde also may be liberated from the DPT-complex in the presence of proton donors; possibly pertinent also is the observation by Nance that acetaldehyde is liberated from some tissues by the addition of chlorophenol or indolephenol. This suggests that free aldehyde liberation depends both upon the particular redox system as well as upon the aldehyde diversion reactions present in tissues or heterogeneous tissue preparations. It would be of considerable interest to establish whether the mechanism indicated in *Figure 9* operates with the indolyl analogue of pyruvic acid, and whether the sequence can be blocked by dimedone or bisulphite. Either of these carbonyl reagents will completely inhibit the conversion of tryptophan to IAA.

The recent work of Leopold and Guernsey (1953), supported in part by that of Siegel and Galston (1953), is appropriate in this connection. It may be recalled from the former work that auxins enhanced sulphydryl oxidation in CoA mixtures; the latter work indicated that esterification of auxin with CoA does occur. Moreover, the results of Leopold and Guernsey show a fascinating correlation between the physiological activity of various auxins and their ability to enhance what is presumably CoA esterification *in vitro*. Additional significance may therefore be attached to the hypothetical scheme. It implies that (1) the process of auxin formation may be channeled directly into the auxin action mechanism without necessarily going to free IAA; (2) administered IAA and other auxins function by backing into the mechanisms of auxin action (as well as auxin 'inactivation') as the acyl ester; (3) the auxin which functions as a hormone, i.e. as a translocated free acid, is the residual of concomitant biosynthetic and depletion mechanisms. Attractive as such a hypothesis may be, the operation of the pyruvate dehydrogenase mechanism upon which it is based is difficult to reconcile with the inhibitions occurring after irradiation by X-rays. The enzymatic conversions of tryptophan and indoleacetaldehyde are highly radiosensitive, whereas very large doses of radiation have no observable effect on the enzymatic transformation of indolepyruvate to IAA in the same plant material.

Finally, we may glance again at *Figure 1* and comment briefly about the nitrile (IAN). Although the existence of IAN in one family of plants may be considered as established, the mechanisms of nitrile biosynthesis and of hydrolysis to IAA indicated in *Figure 1* are very hypothetical. There is no evidence that the nitrile arises from tryptophan *in vivo*, or even that a mechanism for the transformation of tryptophan to IAN exists in plant tissue. While hydrolysis of the nitrile to IAA in a number of plant tissues does occur, apparently the amide is not an intermediate as suggested by Jones *et al.* (1952). In the chromatographic examination of IAN hydrolysed by plant preparations, Stowe and Thimann (1954) could find no trace of the amide, though they did identify IAA. The lack or low activity of IAN as an auxin in a number of plant tissues where IAA is active, and the absence of a mechanism converting the nitrile to an acid in many tissues able to utilize tryptophan, makes it rather unlikely that IAN is a normal intermediate in the conversion of tryptophan to IAA.

In brief, at this time it can be said that tryptophan quite likely is the primary precursor of IAA, that indoleacetaldehyde probably is involved either as a free or complexed carbonyl, that indolepyruvate may be involved, and that tryptamine and indoleacetonitrile probably are not involved in normal auxin production (see also Gordon, 1954). If the keto-acid does participate, the possibility of a pyruvate dehydrogenase mechanism has interesting implications.

In conclusion, I hope I have left the impression that pathways of auxin biosynthesis and interconversion are by no means clearly understood. In a very real sense the work is just beginning, because we have only now reached the stage of being able to define the problem. The field of auxin anabolism merits a concerted attack—not only as a provocative problem in biochemistry, but also as a physiological sequence functioning as a morphogenetic determinant.

REFERENCES

GORDON, S. A. (1954). Occurrence, formation, and inactivation of auxins. *Annu. Rev. Pl. Physiol.* **5,** 341.

GORDON, S. A. (1955). Studies on the mechanism of phytohormone damage by ionizing radiation. *Proc. int. Conf. Atomic Energy*, A/8/P/97, Geneva, Switzerland.

GUNSALUS, I. C. (1954). Oxidative and transfer reaction of lipoic acid. *Fed. Proc.* **13,** 715.

GUNSALUS, I. C., HORECKER, B. L., and WOOD, W. A. (1955). Pathways of carbohydrate metabolism in microorganisms. *Bact. Rev.* **19,** 79.

JONES, E. R. H., HENBEST, H. B., SMITH, G. F., and BENTLEY, J. A. (1952). 3-indolylacetonitrile: a naturally occurring plant growth hormone. *Nature*, **169,** 485.

KREBS, H. A. (1936). Metabolism of amino acids and related substances. *Annu. Rev. Biochem.* **5,** 247.

LEOPOLD, A. C., and GUERNSEY, F. S. (1953). A theory of auxin action involving coenzyme A. *Proc. Nat. Acad. Sci., Wash.* **39,** 1105.

REINERT, J. (1954). Wachstum. *Fortschr. Bot.* **16,** 330.

SIEGEL, S. M., and GALSTON, A. W. (1953). Experimental coupling of indoleacetic acid to pea root protein *in vivo* and *in vitro*. *Proc. Nat. Acad. Sci., Wash.* **39,** 1111.

SKOOG, F. (1937). A deseeded *Avena* test method for small amounts of auxin and auxin precursors. *J. gen. Physiol.* **20,** 311.

STOWE, B., and THIMANN, K. V. (1954). The paper chromatography of indole compounds and some indole-containing auxins of plant tissues. *Arch. Biochem. Biophys.* **51,** 499.

THIMANN, K. V. (1935). On the plant growth hormone produced by *Rhizopus suinus*. *J. biol. Chem.* **109,** 279.

WILDMAN, S. G., FERRI, M. G., and BONNER, J. (1947). The enzymatic conversion of tryptophan to auxin by spinach leaves. *Arch. Biochem.* **13,** 131.

GEOTROPIC RESPONSES IN ROOTS. SOME THEORETICAL AND TECHNICAL PROBLEMS

P. LARSEN

Botanical Laboratory, University of Bergen

THE AUXIN THEORY OF GEOTROPISM

THE auxin theory of geotropism offers a logical explanation of the upward curvature of stems and coleoptiles. The theory has been extended to explain the downward curvature of main roots as well. At least in the textbooks, the existence of a supra-optimal auxin content in roots is generally accepted. The well-known schematic curve (*Figure 1*), representing the relationship between growth rate and internal auxin concentration in the elongation zone of roots, is the basis of the explanation of the downward curvature. We assume that the internal auxin concentration is supra-optimal for growth (point *A* on the curve of *Figure 1*). An additional supply of auxin to the

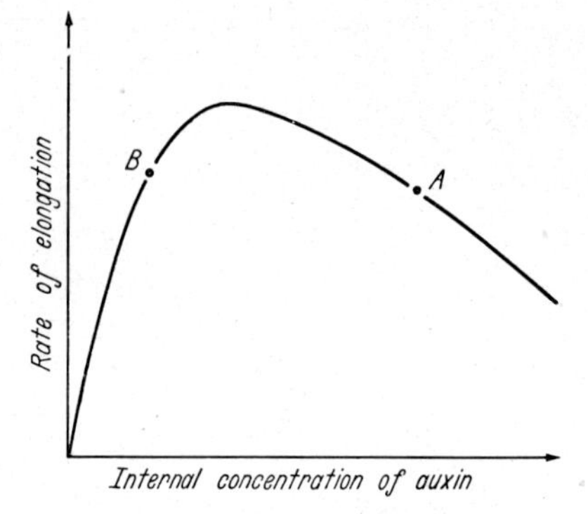

Figure 1. Schematic representation of the relationship between growth rate and internal auxin concentration in roots.

lower side of a main root placed in the horizontal position will thus retard the growth rate of that side, and consequently the root will curve downward. The theory seems to be well founded since both the higher auxin concentration in the lower half of the root and the retarding effect of added auxin on the rate of root elongation have been demonstrated experimentally.

There are, however, various points in this theory which need clarification.

1. Firstly, is the internal auxin concentration really supra-optimal? This problem has been approached by observation of the effect of decapitation on the rate of elongation of roots. In several cases, decapitation results in an increase of the rate of elongation and this has been interpreted as a consequence of reducing the supra-optimal, internal auxin concentration to values closer to the optimum. The operation itself may have an influence on the growth rate, but one would expect that the effect of wounding would most likely be a retardation of growth. In various cases, decapitation actually decreases the growth rate; in those instances, however, in which a growth acceleration was noted, the result favours the concept that the normal, internal auxin concentration is supra-optimal.

Another method of approach has involved the external application of auxins to the roots. In this connection, only normal intact roots are of interest. The response of isolated or decapitated roots, in which the auxin level has been reduced artificially, permits no conclusions as to the auxin level in intact roots.

A mostly slight, but significant acceleration of root elongation following the addition of auxin has been demonstrated in a number of roots (*Table 1*). These results seem to indicate a sub-optimal auxin concentration in the roots (point *B* in *Figure 1*). It would still be possible to apply the classical auxin theory of geotropism to such roots. The change in auxin concentration would only have to be large enough to bring the concentration in the lower half of the root well above the optimum. Theoretically, one would expect that very slight geotropic stimulations would result in negative curvatures, but these might be so small and transitory that they would escape observation.

Table 1

Examples of stimulation of elongation in intact roots after application of IAA

Reference	*Plant*	*Time of observation*†	*Concentration, mols/l.*	*Elongation, % of control*
Macht and Grumbein, 1937	Lupinus	24 hours‡ 24 hours§	$5{\cdot}7 \times 10^{-9}$ $1{\cdot}1 \times 10^{-9}$	115 112
Thimann and Lane, 1938	Avena	24 hours 48 hours	$5{\cdot}7 \times 10^{-11}$ $5{\cdot}7 \times 10^{-11}$	136 117
Naundorf, 1940	Helianthus	5 hours	10^{-8}	220
Lundegårdh, 1942	Triticum	6 days	10^{-8}	120
Moewus, 1949	Lepidium	17 hours	$5{\cdot}7 \times 10^{-11}$	115
Linser, 1949	Lepidium	17 hours	$5{\cdot}7 \times 10^{-11}$	110
Pohl and Ochs, 1953	Lepidium	17 hours	$5{\cdot}7 \times 10^{-13}$	114
Pilet, 1951,	Lens‖			
Fig. 19	1 day old	24 hours	10^{-7}	909
Fig. 20	6 days old	24 hours	10^{-9}	185
Fig. 21	12 days old	24 hours	10^{-11}	151
Ashby, 1951	Artemisia	24 hours	$5{\cdot}7 \times 10^{-10}$	114

† After application of IAA.
‡ § Auxin treatment 15 and 40 minutes, respectively.
‖ Treated with K-salt of IAA.

It can be questioned, however, whether the reported results really indicate sub-optimal auxin concentrations. As far as can be seen from the papers cited (*Table 1*), the positive response to added auxin was noted only after several hours, generally 17 hours or more. Only Naundorf (1940) reported a considerable increase in root length (in *Helianthus*) 5 hours after the addition of auxin. But even 5 hours is a very long time as compared with the time required for a geotropic response to become manifest. In *Artemisia* roots, the geotropic reaction time is less than 8 minutes. Thus in order to test the auxin theory of geotropism in roots we need information on the response of the roots within, say, less than half an hour after the application of auxin. There are but few studies on the effect of auxin on the elongation of roots within such a short time, and all of these show retardation rather than acceleration of growth. Some observations showed that a growth acceleration, if found, was preceded by a retardation of elongation (e.g. Thimann and Lane, 1938), but there are several cases in which retardation only, with no acceleration of root growth, was found. Thus, for example, Seiler (1951) measured the elongation of maize roots at 20-minute intervals and found that the application of IAA for 30 seconds resulted in a transitory retardation of elongation, no acceleration of growth being observed up to 4 hours after treatment with IAA. Lundegårdh (1949) was able to measure root elongation at 4-minute intervals, and although he had previously reported acceleration of the elongation of wheat roots 6 days after the addition of auxin (Lundegårdh, 1942), he found only retardation when the response was recorded after a few hours (1942) or after less than one hour (1949). Similarly Ashby (1951) showed that auxin increased the growth rate of *Artemisia* roots when measured 24 hours after the application of auxin, but found no effect, or even a slight retardation, after 4 hours (*Table 2*).

Table 2

The time factor in auxin-induced stimulation of root elongation

Reference	*Plant*	*Time of observation*†	*Concentration of IAA. mols/l*	*Elongation, % of control*
Lundegårdh, 1942	Triticum	6 days	10^{-8}	120
		3–6 hours	10^{-8}	77
		0–3 hours	10^{-8}	53
Lundegårdh, 1949	Triticum	32–60 minutes	10^{-8}	34
		0–4 minutes	10^{-8}	34
Ashby, 1951	Artemisia	24 hours	$5{\cdot}7\times10^{-10}$	114
		4 hours	$5{\cdot}7\times10^{-10}$	94

† After application of auxin.

According to Burström (1942, 1950, 1954), an auxin-induced acceleration of elongation in individual root cells, when such acceleration occurs, is caused by a stimulation of the first phase of cell stretching (characterized by a dissolution of the cell-wall material). The second phase of cell elongation (characterized by intussusception of new cell-wall material) can only be retarded by auxin. Thus, an over-all acceleration of elongation can be brought about by the addition of auxin only if its concentration is so low that the acceleration of the first phase of growth is not completely masked by a retardation of the second phase. However, since the rate of cell elongation during the first phase is low, it is reasonable to assume that the immediate effect of added auxin on total root elongation will be dominated by the influence of the auxin on the second phase of elongation. We should, therefore, expect that the effect, if any, which can be recorded within a few minutes would be a retardation of elongation. The effect of a stimulation of the first phase may not contribute materially to the rate of total elongation until much later. An increase in growth rate observed several days after the addition of auxin can further be in part attributed to a possible adaptation to higher auxin concentrations.

When a root is placed in the horizontal position, the auxin concentration soon increases in the lower half of the root. In view of the above considerations, one would expect that the immediate effect of the local excess of auxin on the second phase of cell stretching would dominate over any effect on the first phase, giving rise to an over-all retardation of growth in the lower half of the root.

It thus seems that we can still apply the classical auxin theory to the geotropic responses of main roots, even to such roots which in long-term experiments have shown a significant acceleration of elongation as a consequence of external additions of suitable concentrations of auxin. It is entirely possible, and indeed most likely, that the observed acceleration of elongation has been preceded by a retardation of growth. The reported cases of an auxin-induced acceleration of the growth of intact roots do not necessitate modifications of the classical auxin theory of geotropism until such accelerations have been found to be manifest within less than 30 or 60 minutes (see, for example, Pilet, 1953).

2. Another problem is the nature of the mechanism which leads to the unequal distribution of auxin in geotropically stimulated roots. It is a widely accepted idea that in horizontally placed roots auxin moves from the upper to the lower side within the root tip itself, and thereby the supply of auxin to the elongation zone increases in the lower half of the root and decreases in the upper. However, it has been suggested that other mechanisms may also be operative. The idea of an acropetal flow of auxin has been put forward by Czaja (1935) and by Pilet (1951). If such a current exists, its role in normal geotropic responses should be considered. It should be made clear whether the acropetal current carries an auxin or an auxin precursor.

3. A third point is the possibility of a synthesis of auxin as a consequence of geotropic stimulation. Such a synthesis has been demonstrated by Schmitz (1933) in stems of grasses rotating parallel to the horizontal axis of the klinostat. Similarly rotated hypocotyls of *Lupinus* have been shown to yield more auxin than upright ones (Brain, 1942). Van Overbeek and his co-workers (1945) demonstrated a production of auxin in the so-called growth ring of sugar cane after placing stem portions of this plant in the horizontal position. Bünning (1948, p. 418) has suggested that the geotropically induced synthesis of auxin in nodes of grasses may not be a phenomenon peculiar to this particular organ, but may be of general occurrence. This is a point which should also be studied in the case of roots. Again, however, geotropically induced synthesis of auxin has been demonstrated only in experiments of comparatively long duration. Such synthesis may, therefore, be of no significance for the performance of normal geotropic curvatures which become visible after a few minutes exposure to 1 *g*.

THE TECHNIQUE OF GEOTROPIC EXPERIMENTS

The preceding section served to point out a few auxin problems connected with the geotropic responses of roots. There are, of course, other problems, such as those concerning the nature of statoliths, and geo-perception as a whole. Although the writer would like to investigate some of these problems, it soon became clear that a number of technical problems had to be solved first. The studies reported in the following pages were considered a necessary prerequisite for an investigation of the role of auxin in geotropism and also for the study of other aspects of geotropic responses.

Cultivation—The classical culture method used in geotropic experiments, particularly with roots, consists in growing the plants in a so-called moist chamber. In geotropic experiments it is necessary to change the position of the plants during an experiment or to investigate the growth and responses of plants placed in different positions. The direction in which the root tip is pointing may influence the rate of elongation of the roots. The study of this influence, however, is complicated by the fact that moisture condenses on the root in a moist chamber. When roots are growing in the normal, vertical position, moisture will accumulate at the root tip as a drop of liquid. It has been shown by Cholodny (1932) and by Navez (1933) that such a drop of water at the root tip will decrease the rate of elongation of the root. On the other hand, when a root is placed in the inverted position, the moisture does not accumulate at the tip and the growth rate of inverted roots will not be diminished on *this* account. The experiment will, however, give the entirely false impression of a growth acceleration as a consequence of the inversion (cf. Larsen, 1953). When a root is placed in the horizontal position, moisture may be more or less evenly distributed at the start. As the geotropic bending proceeds, however, moisture may start accumulating at the tip. Thus, it is to be expected that the distribution of moisture on the root will influence its geotropic responses by way of the rate of elongation.

One can avoid this difficulty by using a liquid medium. Such a technique will, however, give rise to new problems if one wishes to rotate the plants on a klinostat. Moist sawdust has been used extensively in both older and quite recent studies. Cultures in sawdust may be rotated on a klinostat, but in most cases the plants have to be removed from the sawdust for observation; and even in sawdust the moisture conditions around the root may not be uniform. In order to overcome such difficulties it was decided to use agar as a medium in the present series of experiments.

An agar platelet (20×25 mm; 1 mm thick) was placed on an ordinary glass slide (see *Figure 2*). Twelve sterilized seeds of *Artemisia absinthium* (wormwood) were arranged in a row along the edge of the agar platelet. The seeds were then covered by a second agar platelet, similar in size to the first, so that the roots would develop between two layers of agar. Finally, a plastic cover was placed over the agar platelets. By using this technique the moisture conditions round the roots are made identical regardless of the orientation of the plants, the roots can be observed or photographed through the slide and the agar, and the whole plant chamber can be easily accommodated on a klinostat and rotated. Roots were used for experiments when most of them were about 2·4 mm long (actual range was 0·9 to 4·7 mm). A full description of this technique will be given elsewhere.

Klinostat rotation—When necessary, the seedlings were rotated parallel to the horizontal axis of a klinostat. The klinostat has been described previously (Larsen, 1953). It was powered by a synchronous motor, which secures a high degree of regularity in motion. In the present experiments, the 2-watt motor of the klinostat used in earlier work was exchanged for an 18-watt motor. The klinostat was further equipped with an automatic recording 24-mm camera (Robot) and a counterweight. The camera was rotated together with the plants and by means of micro-switches, the camera would make an exposure every 32 minutes or every 64 minutes. In addition, manual exposures could be made at any time during the rotation.

Measurement of the geotropic responses—One of the purposes of the present study was to determine the so-called presentation time under various conditions. For mass-acceleration of a certain strength, for instance 1 *g*, the presentation time is generally defined as the time during which the root must be stimulated in order that a minimum response may sooner or

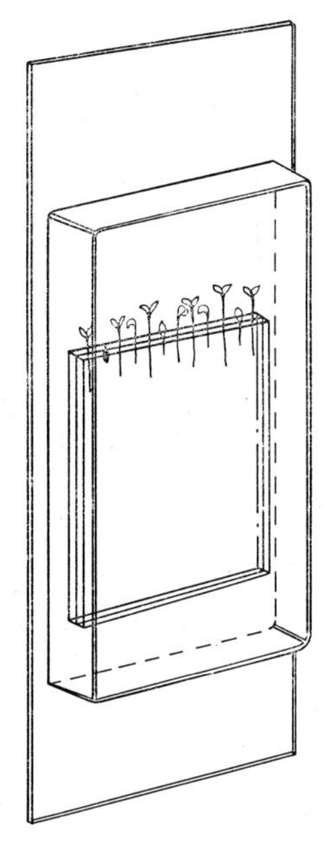

Figure 2. Plant chamber. Artemisia *seedlings growing between agar platelets on a glass slide and protected by a plastic cover.*

later become manifest. A minimum response is often defined as the development of curvatures in 50 per cent of the stimulated roots. The percentage of curving roots, however, is a very crude measure of the response and rather inconvenient for statistical treatment. If one is particularly interested in the magnitude of the reaction under various conditions, it is necessary to measure the curvature itself, and not the number of reacting roots.

Photographic recording (*Figures 3, 4,* and *5*) was used in most of the experiments. White or orange light did not show much effect, if any, on the responses. Individual angles were measured to the nearest degree by means of a suitably equipped horizontal microscope.

The effect of continuous, unilateral geotropic stimulation

Figure 3 and the upper curve in *Figure 6* show the development of curvatures in roots exposed continuously to unilateral geotropic stimulation in the horizontal position. For about 70 minutes they seem to curve at an approximately constant rate of about one-half of a degree per minute. As the angle of curvature increases, however, the intensity of the geotropic stimulus decreases with the sine of the angle which the root tip makes with the plumb

Figures 3, 4, and 5. Development of curvatures in Artemisia *roots under various experimental conditions. Prints reduced to* × 0·7. *Curvatures were measured directly on the negatives at a magnification of* ×35.

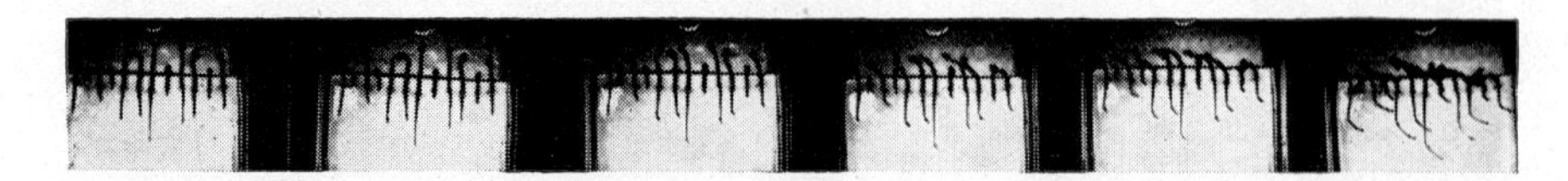

Figure 3. Continuous, unilateral exposure to gravity. Plants not rotated. Photographed at 0, 32, 64, 128, 192 *minutes, and* 10 *hours.*

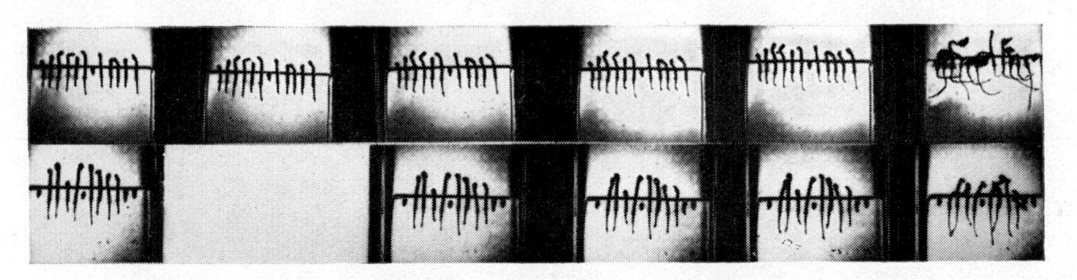

Figure 4. Rotation at 1 *revolution per* 0·5 *minutes* (*R*/0·5). Upper series: *horizontal exposure* (*E*) *for* 32 *minutes before rotation. Photographed at* 0, 32, 64, 128, 192 *minutes, and* 23·5 *hours.* Lower series: *no horizontal exposure. Photographed at* 0, 64, 128, 192 *minutes, and* 8·5 *hours.*

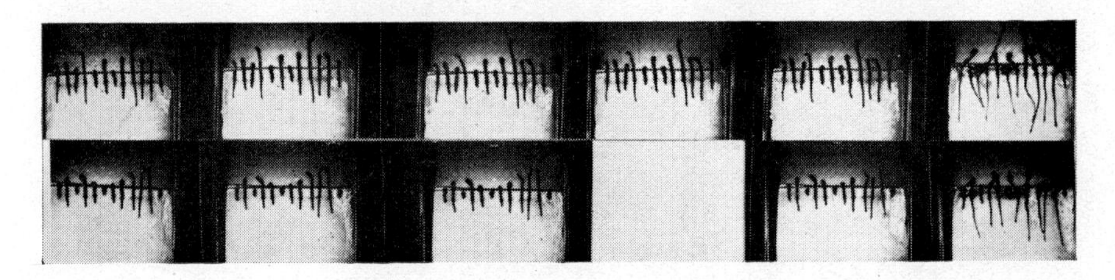

Figure 5. Rotation at 1 *revolution per* 32 *minutes* (*R*/32). Upper series: *horizontal exposure* (*E*) *for* 32 *minutes before rotation. Photographed at* 0, 32, 64, 128, 192 *minutes, and* 22 *hours.* Lower series: *no horizontal exposure. Photographed at* 0, 32, 64, 224 *minutes, and* 22 *hours.*

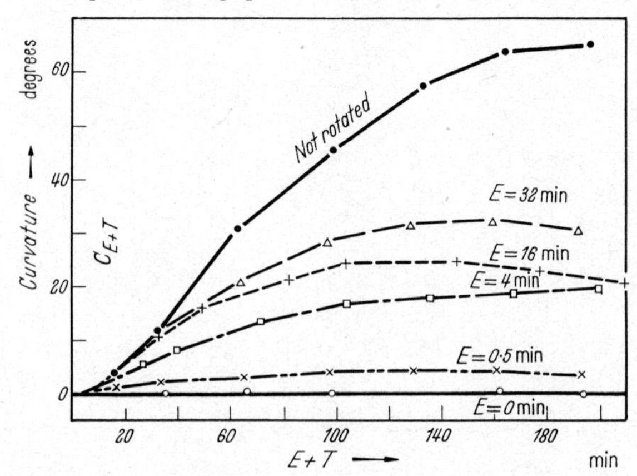

Figure 6. Development of geotropic curvatures. Ordinate: *total curvature* (C_{E+T}). Abscissa: *sum of exposure* (*E*) *in the horizontal position and the time* (*T*) *of rotation at* 1 *revolution per* 0·5 *minutes*(*R*/0·5). Upper curve: *continuous stimulation,* $T = 0$.

line. If the position of the plant were constantly adjusted in such a manner as to maintain the root tip in the horizontal position, one might expect the curvature to continue at the same constant rate for a considerable length of time.

It is clear from the upper curve in *Figure 6* that the reaction time is surprisingly short, at the most about 8 minutes. Definite curvatures could be observed after 10 minutes. Whether the curve should be extrapolated back as a straight line so as to cut the abscissa at 8 minutes, or whether it should be extrapolated as a smooth curve approaching a point closer to the origin, cannot be decided on the basis of these experiments. The latter procedure has, however, been chosen in the present work.

The approximately linear course of the curve is followed until the curvature has reached a value of about 35°. At this point the sine of the angle of attack of gravity is still large, about 0·91. After 20 hours the mean curvature is *ca.* 87°.

The effect of klinostat rotation on the development of curvatures

Plant chambers which were to be rotated were placed on the klinostat in such a position that the slides and agar slices were initially vertical, and the roots were parallel to the horizontal axis of the klinostat. Geotropic curvatures would thus develop in the plane between the agar slices.

Rotation was begun after given periods of exposure (E) in the horizontal position (mainly 0, 0·5, 4, 16, or 32 minutes). Curvatures were recorded after rotation for various lengths of time (T). Only two rates of rotation were used: 1 revolution in 0·5 minutes ($R/0{\cdot}5$), and 1 revolution in 32 minutes ($R/32$). The centrifugal forces developed by rotation were $1{\cdot}3\times10^{-4}\times g$ and $3{\cdot}2\times10^{-8}\times g$, respectively, i.e. they are entirely negligible as compared with gravitation.

Rotation at $R/0{\cdot}5$—The results of rotation at 1 revolution in 0·5 minutes are shown in *Figures 4* and *6*. If roots are first exposed for 32 minutes in the horizontal position and then rotated at $R/0{\cdot}5$, they will have developed a curvature of about 12° at the end of the exposure. They gradually enlarge their curvature during the rotation until they reach a maximum value of about 30° after some 100 minutes of rotation. The course of the curvature after that time is rather uncertain because the variability increases as a linear function of time, a consequence of the spontaneous movements (see later). After an initial exposure of 16 minutes the curvatures follow a similar, but lower course. If rotation is begun after 4 minutes of exposure, no measurable curvature has developed at the start of the rotation. Otherwise, the development of the response follows the same type of curve as in the case of longer exposures. An exposure for 0·5 minutes yields positive mean values, whereas the curvatures recorded during rotation without a preceding exposure are, on average, practically zero. After about 32 minutes of rotation, the curvatures in roots stimulated for 0·5 minutes are significantly higher than in the rotated, unstimulated roots (cf. *Figure 11*). Since the variability increases with time, a statistically significant difference could not be demonstrated after longer periods of rotation using the present set of data for exposures of 0 and 0·5 minutes. Nevertheless, we may conclude that the presentation time is shorter than 0·5 minutes.

It is now of interest to compare the course of the rotation curves from the beginning of rotation and onwards, i.e. after they leave the curve for continuous exposure, and this has been done in *Figure 7*. In the case of exposures for 16 and 32 minutes, the curvature present at the end of the exposure was subtracted from all the later values. The abscissa is the time (T) after

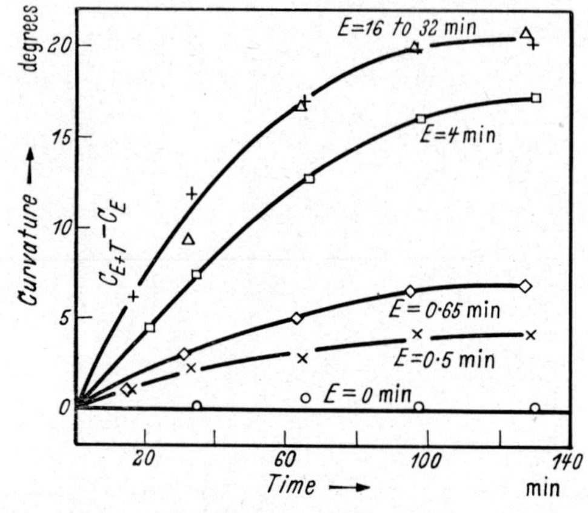

*Figure 7. Development of geotropic curvatures during rotation at R/*0·5 *on the klinostat.* Ordinate: *increase in curvature* ($C_{E+T}-C_E$) *during the period of rotation.* Abscissa: *time* (T) *after beginning of rotation. Duration of preceding horizontal exposure* (E) *indicated for each curve. Data from Figure 6.*

beginning of rotation. When it comes to exposures of 4 and 0·5 minutes, the graphic transposition requires an assumption as to the course of the lower part of the reaction curve for non-rotated roots. If this curve were to

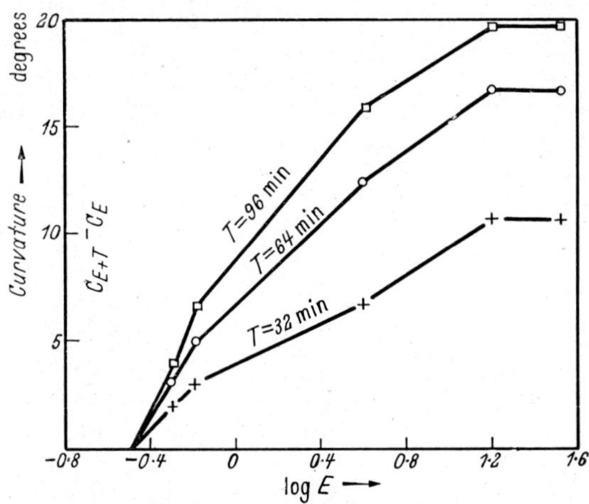

Figure 8. Attempt at an estimation of the presentation time. Ordinate: *increase in curvature during the rotation* ($C_{E+T}-C_E$), *read on curves in Figure 7 at times* (T) *indicated for each curve.* Abscissa: *logarithm of the duration of horizontal exposure* (E). *The logarithm of the presentation time (the shortest exposure which will produce a response later) estimated by extrapolation to* —0·5, *corresponding to a presentation time of* 0·3 *minutes.*

be extrapolated back as a straight line, a fictitious negative angle would be present at the beginning of rotation, and a corresponding angle should be *added* as a correction. In making this set of curves, however, it was assumed that a positive angle of about 1° was present after 4 minutes of exposure and that practically no curvature was present after 0·5 minutes.

It is seen that the development of curvatures during the rotation is practically the same after 16 and 32 minutes of exposure. Roots exposed for 0·5 and 4 minutes, on the other hand, increase their curvature at a lower rate, and they reach lower maximum values.

The initial velocity of each of the individual curves probably indicates the velocity of geotropic curvature at the end of the horizontal exposure. This is the reason for assuming an accelerated course of the lower portion of the curve for continuous exposure. It is not certain, however, whether the course of the curves in *Figure 7* reflects the velocity of the actual curvature or the velocity of some limiting process controlling the rate of geotropic bending, a process which is accelerated from almost the beginning of exposure, but which reaches a constant rate after 16 minutes, or perhaps sooner.

It may now be possible to estimate the length of the presentation time by plotting the angles of $(C_{E+T}-C_E)$ (*Figure 7*) after various times of rotation and extrapolating the resulting curves. In an attempt to do this, the angles at $T = 32$, 64, and 96 minutes were plotted against the logarithm of E (see *Figure 8*). Extrapolation yields a presentation time of 0·3 minutes.

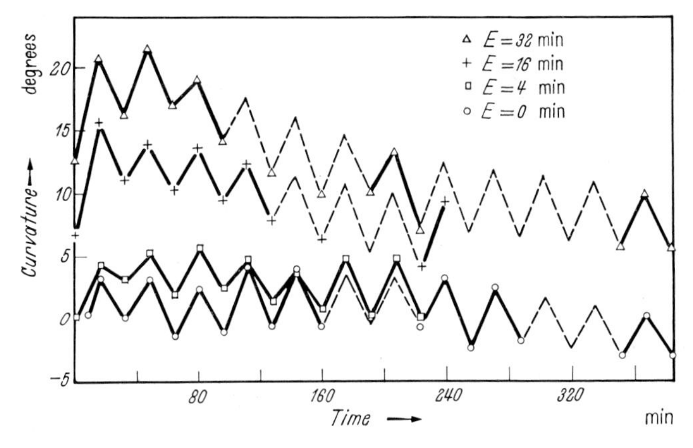

Figure 9. Development of geotropic curvatures during rotation at 1 *revolution per* 32 *minutes* (*R*/32). Ordinate: *total curvature* (C_{E+T}). Abscissa: *time* (*T*) *after beginning of rotation. Duration of preceding horizontal exposure* (*E*) *indicated. Curvature at the end of exposure can be read at* $T = 0$. *Symbols indicate actual determinations. Other maxima and minima were interpolated.*

The procedure applied here was chosen arbitrarily and other methods of graphic presentation are possible. At any rate, however, the true presentation time must be somewhat shorter than 0·5 minutes, though it is probably of this order of magnitude.

Rotation at R/32—If unstimulated roots are rotated at *R*/32, the root tips bend back and forth with an amplitude very close to 5° (*Figure 9*). This result was to be expected on the basis of the known velocity of curvature during continuous exposure to 1 *g* and the size of the opposing stimuli received during the rotation. Measurements were made at 16-minute intervals, approximately when maxima and minima were to be expected.

It was mentioned in a previous publication (Larsen, 1953) that prestimulated roots tend to straighten out again if they are rotated slowly, whereas their curvatures will increase if the plants are rotated at a higher velocity. This has been confirmed in the present experiments (*Figure 5*). The roots do not straighten out simply by curving in the direction opposite to the initial one; they follow the motion of the klinostat just as unstimulated roots do. The *spontaneous* movements which develop during rotation at *R*/0·5 seem to occur only in the plane of the interface between the two layers of agar, probably because the resistance is lower there than in other directions. The *geotropic* movements induced during rotation at *R*/32, on the other hand, most likely take place in all directions, so that the root tip follows a spiral. Deviations as small as $\pm 2{\cdot}5°$ would not be hindered much by the agar. The upper curve in *Figure 9* shows the course of the curvatures of roots which have been stimulated in the horizontal position for 32 minutes. The average curvature at the end of the exposure was about 13°. The curvatures increase during the first 16 minutes of rotation at *R*/32 and reach a maximum of about 21°. During the second half of the revolution the curvature

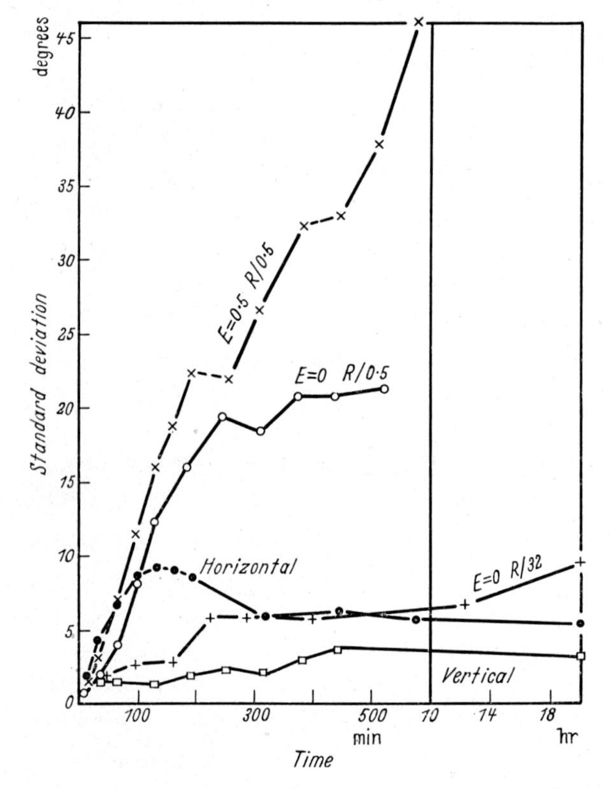

Figure 10. Variability of curvatures, a measure of the extent of the spontaneous movements. Ordinate: *standard deviation of changes in curvature from zero time to the time of each of the subsequent readings.* Abscissa: *time after first reading. Most points based on* 25–35 *degrees of freedom* (*exception*: 6 *upper* x's; $f = 17$ *or* 8).

is reduced by about 5°. During subsequent revolutions the amplitude is approximately constant, but both the maxima and the minima become lower and lower, so that after about 10 hours the root tip is pendling between 3 and 8 degrees. This pendling, probably a spiral movement, goes on for at least 12 more hours.

Spontaneous movements. Variability

When unstimulated roots are rotated at *R*/32, they remain approximately straight, apart from the spiral pendling of their tips. At *R*/0·5 on the other hand, the roots will carry out spontaneous movements, resulting in large irregular curvatures. A measure of these spontaneous movements may be obtained by taking the standard deviation of the changes in curvature which take place after the initial measurement.

Figure 10 shows the magnitude of the standard deviation of the curvatures of roots under various conditions. The squares represent roots kept in the normal, vertical position. Their spontaneous movements are small, since they are constantly being corrected by gravitational stimulation. The upright crosses represent roots which were rotated at *R*/32 without preceding stimulation. Their variability is somewhat greater than that of vertical roots, but still quite low.

If roots are placed in the horizontal position, they start carrying out geotropic movements, and this is attended by a sudden increase in their variability (filled-in circles). Part of this variability is probably due to differences in the geotropic sensitivity and reactivity of the roots. After about 100 minutes, when the roots have reached an average curvature of about 45°, the variability starts decreasing again, and at 5 hours the variability of the previously horizontal roots is the same as in roots rotated at *R*/32.

When roots are rotated at *R*/0·5, the picture is entirely different. They are subjected only to small and insignificant geotropic stimuli on the klinostat, and are free to perform spontaneous movements which are only slightly, if at all, modified by gravitational influences.

The open circles represent roots which were rotated without preceding stimulation. Their variability increases as an almost straight line for about 200 minutes and then levels off at a value (about 22°) much higher than in roots rotated at *R*/32. It should be borne in mind that the mean curvature of these roots is very close to zero.

When roots were first stimulated in the horizontal position for 0·5 minutes and then rotated at *R*/0·5 their variability followed a similar course (x's), but did not level off at 22°. After 10 hours, the variability still seemed to be increasing. The standard deviation was 46°, and the mean curvature 2·9°.

When roots are geotropically stimulated for longer periods before rotation, the spontaneous movements are superimposed on the actual response to the stimulation.

DISCUSSION AND CONCLUSIONS

The klinostat is an interesting instrument, and the present series of results do contribute to the discussion of the theory of the klinostat effect. In this communication, however, only a few points which may be considered of practical importance for the carrying out of geotropic experiments will be considered.

1. *Measurement of the response*—As pointed out previously, the practice of recording the percentage of curving roots is inconvenient for various reasons. Since the technique used in the present study permitted the detection of very small curvatures, few roots could be considered absolutely straight, even when kept in the vertical position. This is not surprising in view of the spontaneous movements which have been demonstrated.

In individual roots, the curvature present at the start rarely exceeded ±5°. A deviation of as much as ±8°, however, will have no measurable influence on the early response when a group of such roots is placed in the *horizontal* position, since the sine of 82° is still 0·99. On the other hand, roots deviating as little as 3° from the *vertical* line will be stimulated by 5 per cent of the force of gravity and thereby induced to straighten out (sin 3° = 0·05).

In the present study, the change in curvature from the start of exposure to the time of subsequent recordings was regarded as a response. *Figure 11* shows an example of the distribution of curvatures in samples of individual roots under the influence of two different treatments. If a sufficiently fine technique of measuring could be applied, nearly 50 per cent positive curvatures would be present at any time in unstimulated roots. In general practice, however, workers using 50 per cent positive curvatures as a criterion for the development of a minimum response have fixed a certain angle as a limit below which all curvatures are neglected. The size of this minimum angle depends mainly on the technique of observation. It is thus clear that, whenever such a limiting angle has been chosen, the recorded result,

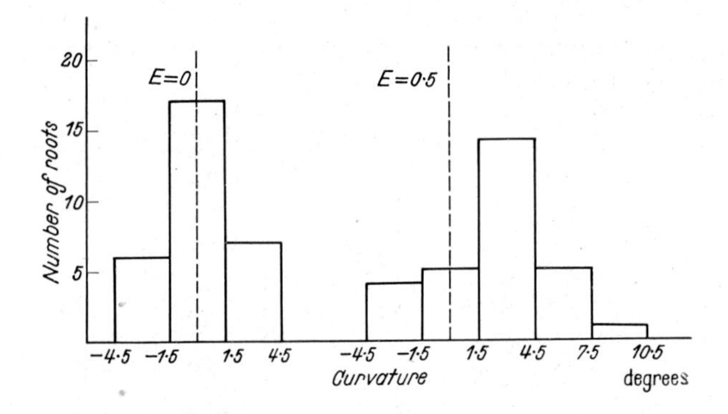

Figure 11. Distribution of changes in curvature from 0 *to* 32 *minutes in* 30 *unstimulated roots* ($E = 0$) *and in* 29 *roots exposed for* 0·5 *minutes to* 1 *g* ($E = 0·5$). *Curvatures measured after* 32 *minutes of rotation at* $R/0·5$. *Note increase in variability, cf. Figure 10.*

expressed as per cent positive curvatures, is not a minimum response but a reaction of a certain magnitude. Possible negative curvatures, and positive curvatures smaller than the fixed minimum, are not considered by this method. On the other hand, the recorded result (per cent) may include a number of much greater curvatures which are not evaluated quantitatively. In order to detect a minimum response, therefore, the writer would strongly recommend determination of the mean curvature. The presentation time may then be determined by simple or logarithmic extrapolation, as shown for example in *Figure 8*. This does not mean extrapolating back until the first root has curved, but until the mean value about which the roots perform their spontaneous movements is just barely positive.

If the chosen technique is such that curvatures smaller than, for example, 10° are neglected, 50 per cent positive curvatures will correspond to a mean curvature of roughly 10°. The exposure, E_{50}, which yields this mean value at the time of recording (e.g. 30 minutes after the end of the exposure) is longer than the presentation time. If we find that E_{50} is prolonged, for example by the addition of auxin, this does not necessarily mean that the presentation time has been prolonged. The result would be the same if the presentation time were unchanged and only the velocity of bending had been reduced. At the time of recording, a positive mean curvature, although smaller than 10°, may actually have developed after an exposure of the same duration as in the auxin-free control.

Similar considerations can be applied to determinations of the reaction time.

2. *Klinostat rotation*—If the curvatures are to be recorded after rotation on a klinostat, the rate of rotation should be fast enough to permit the curvatures to develop freely, and the measurements should be made so early that the spontaneous movements do not create an excessive variability. If klinostat rotation is too slow, the roots will follow the motion of the klinostat, and the presence of maxima and minima of curvature will create difficulties in measuring.

3. *Time of recording*—When studying the development of curvatures, particularly after a stimulation of such duration that measurable angles are present before the end of the exposure, the problem arises as to the correct time of recording the response. It seems impossible *a priori* to fix any particular time at which the observed curvatures may be taken as an adequate measure of the response to the stimulus applied. If one wants to fix a definite time at which to record the curvature, it is difficult to decide whether the starting point should be the beginning, the middle, or the end of the exposure. Another possibility would be to take the maximum curvature as a measure of the response, regardless of when it occurs.

A way out of this difficulty, especially when studying the influence of external auxin on the geotropic responses, would be to determine the *velocity* of curvature under the influence of a stimulation of constant intensity, for example 1 *g*. Changes in this velocity will probably be a satisfactory criterion for the effect of changes in the experimental conditions.

SUMMARY

1. The acceleration of root elongation by added auxin reported in the literature does not necessarily indicate a sub-optimal auxin concentration in the elongation zone of normal intact roots. Such acceleration has not been recorded until several hours after the addition of auxin, whereas the immediate response, the one which has any bearing on normal geotropic reactions, is a retardation of elongation. There is, therefore, at present no necessity for changing the classical auxin theory of geotropism, which is based on the assumption of a supra-optimal auxin concentration in the root.

2. The behaviour of stimulated and unstimulated roots of *Artemisia absinthium* (wormwood) when rotated parallel to the horizontal axis of a synchronous klinostat at two velocities of rotation is described. At a velocity of 1 revolution per 0·5 minutes, geotropically induced curvatures are gradually enlarged during rotation. Large spontaneous movements, however, are superimposed on the actual geotropic response. The variability, therefore, increases enormously with the length of time of rotation. At 1 revolution in 32 minutes the variability is much lower, but the root tips follow the motion of the klinostat, i.e. they perform spiral movements with an amplitude of 5°.

3. Certain precautions to be taken in the recording of geotropic responses are pointed out. It is recommended that the mean curvature rather than the percentage of positive curvatures should be used as the measure of a geotropic response.

REFERENCES

Ashby, W. C. (1951). Effects of certain acid growth substances and their corresponding aldehydes on the growth of roots. *Bot. Gaz.* **112,** 237.

Brain, E. D. (1942). Studies in the effects of prolonged rotation of plants on a horizontal klinostat. III. Physiological reactions in the hypocotyl of *Lupinus albus. New Phytol.* **41,** 81.

Bünning, E. (1948). *Entwicklungs- und Bewegungsphysiologie der Pflanze,* Heidelberg (Springer).

Burström, H. (1942). The influence of heteroauxin on cell growth and root development. *Ann. agric. Coll. Sweden,* **10,** 209.

Burström, H. (1950). Studies on growth and metabolism of roots. IV. Positive and negative auxin effects on cell elongation. *Physiol. Plant.* **3,** 277.

Burström, H. (1954). Studies on growth and metabolism of roots. XI. The influence of auxin and coumarin derivatives on the cell wall. *Physiol. Plant.* **7,** 548.

Cholodny, N. (1932). Ist die Wachstumsgeschwindigkeit der Wurzel von deren Lage abhängig? *Planta,* **17,** 794.

Czaja, A. Th. (1935). Polarität und Wuchsstoff. *Ber. dtsch. bot. Ges.* **53,** 197.

Larsen, P. (1953). Influence of gravity on rate of elongation and on geotropic and autotropic reactions in roots. *Physiol. Plant.* **6,** 735.

Linser, H. (1949). Die Wuchsstoffwirksamkeit von 2,4-Dichlorphenoxyessigsäure und Phenoxyessigsäure. *PflSchBer.* **3,** 131.

Lundegårdh, H. (1942). The growth of roots as influenced by pH and salt content of the medium. *Ann. agric. Coll. Sweden,* **10,** 31.

Lundegårdh, H. (1949). The influence of auxin anions on the growth of wheat roots. *Arkiv för Bot.* **1,** 289.

Macht, D. J., and Grumbein, M. L. (1937). Influence of indole acetic, indole butyric, and naphthalene acetic acids on roots of *Lupinus albus* seedlings. *Amer. J. Bot.* **24,** 457.

Moewus, F. (1949). Der Kressewurzeltest, ein neuer quantitativer Wuchsstofftest. *Biol. Zbl.* **68,** 118.

Naundorf, G. (1940). Untersuchungen über den Phototropismus der Keimwurzel von Helianthus annuus. *Planta,* **30,** 639.

Navez, A. E. (1933). 'Geo-growth' reactions of roots of *Lupinus. Bot. Gaz.* **94,** 616.

Overbeek, J. van, Dávila Olivo, G., and Santiago de Vázques, E. M. (1945). A rapid extraction method for free auxin and its application in geotropic reactions of bean seedlings and sugar cane nodes. *Bot. Gaz.* **106,** 440.

Pilet, P. E. (1951). Contribution à l'étude des hormones de croissance (auxines) dans la racine de *Lens culinaris* Medikus. *Mém. Soc. vaud. Sci. nat.* **10,** 137.

Pilet, P. E. (1953). Auxines et amidon. IV. Essais d'interprétation du géotropisme des racines de *Lens culinaris* Medikus. *Bull. Soc. vaud. Sci. nat.* **65,** 409.

Pohl, R., and Ochs, G. (1953). Über die Wuchsstoffwirkung beim Streckungswachstum der Wurzel. *Naturwissenschaften,* **40,** 24.

Schmitz, H. (1933). Über Wuchsstoff und Geotropismus bei Gräsern. *Planta,* **19,** 614.

Seiler, L. (1951). Über das Wurzelwachstum und eine Methode zur quantitativen Untersuchung des Einflusses von Wirkstoffen. *Ber. schweiz. bot. Ges.* **61,** 622.

Thimann, K. V., and Lane, R. H. (1938). After-effect of the treatment of seed with auxin. *Amer. J. Bot.* **25,** 535.

II

CHEMICAL STRUCTURE AND BIOLOGICAL ACTIVITY

ON THE EFFECTS OF *PARA*-SUBSTITUTION IN SOME PLANT GROWTH REGULATORS WITH PHENYL NUCLEI

B. ÅBERG

Institute of Plant Physiology, Royal Agricultural College, Uppsala, Sweden

INTRODUCTION

THE remarkable effect of introducing a *para* chlorine atom into the phenoxyacetic acid molecule, thereby changing the physiological character of this substance from weakly anti-auxinic (or better: intermediate) to strongly auxinic, has also been found to have its counterpart among the more typical auxins and anti-auxins. The strong increase in the auxin activity from 2-chloro- to 2:4-dichlorophenoxyacetic acid is well known, and among the anti-auxins such a *para chlorine effect* upon the activity has been found for the phenoxy*iso*butyric acids (Burström, 1951a) as well as for different types of substituted phenoxyacetic acids (see Åberg, 1954).

Under the circumstances it was thought pertinent to make a more extensive study of several pairs of substances differing only with respect to a *para* chlorine substituent. Some insight into the nature of its function could be expected from studies on the effects of other *para* substituents. A number of phenoxyacetic acids with such substituents have therefore been included in the present connection.

Most of the substances used have been synthesized by Prof. A. Fredga and Dr. M. Matell of Uppsala, to whom I tender my sincere thanks for their generous and unfailing co-operation. The following abbreviations will be used:

- POA: phenoxyacetic acid, $C_6H_5 \cdot O \cdot CH_2 \cdot COOH$; substituents in the phenyl nucleus are indicated in the usual manner, Me signifying a methyl group, Et an ethyl group, *i*P an *iso*-propyl group, and *t*B a *tert.*-butyl group. Some phenoxyacetic derivatives have been further abbreviated, according to common usage: 2:4-D = 2:4-Cl_2POA, 2:6-D = 2:6-Cl_2POA, 2:4:6-T = 2:4:6-Cl_3POA.
- Th: thymoxyacetic acid, 2-*i*P-5-MePOA.
- ClTh: chlorothymoxyacetic acid, 2-*i*P-4-Cl-5-MePOA.
- POP: α-phenoxy-propionic acid, $C_6H_5 \cdot O \cdot CH(CH_3) \cdot COOH$.
- PO*i*B: α-phenoxy*iso*butyric acid. The 4-chloro derivative, 4-ClPO*i*B, was originally designated PCIB by Burström (1950).
- Tr: *trans*cinnamic acid, $C_6H_5 \cdot CH{:}CH \cdot COOH$.
- PF: phenyl-formic or benzoic acid, $C_6H_5 \cdot COOH$.
- IAA: 3-indolylacetic acid.
- 1-NMSA: 1-naphthylmethyl-sulphide-acetic acid, $C_{10}H_7 \cdot CH_2 \cdot S \cdot CH_2 \cdot COOH$.
- 1-NMSP: the corresponding α-propionic acid.

METHODS

In order to obtain a reasonably complete picture of the growth effects of the different substances, three methods of testing have been used:

(*i*) *The flax root test* (*S*-test, Åberg, 1950; 1953b; 1955) showing preferentially the inhibition of root growth by auxins, and also the restorative effects of anti-auxins upon 2:4-D or IAA inhibited roots. The activity of a certain substance in this test will sometimes be given as the molar concentration (C_{50}) needed for 50 per cent inhibition, or as the negative logarithm of this value (pC_{50}).

(*ii*) *A wheat root test* closely corresponding to the flax root test and showing much more pronounced root-growth stimulations at application of anti-auxins than the latter one (cf. Burström, 1950; 1951a,b; 1955; Hansen, 1954; Åberg, 1952; 1955). The wheat seedlings, var. 'Diamant II', are used when the median root has reached a length of 10 mm, the test period (18 hours), the temperature (25°C), and the basic solution (pH 5·9) being the same as in the flax root test. During the germination period the seedlings grow on moist filter paper in large Petri dishes, and during the test period they are placed in perforated cork disks floating on the solution. Only the median root is measured. The average dispersion of the G values (growth as per cent of control) from independent experiments is $7{\cdot}9 \pm 0{\cdot}5$ per cent (of G) as judged from 25 series, each comprising 7–9 experiments. No clear correlation between the inter-experimental dispersion and the magnitude of the G value is apparent for this material, which fact may be connected with the occurrence of steep parts of the action curves within the whole of the G range covered (63–197) (cf. Åberg, 1955).

(*iii*) *An* Avena *cylinder test* performed mainly as described by Åberg and Khalil (1953), the seedlings being reared, however, on a net of stainless steel placed in a large glass dish immediately over the water surface, and the test period being 18 hours. The average growth of the control sections during this period amounts to $2{\cdot}83 \pm 0{\cdot}04$ mm ($\sigma = 0{\cdot}41$, $N = 120$) or 28 per cent of the initial length. The average inter-experimental dispersion of the G values (expressed in per cent of control growth) is $10{\cdot}7 \pm 0{\cdot}7$ per cent (of G) as judged from 11 series, each comprising 7–10 experiments.

WORKING HYPOTHESIS

There is at present no generally accepted theory as to the mechanism of the physiological action of auxins and related substances. As a guide for our orientation among the multitude of experimental data we will, however, use the following working hypothesis which seems to give a coherent picture of a major part of them.

The auxins are thought to interact with some 'receptor' of protein nature, and to exert their effects only when bound to these 'active sites' or 'growth centres' of the protoplasm. The binding is assumed to be effected by many weak bonds ('multipoint attachment'), thus allowing for a high degree of specificity and taking advantage of the analogy with some better known enzyme-substrate complexes (Veldstra, 1953; Åberg, 1953b).

The question of the function of the hypothetical auxin-receptor complex is a very difficult one, and the solution will certainly depend on the attainment of a better insight into the complex chain of processes connecting the genotype of an organism with the result of its growth processes. Meanwhile we may correlate empirically the action of the auxins with different growth results. The fundamental outcome of such studies is that a substance showing auxin activity in a certain growth process will probably do it also in other connections (Went and Thimann, 1937; Audus, 1953). This could mean that there is a common receptor, but the possibility of several receptors with a similar affinity for different auxins must not be overlooked. It would also be reasonable to expect some variations in the type of the receptor (or group of receptors) for different plant species. In this connection well-documented exceptions from the rule of coupled and general activity may be of considerable interest.

A typical competitive auxin antagonist, or anti-auxin, would now be a substance which is bound to the auxin receptor in the same place as the auxins, but which gives a complex unable to initiate the usual growth responses. There is at present a rather extensive series of substances, for example 1-naphthylmethylsulphideacetic acid and the corresponding α-propionic acid (1-NMSA and 1-NMSP), α-(4-chlorophenoxy)-*iso*-butyric acid, L(—)-α-(2-naphthoxy)-*n*-butyric acid, 4-chloro*trans*cinnamic acid, and 4-*iso*-propyl-phenoxyacetic acid, which may be assumed to behave in this way. All substances mentioned above: (*a*) counteract the inhibiting effects of externally applied auxin upon flax root growth, even if applied in concentrations which are without effect on or slightly depress the growth of control roots, (*b*) stimulate the growth of intact flax roots slightly and that of wheat roots strongly, the latter ones presumably containing a more highly supra-optimal content of native auxin than do flax roots (cf. Åberg, 1955), (*c*) inhibit the growth of *Avena* coleoptile sections. As far as tested, these substances also counteract the effect of externally applied auxins on *Avena* coleoptile sections in the manner expected (McRae and Bonner, 1953; Åberg and Khalil, 1953). Many other anti-auxins are known which are not yet tested by all of the different methods, or which show slight deviations from the pattern mentioned (e.g. no stimulation of flax roots). Such deviations are natural with respect to the occurrence of various complications in the physiological system (competition during uptake and transport, synergism, effects upon auxin metabolism, non-specific toxicity). No alternative to the hypothesis of a competitive auxin antagonism which is able to connect and explain the growth phenomena mentioned above has as yet been proposed.

The counteraction of the effects of externally applied auxins could naturally be partly or wholly related to a hypothetical antagonism during the uptake (see Åberg, 1953b). Owing to the exceedingly low concentrations of the active substances which must be used, such a question is not easily attacked by direct methods, and the possibility of surface effects complicates the situation considerably. A comparison between the antagonistic effects obtained in different tests may, however, give some clues. Preliminary results for a series of homologous L-(—)-2-naphthoxy-alkylcarboxylic acids do indicate that a 'bulky' substituent in the side chain of an anti-auxin may possibly interfere to some extent with its uptake (gradually decreased stimulation of wheat root growth, decreased inhibition of *Avena* cylinder growth), while leaving its antagonistic effects against externally applied auxin intact. However, other explanations may also be possible.

Once the possibility of a competitive inhibition of the auxin effects is accepted, the next step is to inquire into the existence of substances intermediate between the typical auxins and the typical anti-auxins (cf. Åberg, 1952). The molecules of such a substance should have a conspicuously decreased, though not totally eliminated activity in initiating the auxin responses when bound at the proper sites. For the sake of brevity we will denote an activity defined in this way as 'intrinsic auxin activity'. We then have to differentiate between three different ways of defining the activity of a certain regulator as related to a specified growth result:

(*i*) The '*gross activity*' (i.e. secondary activity of Went and Thimann, 1937), expressing the relation between growth result and external amount or concentration of applied regulator; it is conditioned by the 'primary activity' of the regulator and also by such factors as penetration, transport, and destruction.

(*ii*) The 'primary activity' (Went and Thimann, 1937), defined in relation to the amount of regulator immediately available at the active sites.

(*iii*) The '*intrinsic activity*' (McRae, Foster, and Bonner, 1953), defined in relation to the number of regulator molecules bound to the active sites, and thus indicating the specific growth activity of these molecules when properly situated (or of the receptor–regulator complex). Apparently the '*intrinsic activity*' is synonymous with the '*capacity*' as used by Veldstra (1953) and by Jönsson (1955).

In a system previously devoid of auxin, or with a low degree of auxin saturation, a regulator of the intermediate type can apparently be expected to give positive auxin effects. In a system already saturated, or nearly so, with auxin molecules of high *intrinsic activity*, it must on the other hand be able to replace so many of these that the sum of intrinsic activities decreases, that is, a competitive anti-auxin effect will occur.

Substances which behave in this way are already known. As a good example we will mention 4-methyl-phenoxyacetic acid (4-MePOA) (Åberg, 1954). It strikingly increases the growth of 2:4-D-inhibited flax roots, but on the other hand, its own inhibiting effects may be effectively counteracted by an anti-auxin like 1-NMSP. In the *Avena* cylinder test it gives a peculiar action curve (*Figure 1*), an initial inhibition being followed by a growth restoration which, however, does not reach the control level before the ultimate non-specific toxicity sets in. In the wheat root test an action curve of the inverse type is obtained, while the flax roots with their higher auxin sensitivity and lower response to anti-auxins give a simple curve of the 'auxin type'. The ultimate inhibition of the wheat roots may possibly be of complex nature, auxin effects being mixed with non-specific toxicity.

Curves similar to that of 4-MePOA have been found in the *Avena* cylinder test for 1-naphthoxyacetic acid and 2-naphthoxy*iso*butyric acid (Åberg and Khalil, 1953), for 2-naphthylacetic acid, 2:6-dichlorophenoxyacetic acid, 3-methyl-phenoxyacetic acid, etc. Other substances, e.g. 2-methylphenoxyacetic acid and 2-naphthoxyacetic acid, give curves where the initial inhibition is followed by a stimulation up to nearly twice that of the control growth. The action curve of phenoxyacetic acid also seems to belong to this main class, though both the initial inhibition and the final stimulation are comparatively slight.

The very strong difference in the inhibiting activities of 2-naphthoxyacetic acid (2-NOA) upon flax and wheat roots (*Figure 1*) is paralleled by a similar shift in the anti-auxin direction for several other 2-naphthoxy derivatives. It seems probable that here we meet with a case of species difference in the auxin system. For wheat roots and *Avena* coleoptiles, however, the sensitivity might be of the same type, the action curves indicating at first an 'anti-auxin component' of the activity which is, at higher concentrations, superseded by the auxin effects. It is highly interesting to find that 10^{-5} M 2-NOA has a conspicuous restoration effect upon wheat roots inhibited by 3×10^{-7} M 1-naphthylacetic acid (Burström, 1955).

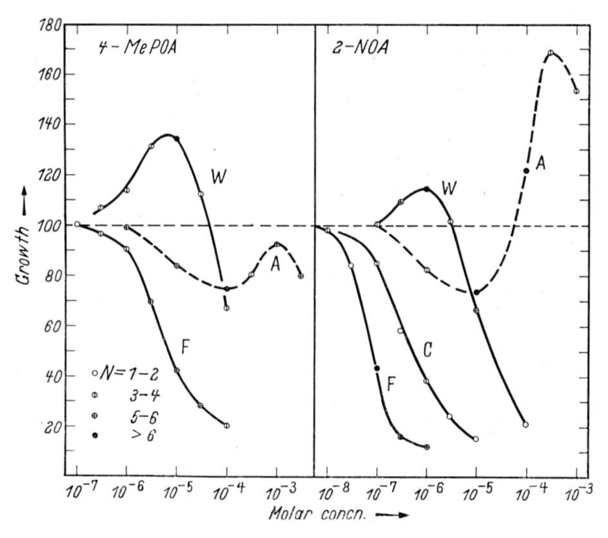

Figure 1. The effects of 4-methylphenoxyacetic acid (4-MePOA) and 2-naphthoxyacetic acid (2-NOA) upon the growth of flax roots (F), cress roots (C), wheat roots (W), and Avena *coleoptile cylinders (A). Growth (G) in per cent of control, plotted against a logarithmic concentration scale. N is the number of independent experiments represented by the points.*

Further data, especially on the interaction of 2-NOA with other growth regulators in the growth of coleoptile cylinders, might be necessary for the final elucidation of these 'anti-auxin' effects (action II according to Burström, 1955).

The quantitative treatment of the auxin–anti-auxin interactions can only be made in a tentative way at present, but analogies from simple model systems are certainly very useful in making more precise hypotheses as to the mechanisms underlying the growth results. It seems reasonable to start from the general laws governing chemical and adsorption equilibria, making as few additional assumptions as possible. This has been done by McRae *et al.* (1952, 1953) in applying the enzyme kinetics of Michaelis and Menten, and by Hellström (1953) in a more general approach. In both cases it must be assumed that a relatively slight proportion of the regulator molecules is actually bound, an assumption that finds good support in the studies of auxin uptake in plant tissues made by Sutter (1944) and by Reinhold (1954). Also, experiments with labelled 2:4-D (Hanson and Bonner, 1955) do seemingly indicate that the concentration of readily exchangeable regulator in the tissue is comparable to that of the surrounding solution. Quite generally we then find:

$$\alpha = \frac{M}{K+M}, \qquad \text{or} \qquad \alpha = \frac{M/K}{1+M/K},$$

where α is the fraction of places in an adsorption system which are occupied by the regulator, M the molar concentration of this regulator, and K the dissociation constant of the receptor–regulator complex. For $\alpha = 0{\cdot}5$ we get $K = M$. Upon addition of another regulator, for example an anti-auxin with the constant K' at the concentration M', we find the α-value for the first substance diminished to

$$\alpha = \frac{M/K}{1+M/K+M'/K'}.$$

Making further the rather bold assumption that the growth results, for example root-growth inhibition, are proportional to α, action curves may be constructed which resemble the empirical curves very closely. The effect of an antagonist in displacing the root-growth inhibition curve to higher auxin concentrations without any fundamental change in its form, is also in good agreement with expectation (Åberg, 1951; Åberg and Jönsson, 1955; Hellström, 1953). Some complications arise, however, from the presence of native auxin in the roots and from the non-specific toxic effects of higher concentrations of the antagonist. The action curve of a pure anti-auxin may be deduced as resulting from an adsorption in two patterns (competition with the native auxin, toxic effect at higher concentrations), the actual growth being determined by the product of both influences (Hellström, 1953).

The Michaelis–Menten formula may be written as follows:

$$\frac{v}{V} = \frac{[S]}{K+[S]} = \frac{M}{K+M},$$

where v is the reaction velocity, V the maximum reaction velocity, $[S]$ or M the substrate concentration at equilibrium, and K the dissociation constant of the enzyme–substrate complex. Now, v is thought to be proportional to the amount of this complex, and v/V is thus equal to α. If we now speak of the plasmatic receptor instead of the enzyme and the growth regulator instead of the enzyme substrate, this type of treatment appears to be identical with the former one. The assumption that a very small proportion of the regulator is actually bound, is made by McRae *et al.* (1952, 1953) by putting $[S]$ equal to the concentration of added regulator.

Though calculations with help of the methods indicated above may often give results which are in good agreement with a limited series of experimental data, difficulties certainly arise when a more extensive set of results have to be treated. This is perhaps not surprising when due respect is paid to the complexity of the situation. The proportionality between the amount of receptor–regulator complex (corrected for variations in *intrinsic activity*) and the growth result may be restricted to a rather limited range. Time and penetration factors have to be considered (see Housley *et al.*, 1954), effects upon the metabolic systems regulating the synthesis and destruction of native auxin are likely to occur and may be especially troublesome in systems involving externally applied indoleacetic acid (see Åberg, 1953a; Åberg and Jönsson, 1955), binding and competition at 'inactive sites' may be of importance, many substances certainly exert a non-specific toxicity at higher concentrations, and so on. In view of these difficulties it is natural that the attempts at quantitative precision must remain tentative. On the other hand, even limited success in such attempts is valuable as a starting point for further comprehensive quantitative treatment.

PHENOXYACETIC ACID AND SOME OF ITS MAIN AUXINIC DERIVATIVES

Phenoxyacetic acid (POA) has often been characterized as wholly inactive as a growth regulator. Some slight positive auxin effects have, however, been reported: e.g. negative stem curvatures induced by highly concentrated lanolin solutions (Zimmerman and Hitchcock, 1942) and positive effects in the *Avena* cylinder test at high concentrations (Muir *et al.*, 1949). On the other hand, the conspicuous restorative effects of POA on flax or cress roots inhibited by 2:4-D (Åberg, 1952; Audus and Shipton, 1952) and the positive effects upon wheat root growth and cell length (Hansen, 1954) might indicate a prevailing anti-auxin activity.

This anti-auxin activity is also clearly shown by the inhibitive action of POA on *Avena* coleoptile growth when using cylinders with a fairly high residual growth (20 per cent) in absence of added auxin (Ingestad, 1953). In our experiments the residual growth has been even higher (28 per cent) and the inhibition by POA appears at about ten times higher concentrations than in Ingestad's experiments. This may be due to the higher pH used (5·9 and 4·5 respectively). It is highly interesting that at strongly increased concentions there is a significant decrease in the inhibition, and that positive effects occur in the range above 10^{-3} M. For example

$$G(10^{-5}) = 98{\cdot}1 \pm 4{\cdot}2; \quad G(10^{-4}) = 83{\cdot}0 \pm 4{\cdot}4; \quad G(10^{-3}) = 103{\cdot}9 \pm 4{\cdot}3;$$

$$G(3 \times 10^{-3}) = 117{\cdot}0 \pm 14{\cdot}0; \quad \Delta[G(10^{-3}) - G(10^{-4})] = 20{\cdot}9 \pm 4{\cdot}9 \ (N = 7).$$

These results, together with the positive effects observed by Muir *et al.* (1949) at lower concentrations (residual control growth 8 per cent and pH probably lower than in the present tests), suggest that the physiological activity of the POA-molecule is of the intermediate type, fairly low *affinity* for the growth centres being combined with very low *intrinsic auxin activity.*

As regards the conspicuous auxin activity of 4-chlorophenoxyacetic acid (4-ClPOA) there can be little doubt. In the pea test and the *Avena* cylinder test, its activity is about 5–10 times less than that of 2:4-D (Fawcett *et al.*, 1953; Wain and Wightman, 1953; Muir and Hansch, 1953) which correlates well with its inhibiting effects on wheat (Hansen, 1954) and flax roots (*Figure 2*).

When comparing the POA and 4-ClPOA curves of *Figure 2* we must remember that the inhibiting effects may be of different types. At the relatively high concentrations where POA begins to inhibit root growth, non-specific toxic effects are certainly possible, and even if the inhibition should be caused by the residual auxin effect of the POA molecules, the *affinity* of these molecules for the growth centres must be higher than indicated by the C_{50}-value (p. 94). A better measure for this affinity may perhaps be obtained from combined experiments with 2:4-D (Åberg, 1952). We will use the concentration of the antagonist which, combined with 10^{-7} M 2:4-D, gives a doubled growth rate as compared to that in 2:4-D alone ($G' = 200$), and this concentration will be denoted C_A (negative logarithm = pC_A). A calculation from a simple competitive model system shows that the C_A-values of pure antagonists may be roughly comparable to the C_{50}-values of

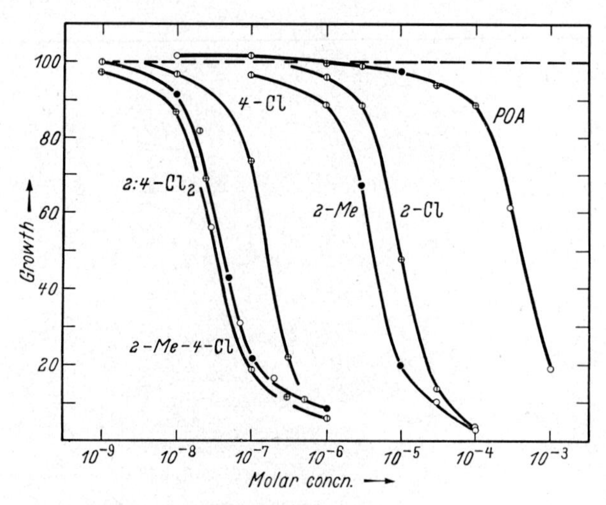

Figure 2. The effects of phenoxyacetic acid (POA) and some of its derivatives upon the root growth of flax seedlings. The derivatives are indicated by means of the substituents: 2-*Cl* = 2-*chloro-phenoxy-acetic acid* (2-*ClPOA*), *and so on. Values presented as in Figure 1.*

typical auxins as *affinity* measures, but because of the complexity of the physiological situation and the complications caused by the variations in *intrinsic activity* we prefer to use them in a purely provisional and exploratory manner in order to see if both sets of values may fit the same general picture.

Even if we use the pC_A-value for POA (4·0) instead of the pC_{50}-value (3·4), the comparison gives an increase in *affinity* of 4-ClPOA ($pC_{50} = 6{\cdot}8$) of about six hundred times.

For 2-chlorophenoxyacetic acid (2-ClPOA) there are clear indications of a weak auxin activity in the *Avena* cylinder test and in the pea test (see, for example, Muir *et al.*, 1949; Wain and Wightman, 1953). Also the experiments with wheat roots (Hansen, 1954) and flax roots (*Figure 2*) indicate weak auxin activity. The growth inhibition of flax roots, however, is strongly counteracted by the anti-auxin 1-NMSP. In 2:4-dichlorophenoxyacetic acid (2:4-D) this weak auxin activity is strongly augmented. As indicated by the *Avena* cylinder test, the increase may be as high as four hundred times (Muir and Hansch, 1953) though the data of Wain and Wightman (1953) give an increase of only about fifty times. From experiments with flax roots

(*Figure 2*) we get an increase of about two hundred times, and from the cell length data of Hansen (1954) about twenty times.

For 2-methylphenoxyacetic acid (2-MePOA), the weak but conspicuous auxin activity is clear from the results of the *Avena* cylinder test (Muir and Hansch, 1953; cf. also above p. 96), the wheat root test (Hansen, 1954), and the flax root test (*Figure 2*; the inhibition is strongly counteracted by 1-NMSP). With this type of compound, the introduction of a *para* chlorine atom to give 2-methyl-4-chlorophenoxyacetic acid strongly augments the auxin activity. Both the flax root test and the cell length data from wheat roots indicate an increase of about one hundred times.

Thus, with the above three pairs of substances, all having at least one *ortho* position free and with acetic acid as a side chain, we have found a very conspicuous increase in the *gross auxin activity* accompanying the introduction of a *para* chlorine atom into the nucleus. In root growth tests the transport factors are to a large extent eliminated, and it also seems probable that the effects of possible differences in the penetration rates are not very pronounced (see the Concluding Remarks, p. 112). Preliminarily, we may therefore assume a real difference in *primary activity*. Much of this difference is probably due to an increased *affinity* to the growth centres, but as is evident from the behaviour of the pair POA–4-ClPOA, we must also reckon with an influence upon *intrinsic activity*. That there may be an anti-auxin component also in the effect of 2-MePOA upon some tissues is suggested by its peculiar type of action curve in the *Avena* cylinder test (p. 96). For 2-ClPOA, an *intrinsic activity* lower than that of 2:4-D is suggested by the difference in the maximum stimulations obtained in the *Avena* cylinder test with these two substances (Muir *et al.*, 1949; Wain and Wightman, 1953).

It is thus possible that the true estimate of the *affinities* of 2-MePOA and 2-ClPOA might be somewhat higher than those indicated by the pC_{50} values, and that the *para* chlorine atom influences *intrinsic activity* as well as *affinity*. The effect of such a substitution must certainly be expected to vary to some extent with the type of the parent substance, and it would not be surprising if the *affinity* of POA is more strongly influenced than that of 2-MePOA or 2-ClPOA.

In order to demonstrate the generality of the *para* chlorine effect among the auxinic phenoxyacetic acids, the following substances may be cited from Wain and Wightman (1953): 3-chloro-, 2:3-dichloro-, and 2:5-dichlorophenoxyacetic acid. With all of these compounds the introduction of a *para* chlorine atom conspicuously increases the auxin activity as judged from the *Avena* cylinder and pea tests.

In the phenylsulphideacetic (or phenylthioglycollic) acid series, the *para* chlorine effect seems to be of exactly the same type as for the phenoxyacetic acids. This is true for unsubstituted phenylsulphideacetic acid and for its 2-chloro-, 3-chloro-, 3-methyl-, and 2:5-dichloro-derivatives (Sugii and Sugii, 1953; Kato, 1954).

There is little doubt that *para*-chlorination will turn out to have a similar effect also in the anilino-acetic acids ($C_6H_5{\cdot}NH{\cdot}CH_2{\cdot}COOH$). The 4-chloro- and 2:4-dichloro-derivatives show conspicuous activity in the *Avena* cylinder and pea tests (Muir and Hansch, 1953; Veldstra and Booij, 1949), while no auxin activity has been reported for anilinoacetic acid itself.

With phenylacetic acid, *para*-chlorination also increases auxin activity considerably, though less than *ortho*-chlorination (Melnikov *et al.*, 1953). The reported decrease in activity from 2-chloro- to 2:4-dichloro-phenylacetic acid makes a more detailed comparison between these substances highly desirable.

SOME α-PHENOXYPROPIONIC ACIDS

The racemic forms of α-phenoxypropionic acid (POP) and its *para*-chloro-derivative (4-ClPOP) have been compared in several tests by Fawcett *et al.* (1953), and their effects upon wheat roots have been studied by Burström (1951b) and Hansen (1954). While decidedly more active in the pea test, for example, racemic 4-ClPOP is only about twice as active as POP in inhibiting the growth of wheat roots. The cell length of wheat roots growing in a solution of 4-ClPOP may even be slightly greater than those in roots growing in an equally concentrated solution of POP.

After resolution of both substances into their optically active forms (Fredga and Matell, 1952; Matell, 1954), the flax root test indicates a five-fold increase in the activity of D-(+)-POP upon *para*-chloro-substitution, while the physiologically inactive L-(—)-POP is changed into a weak auxin antagonist. Detailed data from these experiments will be published in a later communication. The increased activity after *para*-chlorination both in the auxinic D-series and the anti-auxinic L-series might well be caused by a corresponding increase in the *affinity* of the chlorinated molecules to the growth centres.

For the racemic α-(2-methylphenoxy)propionic acid, Synerholm and Zimmerman (1945) found an approximately tenfold increase in cell-elongation activity (tomato shoot) upon *para*-chlorination. With α-(3-methyl-phenoxy)propionic acid, however, the introduction of a *para* chlorine atom resulted in a decrease in activity. The reproducibility of these results is not easily judged, but irrespective of this, the latter pair of substances should not be cited as a case of absent or reversed *para* chlorine effect. We must remember that in this instance we are dealing with a mixture of two optically active forms which are probably of opposite physiological character. In spite of a possible increase in the activity of both forms when tested separately, the effect produced by the racemic mixture may be an unchanged or even decreased activity.

In the present connection, the conspicuous rise in root-growth-inhibiting activity from α-anilinopropionic acid to its 2:4-dichloro-derivative (Åberg, 1953b) is also of some interest as it may be caused to a considerable extent by the *para* chlorine atom.

SOME ACIDS WITH A STRONG ANTI-AUXIN COMPONENT IN THEIR ACTIVITY

The anti-auxin effects of α-(4-chlorophenoxy)*iso*butyric acid (4-ClPO*i*B) on wheat roots were first described by Burström (1950, 1951a), who also found that they occurred at about ten times lower concentrations than the corresponding effects of the unchlorinated α-phenoxy*iso*butyric acid (PO*i*B). Quite similar results have been obtained by Hansen (1954) and the present author (*Figure 3*). This pair of substances have also been studied in the flax root test. The action curves of the pure substances show the expected course with much smaller stimulations than in the case of wheat roots (for PO*i*B see Åberg, 1952; 3×10^{-6} M 4-ClPO*i*B gives a G value of $111{\cdot}3 \pm 1{\cdot}7$). The G'-curves from the combination experiments (*Figure 3*) show about a six-fold increase in the antagonistic activity of 4-ClPO*i*B as compared to PO*i*B. As both substances seem to be completely or almost completely devoid of *intrinsic auxin activity*, and assuming in the first instance a negligible influence of the possible difference in their penetration rates (pp. 101–112), this increase may apparently be related to a corresponding increase in their receptor *affinity*.

4-ClPO*i*B is known to counteract the effect of externally applied IAA or 2:4-D on the growth of *Avena* coleoptile cylinders (McRae and Bonner, 1953); in the concentration range used (about 5×10^{-7} to 5×10^{-6} M) the effect

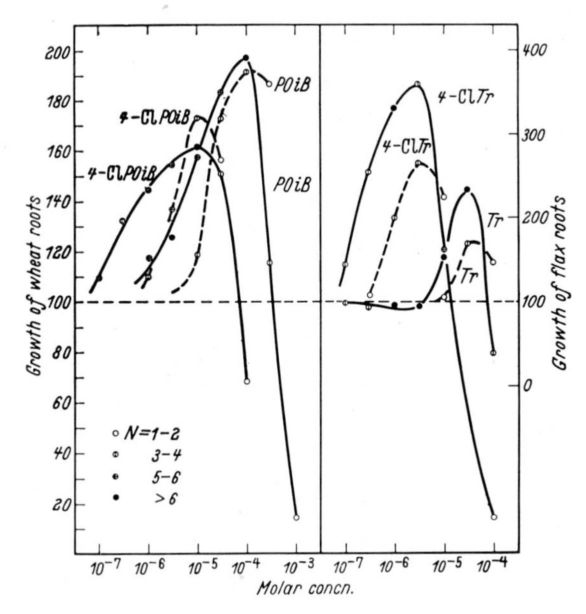

*Figure 3. The effects of phenoxy*isobutyric *acid (PO*i*B),* trans*cinnamic acid (Tr), and their 4-chloro-derivatives (4-ClPO*i*B and 4-ClTr, respectively) upon the growth of wheat roots and 2:4-D-inhibited flax roots. The left scale (G) refers to the growth of wheat roots in per cent of control without added regulator (continuous lines), the right one (G') to the growth of the 2:4-D-inhibited flax roots in per cent of control with 10^{-7} M 2:4-D only (broken lines). The growth values are plotted against a logarithmic concentration scale. N is the number of independent experiments represented by the points.*

upon control sections was negligible. When tested by the present method (p. 94), 4-ClPO*i*B gives a conspicuous inhibition of coleoptile cylinder growth at 10^{-6} M and higher concentrations. Up to 5×10^{-5} M, 4-ClPO*i*B is a stronger inhibitor than PO*i*B, but at higher concentrations the curves tend to cross each other. This phenomenon will be further studied as it could possibly indicate a very faint residual *intrinsic auxin activity* of 4-ClPO*i*B molecules.

As in the case of *iso*butyric acids, there are good reasons to assume that in *trans*cinnamic acids the side chain is of a type normally excluding any conspicuous *intrinsic auxin activity*, while the *affinity* to the growth centres remains fairly high. The anti-auxin effects of *trans*cinnamic acid (Tr) was first demonstrated by Overbeek *et al.* (1951) in experiments with pea stem sections. They have been confirmed here in experiments with flax roots (*Figure 3*). The peculiar form of the action curve of the pure substance (a 'plateau' at $G = 90$ in the range 3×10^{-7} to 3×10^{-6} M) does, however, indicate that complications, in the form of a slight synergistic activity, may perhaps occur. In the wheat root test (*Figure 3*) we found a conspicuous stimulation preceded by faint and uncertain signs of an inhibition at lower concentrations which might again be related to the possible 'synergistic' component of its activity; such a synergistic effect might easily become wholly concealed by the stronger anti-auxin effects in this test. The weak action of Tr in relation to 2:4-D introduces some doubt to such a hypothesis (cf. below), but the synergistic phenomena are not fully understood and may comprise mechanisms of different types (see Åberg and Jönsson, 1955).

In 4-chloro-*trans*cinnamic acid (4-ClTr) the anti-auxin activity is increased by nearly one hundred times in relation to Tr as judged from the effects on wheat roots and on 2:4-D-inhibited flax roots (*Figure 3*). It will be an interesting problem in further studies to decide if the stronger *para* chlorine effect observed in this instance, as compared to that shown by the pair PO*i*B–4-ClPO*i*B, may be related to an elimination of the possible 'synergistic' component of the activity of Tr, or whether in fact it is due to an appreciable difference in the effect upon *affinity*. With 2-chloro-*trans*cinnamic acid (2-ClTr), the optimum stimulating concentration for wheat roots is 3×10^{-6} M, as compared to 3×10^{-5} M in the case of Tr. This may be due to increased toxicity (or the induction of some faint *intrinsic auxin activity*) as a result of *ortho*-chlorination, again perhaps in combination with the elimination of the hypothetical synergistic component in the activity of the unsubstituted acid.

Para-chlorination of 2-ClTr to give 2:4-dichloro-*trans*cinnamic acid (2:4-Cl_2Tr) strongly increases anti-auxin activity (*Figure 4*), though it does not exceed that shown by 4-ClTr. The absence of any strong effect of *ortho*-chlorination on anti-auxin activity is in good agreement with the conditions in the *iso*butyric acid series described by Burström (1951a). It is interesting to note that the increase in 'toxicity' from Tr to 2-ClTr strongly diminishes the apparent anti-auxin effects of the latter substance. Such a phenomenon well illustrates the unreliability of judging anti-auxin effects from one test or one set of conditions only.

Both in the pair PO*i*B–4-ClPO*i*B and in Tr–4-ClTr, the anti-auxin effects on wheat roots become perceptible at considerably lower concentrations than those producing similar effects on 2:4-D-inhibited flax roots, which is only to be expected when one considers the higher total auxin concentration in the last case. With benzoic acid (phenyl-formic acid, PF), however, we meet an instance where the strength of the effects is reversed. The comparatively slight stimulation of wheat root growth (*Figure 4*) has its counterpart in the much lower restorative effect exerted upon IAA-inhibited flax roots (unpublished experiments) than upon the 2:4-D-inhibited ones. The action curve of PF in the flax root test shows some resemblance to that of 2:3:5-triiodobenzoic acid (TIB) (cf. Åberg, 1953a; 1955; Åberg and Jönsson, 1955).

Further studies will also be made in order to test the possibility of a 'synergistic' component in the activity of PF. When tested for auxin effects upon shoot parts, PF has invariably been found inactive. In the *Avena* cylinder test 5×10^{-4} M causes inhibition, while lower concentrations are without effect (Muir and Hansch, 1951).

The introduction of a *para* chlorine atom in PF to give 4-chloro-benzoic acid (4-chloro-phenylformic acid, 4-ClPF) strongly increases the growth-stimulating activity both in respect to wheat roots and to 2:4-D-inhibited flax roots (*Figure 4*). When tested on *Avena* coleoptile sections with the same methods as used for PF, positive auxin effects are still found to be absent, while the inhibiting effects begin to appear at somewhat lower concentrations (10^{-4} M, Muir and Hansch, 1951).

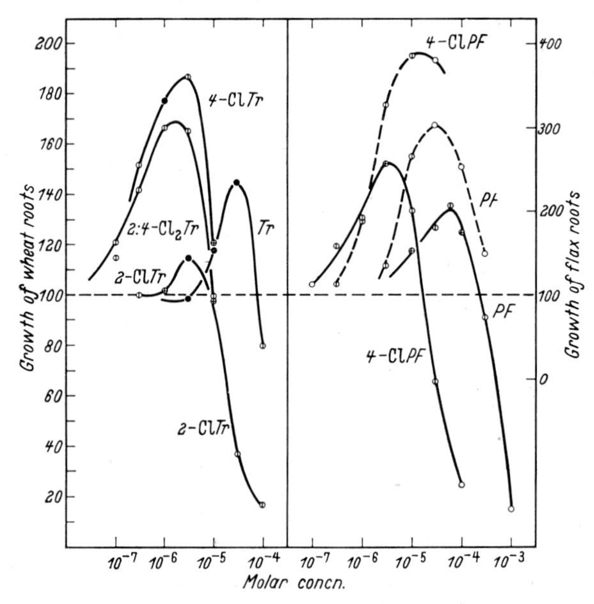

Figure 4. The effects of some chlorinated trans*cinnamic acids* (*Tr*) *on the growth of wheat roots, and the effects of benzoic acid* (*PF*) *and its* 4-*chloro-derivative* (4-*ClPF*) *upon the growth of wheat roots and* 2:4-*D-inhibited flax roots. Values presented as in Figure* 3.

Both thymoxyacetic acid (Th) and its *para*-chloro-derivative (ClTh) have previously been found to exert conspicuous anti-auxin effects in the flax root test when combined with 2:4-D or IAA (Åberg, 1954). Some further data have now been collected, and the G' curves of *Figure 5* clearly show about a five-fold increase in the anti-auxin activity in respect to 2:4-D from Th to ClTh. Also the positive effects on wheat root growth begin at lower concentrations for ClTh than for Th. The action curve of the latter substance also indicates some complications in the form of a possible 'synergistic' component in relation to the natural auxin system, which may be absent in respect to 2:4-D. This could possibly cause the depression of the G curves compared to the G' curves.

For 2:6-dichlorophenoxyacetic acid (2:6-D) both positive auxin effects and anti-auxin effects are well documented. Though this compound exerts a fairly strong antagonistic activity against externally applied 2:4-D and IAA in the *Avena* cylinder test (McRae and Bonner, 1952) and in the flax root test (Åberg, 1954), and is therefore assumed to be a substance of mainly anti-auxin character, it is clear that at high concentrations it may also exert some auxin activity. This was first shown with the pea test by Thimann (1952) and has been corroborated by other workers (Wain and Wightman, 1953; Osborne *et al.*, 1954). In the *Avena* cylinder test it has been found inactive, or at fairly high concentrations, inhibiting (McRae and Bonner, 1952; McRae, personal communication; Muir and Hansch, 1953; Wain and Wightman,

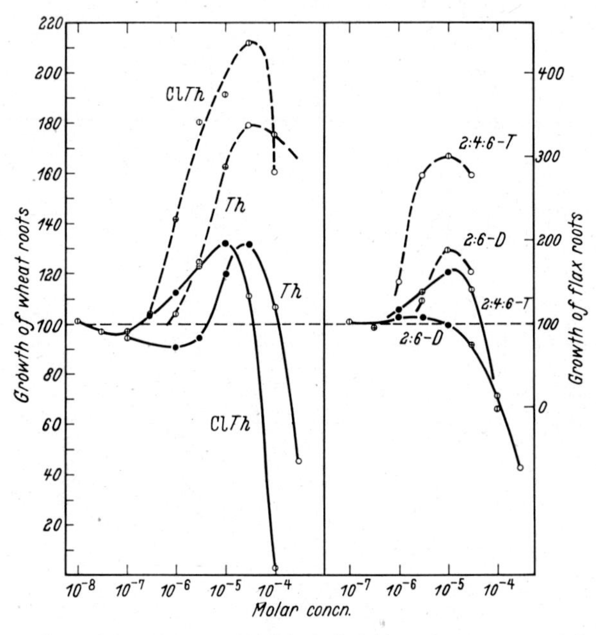

Figure 5. The effects of thymoxyacetic acid (Th), 2:6-dichloro-phenoxyacetic acid (2:6-D), and their 4-chloro-derivatives (ClTh and 2:4:6-T, respectively) upon the growth of wheat roots and 2:4-D-inhibited flax roots (broken curves). Values presented as in Figure 3.

1953). When the concentration is further increased, the growth may, however, be significantly restored, though it usually does not exceed the control growth. The action curve obtained with the present method almost coincides with that of 4-MePOA given in *Figure 1.* When using shorter test periods stimulations over the control growth may even be obtained (Osborne *et al.*, 1954). The existence of a synergistic component in the activity of 2:6-D has also been suggested (Thimann, 1952). The absence of conspicuous stimulations in the wheat root test (*Figure 5*) may under the circumstances be interpreted as the complex result of several different actions; thus the effect of competition with the native auxin is compensated by synergistic effects, the slight *intrinsic* auxin effects, and the toxic effects of 2:6-D molecules.

For 2:4:6-trichlorophenoxyacetic acid (2:4:6-T), no corresponding positive auxin effects on coleoptile sections at high concentrations have been reported in the literature, nor have indications of such effects been found during the present investigation.. A very slight activity is indicated in the pea test (Thimann, 1952; Wain and Wightman, 1953; Osborne *et al.*, 1954), which may, however, possibly be of a synergistic nature (Veldstra, 1953) or due to the combined effect of very weak auxin activity and synergistic activity.

The anti-auxin effects of 2:4:6-T are clearly shown by its inhibiting action on *Avena* coleoptile section growth induced by simultaneously applied 2:4-D or IAA (McRae and Bonner, 1952) and from its growth-restoring effects on 2:4-D-inhibited flax roots (Åberg, 1954; see also *Figure 5*). From the experiments made by Hoffmann (1953) with tomato plants it seems clear that 2:4:6-T not only counteracts externally applied auxins of different types, but also interferes with plant responses controlled by native auxins, such as geotropic curvatures and rooting of cuttings.

In the wheat root test used in the present investigation, 2:4:6-T gives comparatively slight but highly significant stimulations (*Figure 5*). For the cell length, however, Hansen (1954) did not find any corresponding increase. As in the case of 2:6-D we must expect the 2:4:6-T curve to be the complex resultant of counterbalancing effects, and it is quite natural that some differences should occur when using different materials and methods.

On the whole it seems safe to conclude from experiments with wheat roots, with 2:4-D-inhibited flax roots (*Figure 5*), and with *Avena* coleoptile sections (McRae and Bonner, 1952), that the introduction of a *para* chlorine atom in 2:6-D to give 2:4:6-T increases the anti-auxin component of its activity. This increase is probably related to the higher *affinity* of 2:4:6-T molecules for the growth centres, but may also be partly related to a decreased *intrinsic auxin activity* of these molecules.

In the clearly anti-auxinic 3:5-dichlorophenoxyacetic acid (Hansen, 1954), *para*-chlorination to give 3:4:5-trichlorophenoxyacetic acid induces some slight positive auxin activity (e.g. in *Avena* cylinder test and pea test, Wain and Wightman, 1953). Further comparative studies of this highly interesting pair of substances in different types of growth tests, especially those able to show the anti-auxin components of their activity, seem necessary before this phenomenon can be more closely discussed.

THE EFFECTS OF *para* SUBSTITUENTS OTHER THAN CHLORINE

In phenoxyacetic acid the introduction of a *para* chlorine atom results in maximum auxin activity of the new compound. Fluorine or bromine, on the other hand, gives a compound with considerably lower *gross auxin activity* than 4-chlorophenoxyacetic acid, but upon closer inspection the two compounds are found to be of rather different character.

In the flax root test, the growth-inhibiting activity of 4-fluorophenoxyacetic acid (4-FPOA) is five to six times lower than that of 4-ClPOA (*Figure 6*); further, the inhibition caused by 4-FPOA is strongly counteracted by the auxin antagonist 1-NMSP. In the wheat root test, 4-FPOA gives a rather slowly declining curve (*Figure 6*), and no stimulation is apparent at low concentrations, whereas in the *Avena* cylinder test, it causes strong growth stimulations. It seems fairly probable, therefore, that 4-FPOA should be characterized as an auxin with high *intrinsic activity* but with an *affinity* to the active sites which is well below that of 4-ClPOA. The action curve of this latter substance in the wheat root test (*Figure 6*) shows a slight but highly significant stimulation in the range 10^{-7} to 3×10^{-8} M ($G = 105{\cdot}8 \pm 1{\cdot}4$, $N = 10$, and $G = 104{\cdot}9 \pm 1{\cdot}6$, $N = 11$, respectively). Apparently we may assume that even in this fairly strong auxin the *intrinsic activity* is somewhat lower than that of the native auxin of wheat roots, and therefore a weak anti-auxin effect may be demonstrated with this material. Consistent with such an assumption is the lower maximum stimulation obtained in the *Avena* cylinder test with 4-ClPOA than with IAA or 2:4-D (Muir, Hansch, and Gallup, 1949; Wain and Wightman, 1953).

In 4-bromophenoxyacetic acid (4-BrPOA) the *intrinsic auxin activity* is probably further lowered, resulting in a lower root growth-inhibiting activity in the flax root test and stronger stimulations in the wheat root test (*Figure 6*). In the *Avena* cylinder test, 4-BrPOA shows about 30 per cent of the *gross activity* of 4-ClPOA (Muir and Hansch, 1953).

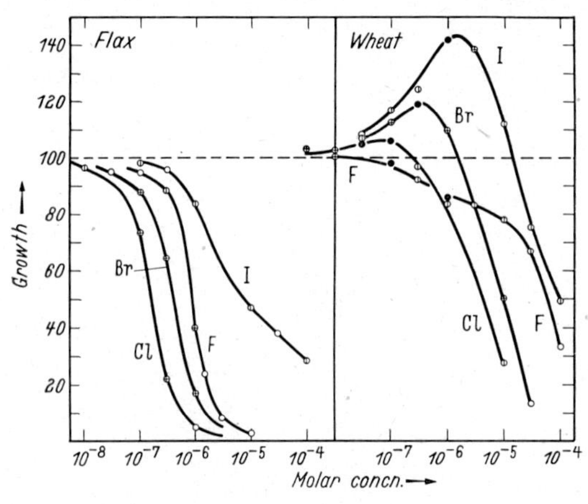

Figure 6. The effects of the para-*halogenated phenoxyacetic acids on the growth of flax and wheat roots. F = 4-fluorophenoxyacetic acid (4-FPOA), and so on. Growth values (G) in per cent of control, presented as in Figure 1.*

In 4-iodophenoxyacetic acid (4-IPOA) the *intrinsic auxin activity* seems to be very weak or absent; Muir and Hansch (1953) report that it is inactive in the *Avena* cylinder test. Its *affinity* to the active sites must be quite considerable, however, as judged from the strong stimulations obtained with this substance in the wheat root test (*Figure 6*). In the flax root test it strongly reduces the inhibition caused by 10^{-7} M 2:4-D when added in a concentration of 10^{-6} M.

It is interesting to compare the halogenated phenoxyacetic acids with the corresponding α-phenoxy*iso*butyric acids, which have been studied by Hansen (1954). The anti-auxin activity of the latter substances increases with the size of the halogen atom. If *intrinsic auxin activity* is wholly absent from the 4-ClPO*i*B molecules, this would suggest that *affinity* progressively increases from 4-ClPO*i*B to 4-BrPO*i*B and 4-IPO*i*B. Alternatively, it could mean that the weak residual *intrinsic auxin activity* is more completely eliminated in the last two substances than in 4-ClPO*i*B.

For 4-methyl- and 4-ethyl-phenoxyacetic acids (4-MePOA and 4-EtPOA), it has earlier (Åberg, 1954) been shown that they are able to counteract the inhibiting effects of 2:4-D upon flax root growth, and also that they produce root inhibitions which may be alleviated by addition of an anti-auxin like 1-NMSP. The anti-auxin component of their activity is most pronounced with 4-EtPOA, and correspondingly we find stronger stimulations in the wheat root test with this substance than with 4-MePOA (*Figure 7*). The intermediate character of 4-MePOA is also apparent from the type of action curve obtained in the *Avena* cylinder test (*Figure 1*).

In the flax root test with externally applied 2:4-D the antagonistic effect of the 4-alkyl-phenoxyacetic acids culminates with 4-*iso*propyl-phenoxyacetic acid (4-*i*P-POA), which also gives a significant stimulation of flax root growth in the range 10^{-5} to 10^{-6} M. With 4-*tert.*-butylphenoxyacetic acid (4-*t*B-POA) both this stimulation and the restorative effect upon 2:4-D-inhibited flax roots are slightly weakened (Åberg, 1954).

For wheat roots, on the other hand, growth stimulations have already

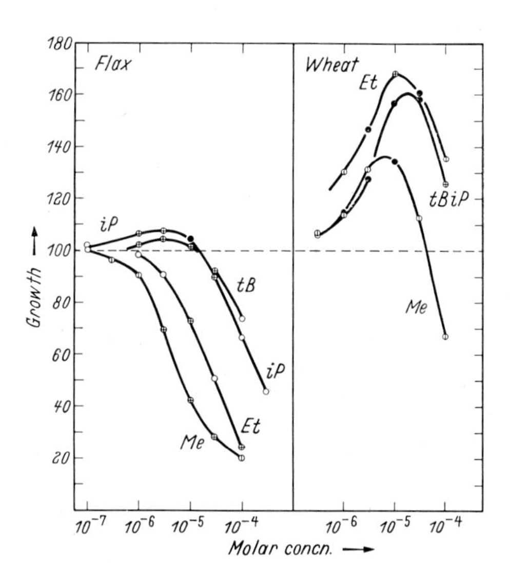

Figure 7. The effects of some para-*alkyl-phenoxyacetic acids on the growth of flax and wheat roots. Me* = *4-methylphenoxyacetic acid* (*4-MePOA*), *and so on. Et* = *ethyl,* iP = iso*propyl,* tB = tert.*-butyl, Growth values* (*G*) *in per cent of control, presented as in Figure 1. The* iP *and* tB *effects on wheat roots do not differ significantly, and the values for both substances have therefore been jointly plotted.*

reached their maximum with 4-EtPOA (*Figure 7*). This is probably partly related to the lower auxin sensitivity of this material as compared with flax roots. To some extent it may perhaps also be caused by a decreased 'uptake' of the substances with 'bulky' alkyl-substituents (cf. p. 95).

Summarizing, it may be said that the highest *intrinsic auxin activity* is possibly attained in the 4-FPOA molecules which, however, show a low *affinity* to the active sites. In 4-ClPOA this *affinity* is much increased, and the *intrinsic activity* is still high, but not high enough to exclude a very faint anti-auxin component of the activity. With further increase in the size of the *para*-substituent we get substances of clearly intermediate character (4-BrPOA, 4-MePOA, 4-EtPOA, and probably 4-IPOA), while the introduction of still larger substituents results in regulators of an almost pure anti-auxin type (4-*i*P-POA, 4-*t*B-POA). The lowering of *intrinsic auxin activity* seems to parallel fairly closely the increase in the van der Waals radius of the *para*-substituent (Pauling, 1948): e.g.

para-substituent:	F	Cl	Br	CH_3	I
van der Waals radius:	1·35	1·80	1·95	2·0	2·15 Å

THE TOXICITY OF PLANT GROWTH REGULATORS

It seems to be a general rule that highly active anti-auxins which stimulate the growth of wheat or flax roots at very low concentrations also show inhibition at lower concentrations than weak anti-auxins. Such a phenomenon could lead to the assumption that the inhibitions exerted by sufficiently high concentrations of all anti-auxins were in some way related to the auxin system. A decrease in the level of active auxin below its optimum value would be a possible explanation, but this is ruled out by the fact that such inhibitions are not relieved by the addition of auxin (Åberg, 1951; 1953a). Instead, it has been assumed that the inhibitions are due to accessory toxic effects which have no connection with the auxin system proper (Åberg, 1951, 1953a; Burström, 1951a,b; Hansen, 1954).

The nature of such a 'toxicity' is, of course, a problem in itself. It is tempting to assume some connection with a general ability of regulator substances to become bound to enzymes and other proteins, thereby upsetting their physiological functions when present in high concentrations. A certain parallelism between the *affinity* of the regulators for the specific growth centres and their general 'toxicity' would then be quite natural. In this connection, it is very interesting to find that there are indications of a parallelism between the bactericidal effect of many phenols and the growth-regulating activity of the corresponding phenoxyacetic acids. As a measure of the bactericidal activity, the 'phenol coefficient', giving the relation between the concentration of unsubstituted phenol and the equi-effective concentration of the substance to be characterized, may be used (see Reddish, 1954).

A rise in the phenol coefficient upon *para*-chlorination is apparent for several pairs of phenols related both to auxinic and to anti-auxinic phenoxyacetic acids. We thus find about a four-fold increase from phenol to 4-Cl-phenol, from 2-Cl- to 2:4-Cl_2-phenol, and from thymol to chlorothymol; from 2:6-Cl_2- to 2:4:6-Cl_3-phenol the increase is approximately two- to three-fold, and from 2-Me- to 2-Me-4-Cl-phenol about five-fold (data obtained from Suter, 1941; McCulloch, 1945; Wolf and Westveer, 1952; Reddish, 1954). Such a *para* chlorine effect is also apparent for many pairs of phenols studied by Blackman *et al.* (1955) in respect to their capacity to induce chlorosis in *Lemna minor*. In this case the rise in activity from phenol to 4-Cl-phenol is 7·3, from 2-Me- to 2-Me-4-Cl-phenol 10·6, and from the 3:5-Me_2-, 2:5-Me_2-, 2:6-Me_2-, and 3-Me-5-Et-phenols to the corresponding *para*-chlorinated compounds 7·3, 9·5, 9·2, and 9·0 respectively.

Hypothetically we may thus assume that *para*-chlorination of phenols and phenol derivatives increases the *affinity* of the substance for receptor places in the cytoplasm, thereby conditioning in part the increased activity of several auxins and also leading to increased activity of many anti-auxins, to higher 'toxicity' (root-growth-inhibiting activity) of anti-auxins and to increased chlorose-inducing and bactericidal effects of many phenols. The strong increase in the rate of hydrolysis of certain chymotrypsin substrates upon *para*-chlorination of a phenylalanine residue (see Neurath and Schwert, 1950; Åberg, 1953b) is relevant in the present connection in that it indicates a corresponding increase in enzyme-substrate affinity. The presence of a *para*-chlorophenyl group in the systemic herbicide 3-(4-chlorophenyl)-1:1-dimethylurea (CMU) is of some interest too. Its action is certainly different from that of the auxins (Christoph and Fisk, 1954; Muzik *et al.*, 1954), but nevertheless the general *affinity* of the *para*-chlorophenyl group to the plasma proteins may be of importance in conditioning it.

Upon closer inspection deviations are likely to occur within the series of phenomena now compared. Though perhaps similar to a certain extent, the receptor sites for such widely different processes may certainly be expected to differ in other respects. For the mainly auxinic substances, the magnitude of the *para* chlorine effect upon *affinity* may be difficult to separate quantitatively from simultaneous effects on *intrinsic activity*, and other difficulties are encountered if regulator substances of clearly intermediate character are included in the comparisons. For an anti-auxin with conspicuous residual auxin activity, the inhibiting effect on root growth exerted by fairly high concentrations may thus be of auxin character, or it may be a mixed effect comprising both an auxin component and a component of 'nonspecific toxicity'. For weak auxins the root inhibitions at high concentrations may likewise be mixed.

CONCLUDING REMARKS

There still remains to be discussed the possible effects of varying penetration rates of the different regulators to the active sites. The exact location of these sites offers immediate difficulties. In the case of surface-controlled reactions of growing cells, the penetration factor may probably be regarded as relatively unimportant when working with such objects as roots. At least in the outer tissues, transport through the cell walls will hardly differ very much for the various substances; when of a purely diffusive character it will naturally be somewhat slower for substances of higher molecular weight.

If, however, it is assumed that a main part of the regulating action takes place after penetration of the plasma membrane, the factors determining the rate of this process may become important, provided that the rate is too slow to permit the equilibrium concentration to be reached under the dynamic conditions of growth. How far this situation is realized cannot be judged at present, and certainly it must differ for different types of material and even for different rates of growth.

Nevertheless, it may be of value to consider briefly two possible sources of variations in the uptake of different regulators. It is fairly certain that most of these substances penetrate into the cell mainly in the form of undissociated, lipophilic molecules, though some uptake in the form of anions may also occur (cf. Simon and Beevers, 1952). A difference in the *dissociation constant* (K) of two regulators tested at the same pH might thus possibly cause a difference in their uptake rates. The effect of *para*-chlorination on the dissociation of some of the substances used in the present study is shown by the following K-values:

POA:	$6{\cdot}8 \times 10^{-4}$,	4-ClPOA:	$7{\cdot}9 \times 10^{-4}$	(Muir *et al.*, 1949).
PO*i*B:	$3{\cdot}8 \times 10^{-4}$,	4-ClPO*i*B:	$3{\cdot}3 \times 10^{-4}$	(Burström, 1951a).
Tr:	$3{\cdot}65 \times 10^{-5}$,	4-ClTr:	$3{\cdot}86 \times 10^{-5}$	(Nivard, 1951).
PF:	$6{\cdot}27 \times 10^{-5}$,	4-ClPF:	$10{\cdot}6 \times 10^{-5}$	(Nivard, 1951).

Apparently there is no consistent effect of such magnitude that it can be related to the observed differences in *gross activity*.

The situation might be influenced, however, by the *degree of lipophily* of the undissociated molecules, which, together with the molecular size, is a very important factor determining the permeation rate (see Collander, 1954). For several aliphatic substances, Collander (1949) found about a five-fold rise in the partition coefficient C_{ether}/C_{water} upon the introduction of a chlorine atom, and the same may be true for aromatic substances. Thus, the water solubility of *N*-phenylmaleimide is about twenty times higher than that of the 4-chloro- derivative, and this has been suggested as explaining, in part at least, the higher physiological activity of the chlorinated compound (Overbeek *et al.*, 1955). As pointed out by these authors, however, such a mechanism cannot fully explain the *specific* effect of a *para* chlorine atom, and such specific effects are clearly apparent with the chloro-phenoxyacetic acids, the chloro-phenoxy*iso*butyric acids and the chloro-*trans*cinnamic acids. It seems, therefore, that we must turn from the less specific solubility effects to the much higher specificity possible in a multipoint adsorption system in order to get a plausible hypothesis as to the nature of the *para* chlorine effect. As a reminder against over-estimating the lipoid solubility factor, the partition coefficients C_{ether}/C_{water} for phenylacetic acid and indoleacetic acid may be cited: PA 37, IAA 20 (Collander, 1949).

Additional evidence for the probable absence of conspicuous penetration factors related to undissociated molecules in a root growth test comes from Burström's (1951a; 1952) studies on the effects of PO*i*B and 4-ClPO*i*B on wheat roots at different pH values. An increase in the pH value from 4 to 7 has, in the presence of a normal calcium supply, no significant effects upon the growth stimulation caused by these substances, in spite of the strongly reduced amount of undissociated molecules present at higher pH values. The non-auxinic inhibitions, on the other hand, are markedly shifted to higher concentrations with increasing pH.

Though *para*-chlorination may certainly influence the permeation rate of a regulator substance, and though this rate may be of importance in conditioning the magnitude of the *gross activity* in some types of tests, nevertheless we may conclude that such a factor is likely to be of little significance in root tests. This may perhaps be connected with the localization of the growth centres at the cell surfaces and with the rapid penetration of the regulators on to these surfaces. Further experimental studies are needed, however, for clarification of the situation, but provisionally the permeation factor may be neglected when considering the results of such tests and the emphasis laid upon the probably more important effects of variations in *affinity* and in *intrinsic activity*.

The effects of *para*-chlorination may then be summarized as follows:

(*i*) It generally increases the auxin activity of weak auxins. In the phenoxyacetic acid series this increase may amount to one hundred times or more, and it appears probable that it is mainly conditioned by an increase in the *affinity* to the growth centres and in the *intrinsic activity* of the molecules.

(*ii*) In the typical anti-auxins, the increase in the growth-stimulating activity upon wheat roots or in the growth-restoring activity upon 2:4-D-inhibited flax roots usually is of the order of about five to ten times or more.

As the *intrinsic activity* of these molecules is thought to be completely or almost completely blocked, this increase may preliminarily be taken as related mainly to the *affinity* for the growth centres.

(*iii*) The *affinity* effect must certainly be expected to vary within fairly wide limits for different types of substances. Tentatively, the estimate obtained from anti-auxins of the phenoxy type may, however, be applied to substances like POA, 2-ClPOA, and 2-MePOA, for which the *para* chlorine effect could then be divided into about a five- to ten-fold increase in receptor *affinity* and about an equal or stronger increase in *intrinsic auxin activity*.

The present hypothesis evidently postulates the existence of a graded series of intermediate growth regulators with *intrinsic activities* between those of the typical auxins and the very low or absent activities of the typical anti-auxins. The interactions of substances like γ-phenylbutyric, 4-methylphenoxyacetic 4-ethylphenoxyacetic, and carvacroxyacetic acid (2-Me-5-*i*P-POA) with 2:4-D and 1-NMSP strongly indicate that they occupy such an intermediate position (Åberg, 1952; 1954). The auxin and anti-auxin effects shown by substances like 2:6-dichlorophenoxyacetic acid or 4-bromophenoxyacetic acid in different types of tests, and the peculiar compound action curves of such substances in the *Avena* cylinder test (p. 96) also point to the same conclusion. That even fairly strong auxins may have an *intrinsic activity* below the possible maximum is evident from the quantitative treatment of the IAA–2:4-D–interactions in the *Avena* cylinder test (McRae, Foster, and Bonner, 1953) and from the slight stimulations of wheat roots by low concentrations of 4-chlorophenoxyacetic acid (*Figure 6*).

The maximum stimulations obtainable under certain conditions with *Avena* coleoptile sections may be directly related to *intrinsic activity*, the maximum stimulations of wheat roots may be inversely related to the same measure, and data for judging the position of a certain substance may be obtained from combination experiments like those made with flax roots. In all these different methods disturbances may be caused in several different ways (uptake and transport factors, non-specific toxicity, synergism, and so on). Therefore, the safest way of approach to a comprehensive quantitative treatment of the primary reaction, or reactions, underlying the diverse growth responses seems to be the parallel use of different test methods and the attempted synthesis of the results into a coherent picture.

REFERENCES

ÅBERG, B. (1950). On auxin antagonists and synergists in root growth. *Physiol. Plant.* **3,** 447.

ÅBERG, B. (1951). The interaction of some auxin antagonists and 2:4-D in root growth. *Physiol. Plant.* **4,** 627.

ÅBERG, B. (1952). On the effects of weak auxins and antiauxins upon root growth. *Physiol. Plant.* **5,** 305.

ÅBERG, B. (1953a). On the interaction of 2:3:5-triiodobenzoic acid and maleic hydrazide with auxins. *Physiol. Plant.* **6,** 277.

ÅBERG, B. (1953b). On optically active plant growth regulators. *LantbrHögsk. Ann.* **20,** 241.

ÅBERG, B. (1954). Studies on plant growth regulators. IX. *Para*-alkyl-phenoxy-acetic and -propionic acids, and some related derivatives of naturally occurring phenols. *Physiol. Plant.* **7,** 241.

ÅBERG, B. (1955). Studies on plant growth regulators. X. On the reproducibility of root growth results. *LantbrHögsk. Ann.* **21** (1954) 197.

ÅBERG, B., and JÖNSSON, E. (1955). Studies on plant growth regulators. XI. Experiments with pea roots, including some observations on the destruction of indole-acid acid by different types of roots. *LantbrHögsk. Ann.* **21** (1954) 401.

ÅBERG, B., and KHALIL, A. (1953). Some notes on the effect of auxin antagonists and synergists upon coleoptile growth. *LantbrHögsk. Ann.* **20,** 81.

AUDUS, L. J. (1953). *Plant growth substances*, Leonard Hill Ltd., London.

AUDUS, L. J., and SHIPTON, M. E. (1952). 2:4-Dichloranisole-auxin interactions in root growth. *Physiol. Plant.* **5,** 430.

BLACKMAN, G. E., PARKE, M. H., and GARTON, G. (1955). The physiological activity of substituted phenols. I, II. *Arch. Biochem. Biophys.* **54,** 45.

BURSTRÖM, H. (1950). Studies on growth and metabolism of roots. IV. Positive and negative auxin effects on cell elongation. *Physiol. Plant.* **3,** 277.

BURSTRÖM, H. (1951a). Studies on growth and metabolism of roots. VI. The relative growth action of different *iso*butyric acid derivatives. *Physiol. Plant.* **4,** 470.

BURSTRÖM, H. (1951b). Studies on growth and metabolism of roots. VII. The growth action of α-(phenoxy)propionic acids. *Physiol. Plant.* **4,** 641.

BURSTRÖM, H. (1952). Studies on growth and metabolism of roots. VIII. Calcium as a growth factor. *Physiol. Plant.* **5,** 391.

BURSTRÖM, H. (1955). Evaluation of the growth activity of naphthalene derivatives. *Physiol. Plant.* **8,** 174.

CHRISTOPH, R. J., and FISK, E. L. (1954). Responses of plants to the herbicide 3-(*p*-chlorophenyl)-1:1-dimethylurea (CMU). *Bot. Gaz.* **116,** 1.

COLLANDER, R. (1949). Die Verteilung organischer Verbindungen zwischen Äther und Wasser. *Acta chem. scand.* **3,** 717.

COLLANDER, R. (1954). The permeability of Nitella cells to non-electrolytes. *Physiol. Plant.* **7,** 420.

FAWCETT, C. H., OSBORNE, D. J., WAIN, R. L., and WALKER, R. D. (1953). Studies on plant growth-regulating substances. VI. Side-chain structure in relation to growth-regulating activity in the aryloxyalkylcarboxylic acids. *Ann. appl. Biol.* **40,** 231.

FREDGA, A., and MATELL, M. (1952). Studies on synthetic growth substances. III. The steric relations of the optically active α-phenoxy-propionic acid. *Ark. Kemi,* **4,** 325.

HANSEN, B. (1954). A physiological classification of 'shoot auxins' and 'root auxins'. I, II. *Bot. Notiser,* 230, 318.

HANSON, J. B., and BONNER, J. (1955). The nature of the lag period in auxin-induced water uptake. *Amer. J. Bot.* **42,** 411.

HELLSTRÖM, N. (1953). An attempt to explain the interaction of auxin and anti-auxin in root growth by an adsorption mechanism. *Acta chem. scand.* **7,** 461.

HOFFMANN, O. L. (1953). Inhibition of auxin effects by 2:4:6-trichlorophenoxy-acetic acid. *Plant Physiol.* **28,** 622.

HOUSLEY, S., BENTLEY, J. A., and BICKLE, A. S. (1954). Studies on plant growth hormones. III. Application of enzyme reaction kinetics to cell elongation in the *Avena* coleoptile. *J. exp. Bot.* **5,** 373.

INGESTAD, T. (1953). Kinetic aspects on the growth-regulating effect of some phenoxy acids. *Physiol. Plant.* **6,** 796.

JÖNSSON, Å. (1955). Synthetic plant hormones. VIII. Relationship between chemical structure and plant growth activity in the arylalkyl-, aryloxyalkyl- and indole-alkylcarboxylic acid series. *Svensk kem. Tidskr.*, **67,** 166.

KATO, J. (1954). Studies on the relation between auxin activity and chemical structure. I. On phenyl- and naphthyl-thioglycolic acid derivatives and related compounds. *Mem. Coll. Sci. Kyoto,* **B21,** 77.

MATELL, M. (1954). Stereochemical studies on plant growth regulators. IX. The enantiomorphic α-(4-chlorophenoxy)propionic acids and their configuration. *Ark. Kemi*, **7,** 437.

MCCULLOCH, E. C. (1945). *Disinfection and sterilization*, 2nd ed., Philadelphia.

MCRAE, D. H., and BONNER, J. (1952). Diortho substituted phenoxyacetic acids as antiauxins. *Plant Physiol.* **27,** 834.

MCRAE, D. H., and BONNER, J. (1953). Chemical structure and antiauxin activity. *Physiol. Plant.* **6,** 485.

MCRAE, D. H., FOSTER, R. J., and BONNER, J. (1953). Kinetics of auxin interaction. *Plant. Physiol.* **28,** 343.

MELNIKOV, N. N., TURETSKAYA, R. KH., BASKAKOV, YU. A., BOYARKIN, A. N., and KUZNETSOVA, M. S. (1953). The structure and the physiological activity of substituted phenylacetic and naphthylacetic acids. *Dokl. Akad. Nauk. S.S.S.R.* **89,** 953 (*Chem. Abstr.* **48,** 6398 (1954)).

MUIR, R. M., and HANSCH, C. (1951). The relationship of structure and plant-growth activity of substituted benzoic and phenoxyacetic acids. *Plant. Physiol.* **26,** 369.

MUIR, R. M., and HANSCH, C. (1953). On the mechanism of action of growth regulators. *Plant Physiol.* **28,** 218.

MUIR, R. M., HANSCH, C., and GALLUP, A. H. (1949). Growth regulation by organic compounds. *Plant Physiol.* **24,** 359.

MUZIK, T. J., CRUZADO, H. J., and LOUSTALOT, A. Y. (1954). Studies on the absorption, translocation, and action of CMU. *Bot. Gaz.* **116,** 65.

NEURATH, H., and SCHWERT, G. W. (1950). The mode of action of the crystalline pancreatic proteolytic enzymes. *Chem. Rev.* **46,** 69.

NIVARD, R. J. F. (1951). Over structuur en eigenschappen bij *cis*- en *trans*-kaneelzuur en verwante verbindingen. Thesis, Leyden.

OSBORNE, D. J., BLACKMAN, G. E., POWELL, R. G., SUDZUKI, F., and NOVOA, S. (1954). Growth-regulating activity of certain 2:6-substituted phenoxyacetic acids. *Nature*, **174,** 742.

OVERBEEK, J. VAN, BLONDEAU, R., and HORNE, V. (1951). *Trans*-cinnamic acid as an antiauxin. *Amer. J. Bot.* **38,** 589.

OVERBEEK, J. VAN, BLONDEAU, R., and HORNE, V. (1955). Maleimides as auxin antagonists. *Amer. J. Bot.* **42,** 205.

PAULING, L. (1948). *The nature of the chemical bond*, 2nd ed., Cornell University Press, Ithaca, New York.

REDDISH, G. F. (Ed.) (1954). *Antiseptics, disinfectants, fungicides, and chemical and physical sterilization*, Lea and Febiger, Philadelphia.

REINHOLD, L. (1954). The uptake of indole-3-acetic acid by pea epicotyl segments and carrot disks. *New Phytol.* **53,** 217.

SIMON, E. W., and BEEVERS, H. (1952). The effect of pH on the biological activities of weak acids and bases. I, II. *New Phytol.* **51,** 163.

SUGII, M., and SUGII, A. (1953). Studies on the phytohormones. I. On the growth-promoting activity for plants of aryl thioglycolic acid derivatives. *Bull. Inst. chem. Res. Kyoto*, **31,** 27.

SUTER, C. M. (1941). Relationships between the structures and bactericidal properties of phenols. *Chem. Rev.* **28,** 269.

SUTTER, E. (1944). Die chemische Bestimmung des Heteroauxins und Versuche über seine Aufnahme durch die Pflanze. *Ber. schweiz. bot. Ges.* **54,** 197.

SYNERHOLM, M. E., and ZIMMERMAN, P. W. (1945). The preparation of some substituted phenoxy alkyl carboxylic acids and their properties as growth substances. *Contr. Boyce Thompson Inst.* **14,** 91.

THIMANN, K. V. (1952). The role of ortho-substitution in the synthetic auxins. *Plant Physiol.* **27,** 392.

VELDSTRA, H. (1953). The relation of chemical structure to biological activity in growth substances. *Ann. Rev. Pl. Physiol.* **4,** 151.

VELDSTRA, H., and BOOIJ, H. L. (1949). Researches on plant growth regulators. XVII. Structure and activity. On the mechanism of the action III. *Biochim. biophys. Acta,* **3,** 278.

WAIN, R. L., and WIGHTMAN, F. (1953). Studies on plant growth-regulating substances. VII. Growth-promoting activity in the chloro-phenoxyacetic acids. *Ann. appl. Biol.* **40,** 244.

WENT, F. W., and THIMANN, K. V. (1937). *Phytohormones,* Macmillan, New York.

WOLF, P. A., and WESTVEER, W. M. (1952). The relationship of chemical structure to germicidal activity as evidenced by chlorinated phenols. *Arch. Biochem. Biophys.* **40,** 306.

ZIMMERMAN, P. W., and HITCHCOCK, A. E. (1942). Substituted phenoxy and benzoic acid growth substances and the relation of structure to physiological activity. *Contr. Boyce Thompson Inst.* **12,** 321.

ON FORM AND FUNCTION OF PLANT GROWTH SUBSTANCES

H. VELDSTRA

Research Laboratory, Combined Quinine Works, Amsterdam

FROM the literature on the subject of our present discussion it is evident that the analysis of structure–activity relationships with plant growth substances continues to fascinate both chemists and plant physiologists. This is not to be wondered at, as there exist hardly any types of naturally occurring, physiologically active substances which have so simple a structure as indole-acetic acid and the features of which, essential for activity, can be incorporated in such a variety of compounds.

It may be useful, however, to see where we actually are at the moment and to ask what one may expect from this work as to the solution of the primary problem: where do these simple substances act and what is the essence of their function?

As to the active agents, in our opinion, we are fairly well informed about the requirements for activity and are able to discern in the chemically different compounds a common active principle (cf. Veldstra, 1953).

We must confess that in recent years we have on several occasions had the impression that the synthetic work would be unlikely to provide further essential information, but as frequently we were intrigued by an unexpected activity or lack of activity and found ourselves again on the synthetic trail, the course of which will be reported upon in this paper.

Moreover, very interesting results obtained by other investigators clearly indicate that the last word with regard to the structure (form) of the active compounds has certainly not yet been said.

Thus Jönsson (1955), in an elegant way, recently analysed in more detail the 'active' position of the side chain by comparing a large number of compounds. His conclusion that the formation of a pseudo-ring with the COOH group near to the centre of the extended ring-system formed seems to be essential, would imply that the position of the carboxyl group in all of the active acids is the same as that in the active di*ortho*-substituted benzoic acids (cf. Veldstra, 1952).

A real surprise in this structure–activity domain was the announcement of plant growth regulating activity of certain dithiocarbamates by van der Kerk *et al.* (1955) as this constitutes the first example of a 'ring-less' growth substance. This most interesting work will be referred to below. Apparently we have not yet exhausted all possible structures active as growth substances.

One has to be aware of the fact, however, that, fascinating as this work may be, it will not afford us the answer to the primary question of the mode of action. We know a lot about the active compounds, while the growth response they bring about as an end-effect of their actions is clearly perceptible and measurable. One has to admit, however, that properly speaking we know nothing for certain about what is going on 'in between' (in the cell). This is apparent also from the large number of theories, always inversely proportional to our factual knowledge of the relative problem. By dealing with half of the problem only (the active growth substances) we shall not be able to unravel the secret of auxin action; to achieve that aim we shall have to know more about 'the other side', viz. the receptor(s) in the cell.

Realizing that the growth response is given by an intact biological system only, it is evident that the primary action cannot be isolated from the cell. In this respect the analysis of localization and mode of action will be even more difficult than it is in enzymatic studies. There, one has the advantage that in several cases free, isolated enzymes are available with which the interaction between agent (substrate or inhibitor) and functioning macromolecule (viz. the primary action) can be studied uninfluenced by secondary factors.

However difficult the task may be, in order to get at the final solution of the problem of auxin action, in our opinion the accent of the investigations will have to shift from studies on structure–activity to a biochemical (physical) approach, while looking more inside the cell. For this perhaps new techniques are needed. The way such research will develop will, of course, depend also on the interpretation of knowledge gained previously in physiological and structural chemical investigations.

From more recent work I have therefore selected a number of experiments which in some respects round off our work on structure–activity relationships, and which in my opinion may guide further analysis in the above-mentioned directions.

SUBSTITUTED BENZOIC AND NAPHTHOIC ACIDS

In my opinion there can be no doubt that the activity of the substituted benzoic acids is essentially linked up with the particular spatial structure, resulting from the steric influence exerted by the di*ortho* substitution. The conjugation between the carboxyl group and the ring-system, which normally causes the molecule to occur in the mean in a flat form, is suppressed by the hindering substituents, and the resulting active form is a non-flat one (see *Figure 1*, also Veldstra, 1952).

Different opinions have been expressed with respect to the role of the nucleus in the active benzoic acids. Muir and Hansch (1951) and also Thimann (1952) ascribed a special function (according to Muir and Hansch a chemically reactive one) to defined positions in the nucleus (2–6, and 5, respectively) with respect to the primary action. We preferred to consider the whole nucleus as an attaching unit, in which special steric requirements as to size and position of substituents have to be met.

Our objections to the view of Muir and Hansch have been expounded elsewhere (Veldstra and Westeringh, 1952; Veldstra, 1953) and need not be repeated here. In our opinion, as to the *o*-substituents it is quite evident that a steric and not a chemically reactive function gives a plausible explanation of the observed facts; however, we desired to know more about the 3-, 5-, and 4-positions.

It is well known that *o*-substituents larger than CH_3 or Cl, though no doubt causing the COOH group to occur in the active spatial position, do not confer activity to benzoic acids. This is caused very probably by masking of the COOH group, thus excluding it from the interaction with its counterpart in the cell.

Figure 1. Molecule models of
Left: Benzoic acid. The molecule tends to take a flat form, as structures like + $C_6H_5{=}C(O^-)OH$ *and* $^+C_6H_5{=}C(O^-)OH$ *contribute to the mean state.*
Right: 2:6-*Dichlorobenzoic acid. Non-flat form, the* o-*substituents causing steric inhibition of resonance.*

As to the 3-position, apparently more latitude is left, as we found 3-cyanomethyl-2:6-dimethylbenzoic acid (I) to be active (*Figure 2*).

COOH; H_3C—; —CH_3; —CH_2CN
I

COOH; —CH_2CH_3; —Cl
II

COOH; —I; —Cl
III

COOH; —CH(CH_3)(CH_3); —Cl
IV

COOH; H_3C—; —CH_3; —CH_3
V

COOH; H_3C—; H_3C—; —CH_3; —CH_3
VI

COOH; Cl—; —Cl; —Cl; F
VII

COOH; Cl—; —Cl; —NO_2; F
VIII

The 3-chloromethyl-derivative proved to be very toxic, probably because of too high a chemical reactivity, as Cl^- was liberated in the medium. The 3-hydroxymethyl-derivative is inactive, which is more or less to be expected, as introduction of hydrophilic substituents in the lipophilic part of the molecule is not generally compatible with activity.

If substituents larger than CH_3 or Cl are introduced in one of the *o*-positions only, some activity is retained, which may be enhanced by a 3-substituent, as for example in 2-ethyl-3-chlorobenzoic acid (II) and 2-iodo-3-chlorobenzoic acid (III) (cf. Veldstra, 1955).

Though these compounds are only weakly active, they are interesting in that they illustrate the sensitivity of the COOH group as to inhibition of conjugation and masking from interaction. In the latter respect it should be noted that 2-*iso*propyl-3-chlorobenzoic acid (IV) is inactive again.

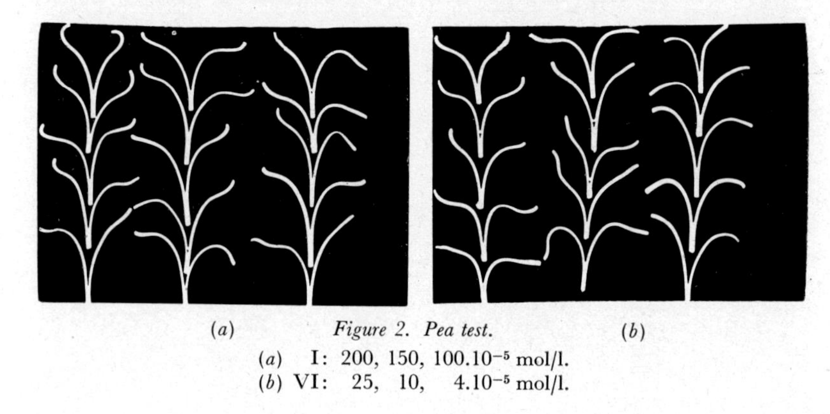

(*a*) *Figure 2. Pea test.* (*b*)

(*a*) I: 200, 150, 100.10^{-5} mol/l.
(*b*) VI: 25, 10, 4.10^{-5} mol/l.

Thimann (1952) considered a free 5-position in 2:3:6-substituted benzoic acids to possess an activating influence with respect to the physiological activity. Although the arguments given in Thimann's paper were already unacceptable from a theoretical chemical point of view, the fact that we found 2:3:5:6-tetramethylbenzoic acid (VI) to be slightly more active than 2:3:6-trimethylbenzoic acid (V) in the pea test at 25 and 10.10^{-5} mol/l., also demonstrates that a free 5-position is not essential. (For activity of VI cf. *Figure 2*.)

However, this proved to be the case until now with respect to the 4-position, all 4-substituted benzoic acids being inactive or in some cases, as with 4-chloro-3-nitrobenzoic acid, possessing antagonistic activity (Minarik *et al.*, 1951).

This latter fact, in particular, suggested to us that a free 4-position implies the absence of a hindrance to the 'active' interaction, rather than the presence of an active binding spot, as, quite generally, introduction of a steric hindrance to the normal interaction results in the appearance of antagonistic activity (cf. the *iso*butyric acid derivatives (Burström, 1951) and the acids with a bulky α-substituent (Veldstra and Åberg, 1953)). In order to verify this view, 2:3:6-trichloro-4-fluorobenzoic acid (VII) was synthesized. This acid and also an intermediate in its synthesis, viz. 2:6-dichloro-3-nitro-4-fluorobenzoic acid (VIII) proved to be distinctly active, both in the pea test and in the straight growth test (see *Figure 3* and *Table 1*). So apparently the restriction of substitution in the 4-position is not an absolute one, but one of maximal (very small) size of the substituent.

(*a*) *Figure 3. Pea test.* (*b*)
(*a*) 2:3:6-*trichlorobenzoic acid*: 50, 25, 10, 4.10^{-5} *mol/l.*
(*b*) VII: 50, 25, 10, 4.10^{-5} *mol/l.*

When surveying the available data on substituted benzoic acids, in our opinion the most plausible conclusions can be summarized as follows:

(i) Activity is dependent on a non-flat structure, caused by di*ortho* substituents of such a size that the COOH group is not masked.

Table 1

Avena *straight growth. Percentage elongation. The mean of* 20 *sections of initial length* 4 *mm, measured after* 24-*hour test*

Compound	*Buffer*	*IAA* 10^{-5} *mol/l.*	*Concentration (mol/l.)*						
			10^{-6}	10^{-5}	10^{-4}	5.10^{-4}	10^{-3}	5.10^{-3}	10^{-2}
II	38	73	40	40	40		17		
III	44	80	53	53	48		28		
IV	40	68	40	33	20		13		
VI	25	70	23	20	30		33		
VII	35	100	33	43	68		60		
VIII	38	83			55	78	83	63	
XI. Cl	16	110	40	68	65		40		
XIV	40	93		25	48		65		40
XVI	35	100		40	55		93		88
XVII	35	95		33	38		43		63
XIX	36	93	49	40	23		18		
XX	40	93	34	36	41		33		
XXI	35	83	35	40	28		23		
XXII	30	70	38	65	48		30		
XXIII	35	100	33	35	98		93		
XXIV	33	103	51	78	123		45		
XXVI	38			50	63		58		
XXIX	43	98	48	54	55		93		
XXX	45	135	55	98	140		140		

(ii) No convincing arguments have been adduced in support of the view that certain separate positions in the nucleus have a special binding function. For the moment the most simple and plausible explanation of the observed facts is that the nucleus with its substituents (other than COOH) as a whole acts as an attaching unit.

(iii) Substituents in 3- and/or 5-positions are allowed (or even desired as they mostly enhance activity as compared with 2:6-di-substitution). The restrictions as to their size are less than those for the *o*-substituents.

(iv) All 4-substituents larger than F are incompatible with activity.

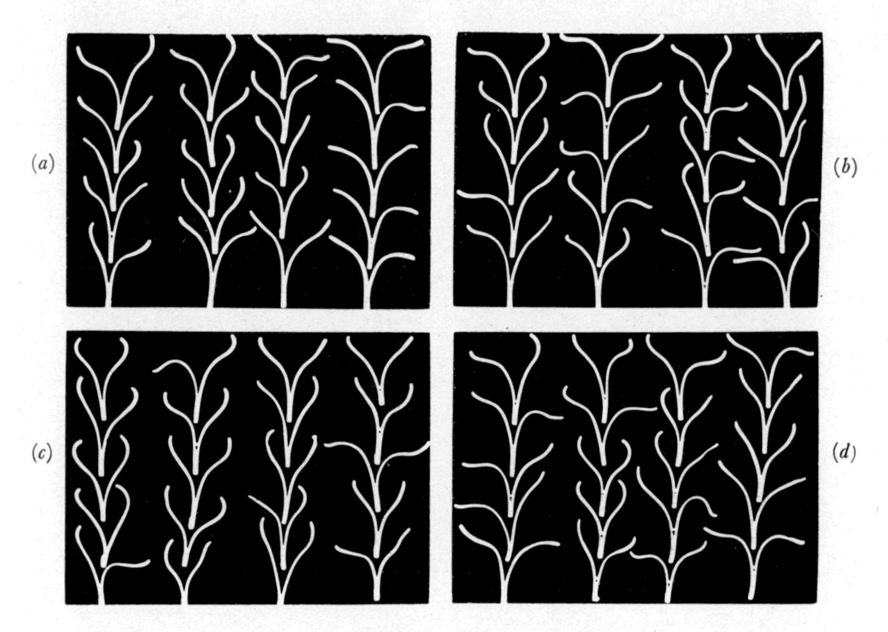

Figure 4. Pea test.

(*a*) XI. CH_3: 25, 10, 4, 1.10^{-5} *mol/l.*
(*b*) XI. Cl: 25, 10, 4, 1.10^{-5} *mol/l.*
(*c*) XI. Br: 25, 10, 4, 1.10^{-5} *mol/l.*
(*d*) XI. I: 25, 10, 4, 1.10^{-5} *mol/l.*

(v) All requirements with respect to the substituents strongly suggest that they imply the absence of hindrances to the fitting of the molecule on to its receptor, rather than the presence of specific binding spots.†

The weak activity of α-naphthoic acid (IX) and its enhancement by 2-substituents (e.g. X) has been explained by us on the same basis as the activity of the di*ortho* substituted benzoic acids (Veldstra, 1952). Studies of

† In the discussions about the kinetics of auxin action and the two-point attachment theory of Bonner (1954), illustrations are used in which besides the COOH group a special position in the active molecule is bound to the receptor. These illustrations are misleading as, apart from the fact that the calculations are based in fact on the assumption that the bindings are spontaneously reversible (so normal chemical bonds must be excluded!), the possible validity of these calculations has nothing to do with *two points* in the molecule. It would merely imply that *two factors* are operating, without informing us in the least about their nature.

molecular models reveal that in fact substituents in the 8-position of the naphthalene ring interfere more with a flat structure than do 2-substituents.

COOH (IX) COOH, —Cl (X) R, COOH (XI) $R = CH_3$, Cl, Br, I

We would expect therefore 8-substituted α-naphthoic acids to be active, as actually was found for 8-methyl-, 8-chloro-, 8-bromo, and 8-iodo-α-naphthoic acid (XI) (*Figure 4*).

In these compounds the COOH group is really fixed in what we indicated as the active spatial position (see *Figure 5*), of which they thus provide one of the best illustrations.

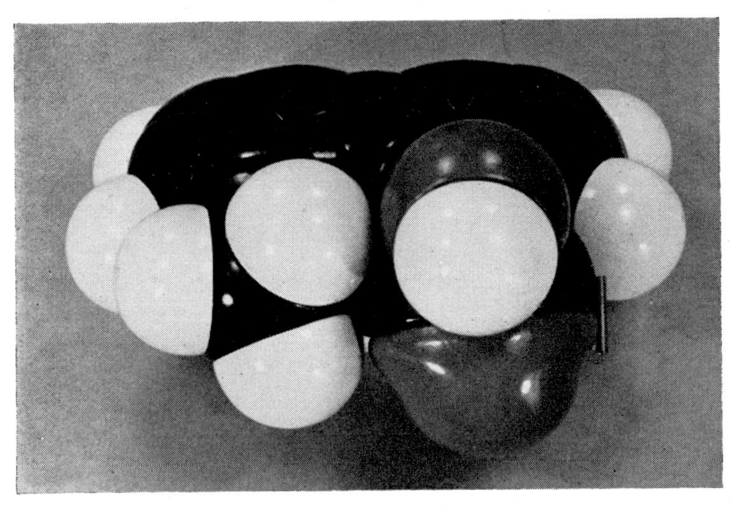

Figure 5. Molecular model of 8-*methyl-α-naphthoic acid, showing the fixed* (*'active'*) *position of the* COOH group.

The fact that for such a rotation of the carboxyl group out of the plane of the ring-system (frequently enough to give the molecule in the mean an active non-planar structure) the 'help' of a steric hindrance is apparently needed, and since this is not effected to the same extent by the forces responsible for the growth substance–receptor interaction it would appear that these forces are weak ones. In our opinion, for this same reason, the participation of the COOH group in a chemical bond (e.g. an amide bond, as proposed throughout the discussions by Muir and Hansch) may be ruled out.

VARIATIONS OF THE POLAR GROUP

It has been shown before that activity is not restricted to carboxylic acids, but that COOH may be replaced by a primary NO_2 group (Veldstra, 1944) or by SO_3H (Veldstra *et al.*, 1954). In the latter case, in a quantitative sense the same growth effect can be obtained as with, for example, IAA, both in the pea and in the straight growth tests provided that very high outside concentrations are used (up to 5×10^{-2} mol). Very probably this will have to be explained by a very poor penetration of these completely dissociated strong acids, which in itself would imply that the primary action resides inside the cell.

In order to analyse further variations of the polar group, in relation to activity, a number of phosphonic and phosphonous acids were synthesized, of which only naphthalene methane phosphonic acid (XIV) had been previously investigated (see Veldstra *et al.*, 1954).

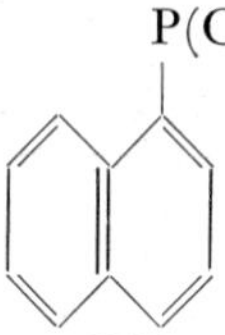

$P(O)(OH)_2$ — XII PO_2H_2 — XIII $CH_2P(O)(OH)_2$ — XIV $CH_2PO_2H_2$ — XV

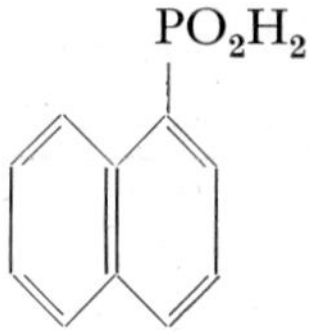

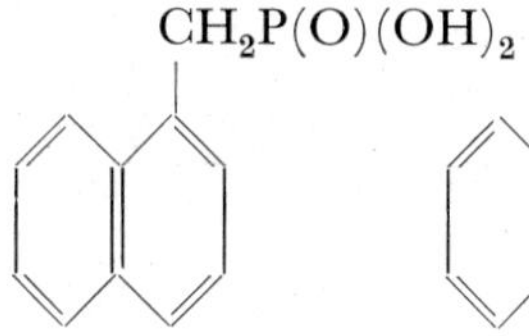

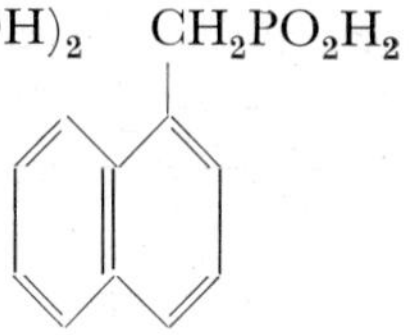

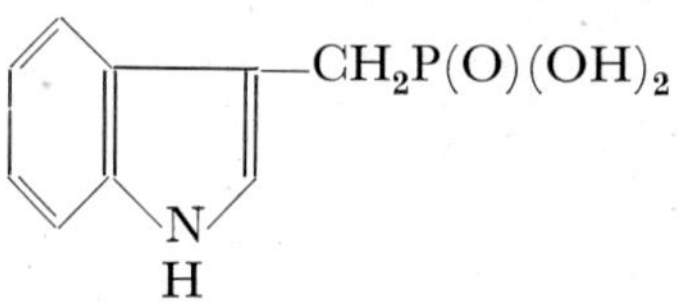

$CH_2P(O)(OH)_2$, N, H — XVI OC_2H_5, $CH_2P(O)(OH)$, N, H — XVII

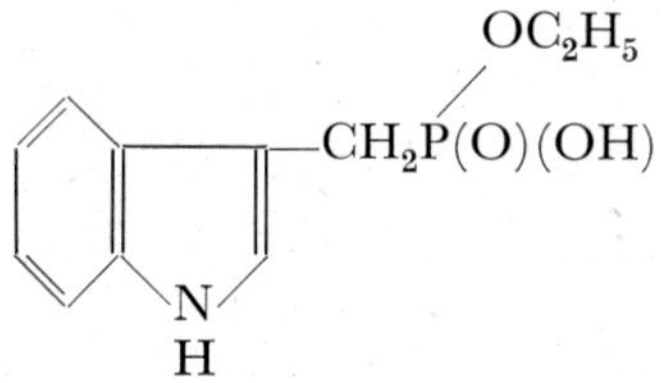

Most of them proved to be active again in both tests at high concentrations (see *Figure 6* and *Table 1*). It is worth mentioning that of the P-analogues of the weakly active naphthoic acid only the phosphonous acid (XIII) is active, whereas naphthalenemethanephosphonous acid (XV) at similar concentrations is more active than the phosphonic acid (XIV). Of the indole derivatives the phosphonic acid analogue of IAA (XVI) and its mono ester (XVII) were investigated, both of them being active.

From these results† it is clear that, though COOH is superior as a polar group in that it confers high activity to the compounds at low concentrations, other negative polar groups can perform the same function, and that their intrinsic activity may well come up to the same level, higher concentrations being required only because of secondary factors.

The fact that the structural specificity of the polar group is low, in our opinion is another argument in support of the view that, in functioning, the growth substance is not incorporated by a chemical reaction into an 'active structure'. From all the evidence available from other domains one would expect rather an antagonistic activity of the sulphonic and the phosphonic acids which, chemically, are not equivalent to the carboxylic acids. As in many respects they are equivalent physico-chemically, however, such a type of auxin action would make it comprehensible that all of these chemically different acids are physiologically active. In our opinion this is the most important conclusion to be drawn from this work on the polar group with respect to mode of action.

† For other phosphoric acid derivatives active as growth substances see Greenham (1953).

Figure 6. Pea test.

(*a*) XII : 1000, 750, 500.10^{-5} *mol/l.*
(*b*) XIII : 1000, 750, 500.10^{-5} *mol/l.*
(*c*) XIV : 1500, 1000, 750, 500.10^{-5} *mol/l.*
(*d*) XV : 1500, 1000, 750, 500.10^{-5} *mol/l.*
(*e*) XVI : 1500, 1250, 1000, 750.10^{-5} *mol/l.*
(*f*) XVII : 1500, 1250, 1000, 750.10^{-5} *mol/l.*

α-SUBSTITUTED PHENYLACETIC ACIDS

The effect of α-alkyl-substituents in phenylacetic acid has been discussed up to three-carbon substituents (Veldstra and Åberg, 1953). This series was extended by investigating the (DL)*n*-butyl-, *tert.*-butyl-, and *n*-amyl-derivatives (XVIII)

$$C_6H_5-CH(COOH)-R \qquad R = \begin{cases} -CH_2CH_2CH_2CH_3 \\ -C(CH_3)_3 \\ -CH_2CH_2CH_2CH_2CH_3 \end{cases}$$

XVIII

All of them are inactive in the pea test and the straight growth test. Judged from their effect on the normal geotropic response in the cress-root test they possess antagonistic properties. This will have to be studied more extensively, however (e.g. in Åberg's tests; also after resolving the racemates), before final information can be given.

We considered it to be of interest to compare α-alkylidene phenylacetic acids with the alkyl analogues, also with respect to the α-hydrogen hypothesis (Wain, 1953), which in our opinion cannot be of general importance for reasons given already elsewhere (Veldstra, 1953).

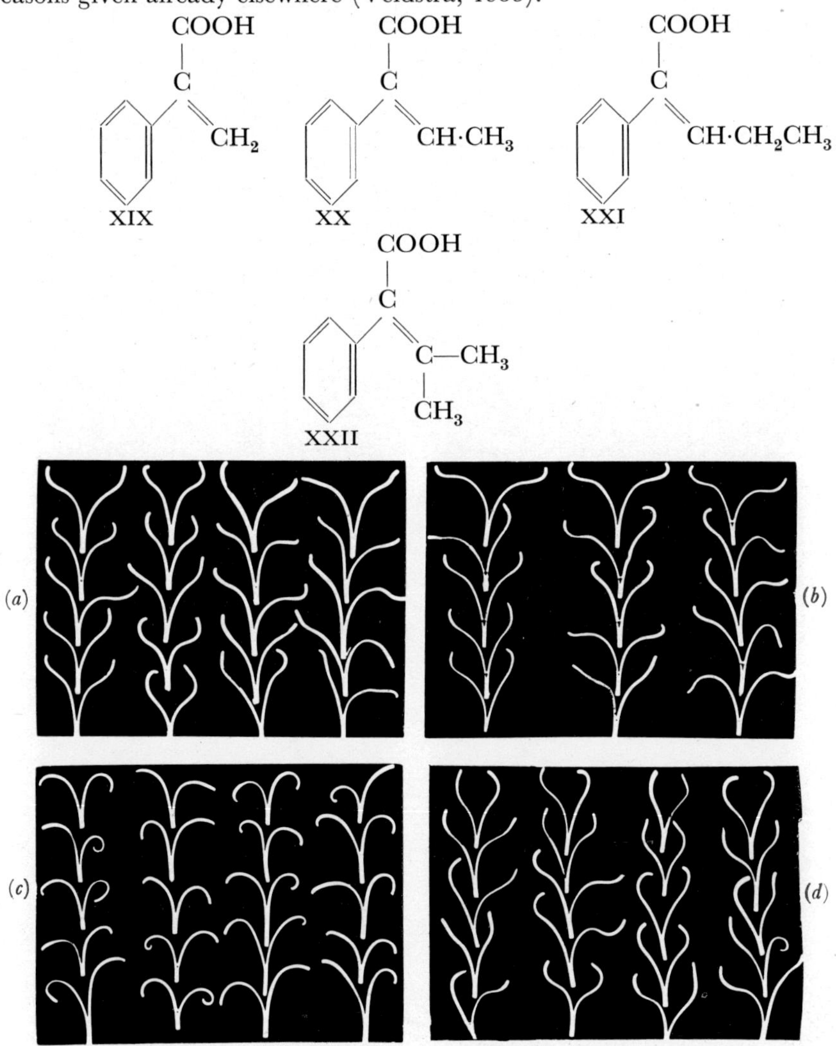

Figure 7. Pea test.

(*a*) *Phenylacetic acid* : 100, 50, 25, 10.10^{-5} *mol/l.*
(*b*) XIX : 50, 25, 10.10^{-5} *mol/l.*
(*c*) (DL)α-iso*propylphenylacetic acid*: 50, 25, 10, 4.10^{-5} *mol/l.*
(*d*) XXII : 50, 25, 10, 4.10^{-5} *mol/l.*

In the pea test α-methylene-phenylacetic acid (XIX) at lower concentrations is somewhat more active than phenylacetic acid, whereas the *iso*-propylidene-derivative is distinctly more active than the parent acid (see *Figure 7*). That these activities cannot be explained by a possible hydrogenation in the tissue to the corresponding alkyl-derivatives must be deduced from the fact that then in the case of *iso*propylidene-phenylacetic acid the antagonistically active *iso*propyl-derivative would result. So apparently an α-hydrogen atom is not essential here.

The great difference in physiological effect of the *iso*propyl- and *iso*propylidene-phenylacetic acid illustrates once more how sensitively the primary active site responds to seemingly small differences in structure. Judging from the ultra-violet absorption spectra, the double bond in the unsaturated acid is co-planar with the benzene nucleus and, in that case, as to its spatial form the acid is to be compared with the active 2-substituted α-naphthoic acids (Veldstra, 1952). We have no plausible explanation to offer, however, for the fact that the ethylidene- and *n*-propylidene- phenylacetic acids are practically inactive. Both of them may exist as *cis*- and *trans*- forms. These have not been separated as yet, and a more conclusive discussion of these interesting relations will have to be postponed for that reason also.

DITHIOCARBAMATES

A most interesting and important contribution to the study of structure–activity has recently been given by van der Kerk, van Raalte, Kaars Sijpesteijn, and van der Veen (1955), when during work on fungicides a notable growth substance activity was found for carboxymethyl dimethyl-dithiocarbamate (XXIII).

$$(H_3C)_2N-C(=S)-S-CH_2COOH \quad \text{XXIII}$$

$$(H_3C)_2N-C(=S)-O-CH_2COOH \quad \text{XXIV}$$

$$(H_3C)_2N-C(=O)-S-CH_2COOH \quad \text{XXV}$$

$$(H_5C_2)_2N-C(=S)-S-CH_2COOH \quad \text{XXVI}$$

$$(H_3C)_2N-C(=S)-S-C(CH_3)_2-COOH \quad \text{XXVII}$$

The activity first reported concerned only epinastic curvature and leaf deformation in tomato plants, whereas the compound also proved to be weakly active in the pea test and in the straight growth test. It was convincingly shown that activity in this type of compound is connected with the possibility and tendency that part of the molecule assumes a flat structure $\overset{+}{\rangle N}=C\langle_{S^-}$, which may be considered to take the place of the ring-system in the well-known growth substances. By kindly putting a number of these compounds at our disposal Dr. van der Kerk enabled us to test them under our conditions. *Figure 8* and *Table 1* show that the compounds XXIII and

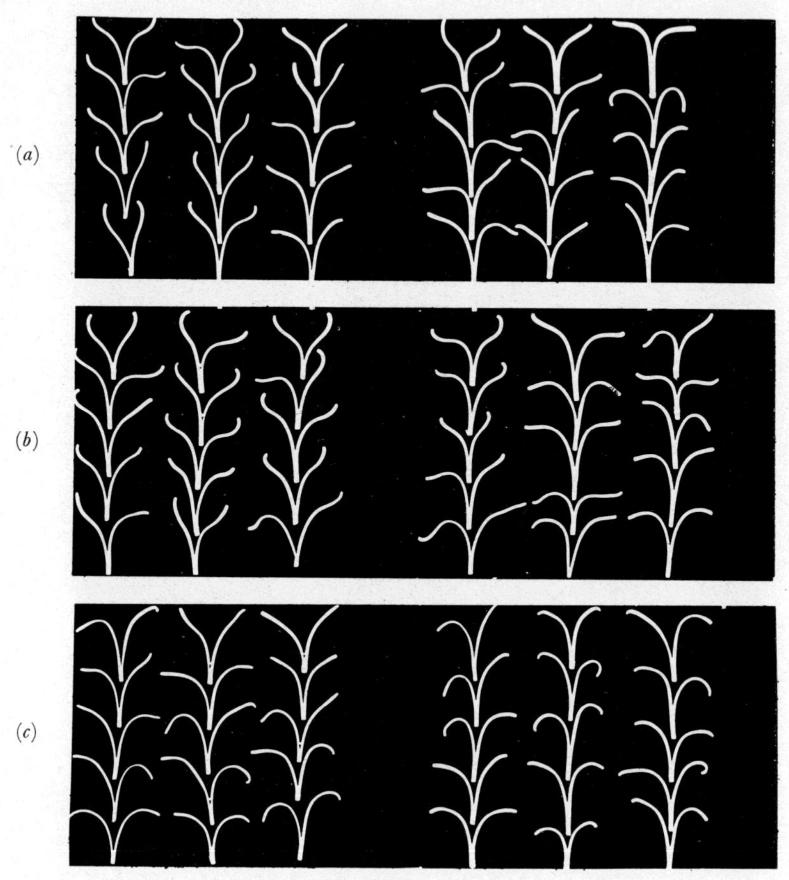

Figure 8. Pea test.
(*a*) XXIII : 500, 300, 100, 25, 10, 4.10^{-5} *mol/l.*
(*b*) XXIV : 500, 300, 100, 25, 10, 4.10^{-5} *mol/l.*
(*c*) XXVI : 500, 300, 100, 25, 10, 4.10^{-5} *mol/l.*

XXIV are distinctly active, XXIV being the most active one. When $N(CH_3)_2$ is replaced by $N(C_2H_5)_2$ (XXVI), or C=S by C=O (XXV), very weak activity or inactivity results, to be expected according to the view expressed by van der Kerk *et al.*, that in these cases the formation of the flat structure with a double bond is favoured less or not at all.

In the *iso*butyric acid derivative (XXVII) indications for antagonistic activity were found in the suppression of the normal geotropic behaviour of the roots in the cress-root test.

The fact that the activity of these compounds is found to be higher in the straight growth test than in the pea test is rather exceptional. It would be worth while investigating whether this might be caused by a higher degree of decomposition in the pea tissue.

Van der Kerk *et al.* have thus shown for the first time that a ring-system is not an absolute requirement for a compound to be active as a growth substance. The polar group apparently may be 'presented' in quite a number of ways, provided that the molecule can assume (or already possesses) the form required for an 'active' fitting on to the receptor.

This again suggests to us that the ring-system or its equivalent as a whole is functioning as an attaching unit and that no localized reactive function can be attributed plausibly to certain 'points' of it.

GROWTH SUBSTANCES WITH A PYRIDINE NUCLEUS

Pyridine compounds have hardly been investigated as growth substances until now. We reported pyridyl acetic acid to be inactive in the pea test (Veldstra, 1952), and supposed that this might be explained by too low a surface activity of the pyridine ring-system (Veldstra, 1944). That this type of compound merits further consideration, however, is shown by recent work of den Hertog *et al.* on pyridoxyacetic acids and related compounds, part of which has been published (Maas, de Graaff, and den Hertog, 1955).

Figure 9. Pea test.

Top XXIX: 500, 250, 100, 50.10^{-5} *mol/l.*
Bottom XXX : 100, 50, 25, 10, 4, 1.10^{-5} *mol/l.*

Prof. den Hertog kindly afforded us an opportunity to test a number of his compounds and with his consent a preliminary account of the results is given (see *Figure 9* and *Table 1*).

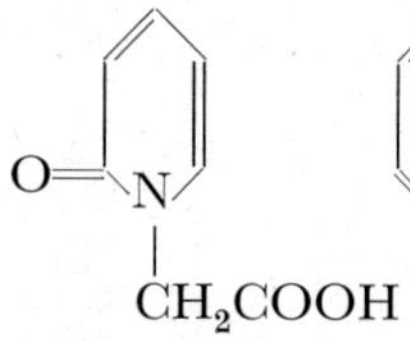

XXVIII: O=N-pyridone with N–CH_2COOH

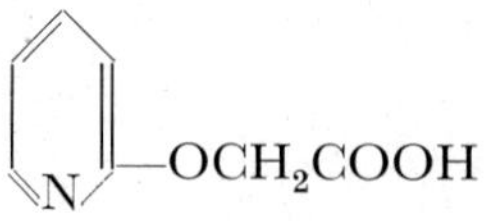

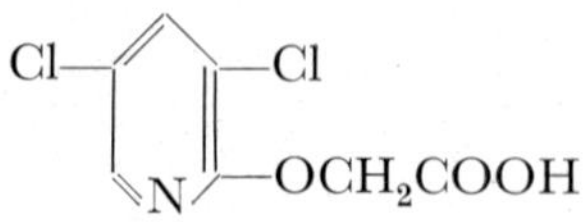

XXIX: pyridine –OCH_2COOH

XXX: Cl, Cl pyridine –OCH_2COOH

Whereas *N*-(2-pyridonyl)acetic acid (XXVIII) is inactive, 2-pyridoxy-acetic acid (XXIX) and its 3:5-dichloro-derivative (XXX) are active both in the pea test and in the straight growth test, the activity of the latter approaching the level of IAA. It is noteworthy that, as compared with 2:4-D, the pyridine analogue shows a far lower phyto-toxicity, at least towards these tissues.

After the other isomeric pyridoxyacetic acids and their derivatives have been investigated, this group of compounds, possibly in connection with the dithiocarbamates, might well enable us to analyse further the details of structure–activity relationships.

In these compounds we are dealing with more precise variations in the ring-system and its influencing by the location of the side chain than have so far been studied with naphthalene and indole ring-systems. Their effect on activity may provide a possibility to 'reconnoitre' some aspects of the receptor surface.

ON THE FUNCTION OF GROWTH SUBSTANCES

As stated above, for fundamental reasons we cannot expect to solve the problem of auxin function by exclusively studying their form (structure) and its influence on activity. Such work may certainly provide information, however, as to dimensions and nature of the receptor(s) as well as to the type of auxin action.

The various interpretations of results obtained in the structure–activity domain have led to different attempts to solve the primary question. We have to admit, however, that despite all these efforts, our joint explorations have so far not yielded real basic information as to the mode of action (cf. the reviews by Bonner and Bandurski, 1952, and by Gordon, 1953); for, as Gordon has expressed it, 'the biochemical mechanism of auxin action still remains as one of the pressing and challenging problems in plant physiology'.

So apparently more data are needed and a constant re-evaluation of those already obtained (even if affecting beloved theories) will be compulsory too.

When deciding to shift the accent from an analysis of structure–activity to a biochemical one (in the cell), our way of analysing will obviously be determined to a large extent by the conclusions about the type of action referred to above.

Thus, when trying to 'visualize' auxin function as a physico-chemical action of an amphipatic organic anion with a particular spatial pattern, an interaction at a functioning macromolecular surface and/or at interfaces in the cell, in our opinion is the most plausible starting point.

We had previously, therefore, considered the possibility that auxins might 'start' activity of potential, but 'masked' enzymes (Veldstra and Booij, 1949) (cf. also the discussion by Söding (1953), a theme further elaborated by Booij (1953)).

While at the moment no direct evidence in support of these views can be given and work in this domain is still in a preliminary stage, it may be useful to focus attention on other possibilities of a physico-chemical action.

Since auxins, in addition to promoting growth, are acting also in differentiation (initiation of root formation, control of flower initiation) and are morphological determinants too, it may well be that, apart from actions at protein surfaces, the site of action will have to be looked for 'higher up' in the hierarchy of the cell, viz. with the nucleic acids.

In fact, Skoog (1950; 1953) already concluded that the action of auxins in growth is intimately concerned with nucleic acid metabolism (DNA/RNA balance), on account of evidence for IAA-adenine interactions in growth and in organ formation and of IAA effects on nucleic acid content of the cells (cf. also Galston *et al.*, 1953, and Ber, 1953).

In this connection we should like to point out the well-known facts that in certain cases the deformations in plants, caused by an over-dosage of growth substances (e.g. by 2:4-D), hardly can be distinguished from the symptoms of a virus infection and that growth substances are able to influence the course of virus infection in plants. Here one gets the impression that influencing of synthesis (and/or functioning) of nucleic acids by growth substances are involved or, perhaps, nucleic acid dynamics are interwoven with auxin balances.

Moreover, in recent work on animal cell physiology and embryonic development, the possibility emerges that the action of oestrogens may be directly connected with nucleic acid synthesis (Töndury, 1955). Since there are connections between oestrogens and plant growth substances, with regard to type of compounds and importance of spatial structure (cf. the doisynolic acids (Miescher, 1946)) as well as to action (see, for example, Helmkamp and Bonner, 1953), all possibilities of putting the pieces of this jigsaw puzzle together should be sought.

While expecting that they may be put together, we are convinced that progress in our understanding of auxin action not only will imply a contribution to the solution of one of the main problems of plant physiology, but also to our insight into mechanisms which govern development and differentiation in general.

REFERENCES

Ber, A. (1953). Studien über Auxinwirkung. *Endokrinologie*, **30,** 329.

Bonner, J. (1954). The hormonol control of plant growth. *The Harvey Lectures, Series XLVIII*, I.

Bonner, J., and Bandurski, R. S. (1952). Studies of the physiology, pharmacology, and biochemistry of the auxins. *Annu. Rev. Pl. Physiol.* **3,** 59.

Booij, H. L. (1953). Lecture given at Plant Growth Substance Conference, Lund; see review by R. L. Wain, *Nature*, **172,** 710.

BURSTRÖM, H. (1951). Studies on growth and metabolism of roots. VI. The relative growth action of different *iso*butyric acid derivatives. *Physiol. Plant.* **4,** 470.

GALSTON, A. W., BAKER, R. S., and KING, J. W. (1953). Benzimidazole and the geometry of cell growth. *Physiol. Plant.* **6,** 863.

GORDON, S. A. (1953). Physiology of hormone action, *Growth and Differentiation in Plants*, ed. W. E. Loomis, p. 253.

GREENHAM, C. G. (1953). Phosphonic acids as auxins and substances affecting growth. *Austr. J. Sci.* **16,** 66: see also Maguire, M. H., and Shaw, G. *J. chem. Soc.* (1953) 1479; (1955) 1756; Craniades, P., and Rumpf, P. *Bull. Soc. chim. Fr.* (1952) 1063; (1954) 719; Pastac, J., and Craniades, P. *C.R. Soc. Biol., Paris*, **148** (1954) 35; *Bull. Soc. Chim. biol., Paris*, **36,** (1954) 675.

HELMKAMP, G., and BONNER, J. (1953). Some relationships of sterols to plant growth. *Plant Physiol.* **28,** 428.

JÖNSSON, Å. (1955). Synthetic plant hormones. VIII. Relationship between chemical structure and plant growth activity in the arylalkyl-, aryloxyalkyl-, and indolealkylcarboxylic acid series. *Svensk kem. Tidskr.* **67,** 166.

KERK, G. J. M. VAN DER, RAALTE, M. H. VAN, KAARS SIJPESTEIJN, A., and VEEN, R. VAN DER (1955). A new type of plant growth-regulating substances. *Nature*, **176,** 308. (First communication at S.E.B. Conference, Groningen, April, 1955).

MAAS, J., GRAAFF, G. B. R. DE, and HERTOG, H. J. DEN (1955). The action of diazoacetic ester on pyridone-2. A new synthesis of 2-pyridoxyacetic acid. *Rec. Trav. chim. Pays-Bas*, **74,** 175.

MIESCHER, K. (1946). Recherches récentes en Suisse dans le domaine des hormones. *Experientia*, **2,** 237.

MIESCHER, K. (1948). On the relation of activity to constitution in the sexogens, with special reference to the doisynolic acids. *Recent Progr. Hormone Res.* **3,** 47.

MINARIK, C. E., READY, D., NORMAN, A. G., THOMPSON, H. E., and OWINGS, J. F. (1951). New growth-regulating compounds. II. Substituted benzoic acids. *Bot. Gaz.* **113,** 135.

MUIR, R. M., and HANSCH, C. (1951). The relationship of structure and plant-growth activity of substituted benzoic and phenoxyacetic acids. *Plant Physiol.* **26,** 369. See also Hansch, C., Muir, R. M., and Metzenberg, R. L. Further evidence for a chemical reaction between plant growth regulators and a plant substrate. *Plant Physiol.* **26** (1951) 812.

SKOOG, F. (1950). Chemical control of growth and organ formation in plant tissues. *Année biol.* **26,** 545.

SKOOG, F. (1953). Substances involved in normal growth and differentiation of plants. *Brookhaven Symp. Biol.* **6,** 1.

SÖDING, H. (1953). Die Wuchsstoffe und ihre Bedeutung im der höheren Pflanze. *Ber. dtsch. bot. Ges.* **66,** 383.

THIMANN, K. V. (1952). The role of *ortho* substitution in the synthetic auxins. *Plant Physiol.* **27,** 392.

TÖNDURY, G. (1955). Entwicklungsstörungen durch chemische Faktoren und Viren. *Naturwissenschaften*, **42,** 312. See also Duspiva, F. *ibid.* **42,** (1955) 305. Zur Biochemie der normalen Wirbeltierentwicklung.

VELDSTRA, H. (1944). Researches on plant-growth substances. V. Relation between chemical structure and physiological activity. II. Contemplations on place and mechanism of the action of the growth substances. *Enzymologia*, **11,** 137.

VELDSTRA, H. (1952). Plant growth regulators. XXI. Structure and activity. VI. Halogenated benzoic acids and related compounds. *Rec. Trav. chim. Pays-Bas*, **71,** 15.

VELDSTRA, H. (1953). The relation of chemical structure to biological activity in growth substances. *Annu. Rev. Pl. Physiol.* **4,** 151.

VELDSTRA, H. (1955). Stereochemie in de levende cel. *Chem. Weekbl.* **51,** 158.

Veldstra, H., and Åberg, B. (1953). Aryl- and aryloxy-acetic acids with a 'bulky' α-substituent. *Biochim. biophys. Acta*, **12,** 593.

Veldstra, H., and Booij, H. L. (1949). Researches on plant growth regulators. XVII. Structure and activity. On the mechanism of the action. III. *Biochim. biophys. Acta*, **3,** 278.

Veldstra, H., Kruyt, W., Steen, E. J. der, and Åberg, B. (1954). Researches on plant growth regulators. XXII. Structure and activity. VII. Sulphonic acids and related compounds. *Rec. Trav. chim. Pays-Bas*, **73,** 23.

Veldstra, H., and Westeringh, C. van de (1952). On the growth substance activity of substituted benzoic acids. *Rec. Trav. chim. Pays-Bas*, **71,** 318.

Wain, R. L. (1953). Plant growth substances. *The Royal Institute of Chemistry, Monograph No.* 2.

Gorter, physiol plantarum 10, 858 (1957

THE MODE OF GROWTH ACTION OF SOME NAPHTHOXY COMPOUNDS†

H. BURSTRÖM and BERIT A. M. HANSEN
Botany Laboratory, University of Lund

INTRODUCTION

It has been shown in a previous communication (Burström, 1955) that naphthalene acetic and naphthoxyacetic acids increase and decrease root elongation according to a fairly complicated pattern.

By testing combinations of these acids it was also shown that some effects of low concentrations of the 2-substituted acids were physiologically independent of the others, and that, at high concentrations, the acids can exert toxic effects which complicate the assessment of real growth activities. Furthermore, 1-naphthalene acetic and 2-naphthoxyacetic acids inhibited root elongation and were classified as auxins, whereas 2-naphthalene acetic and 1-naphthoxyacetic acids increased root elongation and antagonized the two others. They should be classified as root auxins according to Hansen's (1954) terminology; they cannot *a priori* be called anti-auxins in the sense of the semi-official nomenclature (Tukey *et al.*, 1954) because it has not been shown conclusively that they act as competitive inhibitors of auxin. It is also convenient for other reasons to use a term which does not anticipate a special mode of action.

Of the two supposed auxins, 2-naphthoxyacetic acid has unanimously been classified as an auxin in the literature (see Hansen, 1954); Street (1955), however, has questioned whether the root-growth effect of 1-naphthalene acetic acid is physiologically of the same kind.

A tentative explanation of why these two acids are auxins and the other two are not has been given by Jönsson (1955). This implies that they are auxins because the side-chain can form a pseudo-ring in the plane of the naphthalene ring with the carboxyl near the centre of the compound ring system. For sterical reasons this is impossible with the other two acids. This provides an amendment to the commonly accepted structural requirements of auxins, giving a reason for the different activities of these four acids.

In order to test this explanation, experiments have been conducted with a number of chlorine derivatives of the two auxins, all of which were prepared and kindly supplied by Dr. Jönsson. The tests with the derivatives of 2-naphthoxyacetic acid have led to some rather unexpected results, which may be of general importance for elucidating the mode of action of these compounds.

† This paper was read at the Conference by H. Burström.

ACTIVITY OF PURE 2-NAPHTHOXYACETIC ACID DERIVATIVES

The following substances have been tested in addition to the unchlorinated acid (I): 1-chloro-2-naphthoxyacetic acid (II), 3-chloro-2-naphthoxyacetic acid (III), and 1 : 3-dichloro-2-naphthoxyacetic acid (IV).

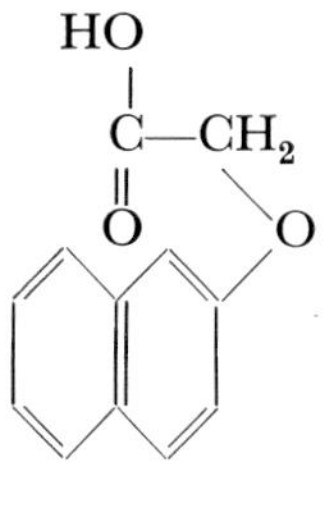

I 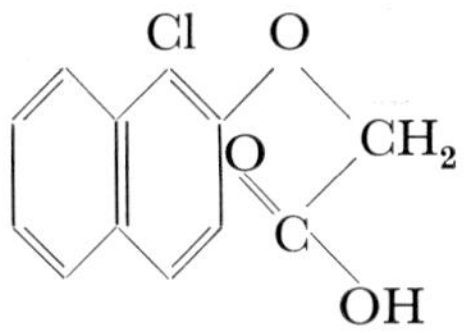 II 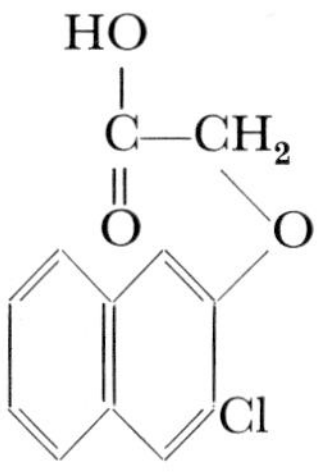 III 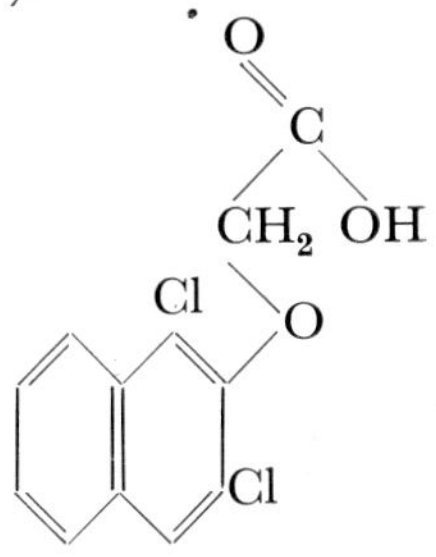 IV

According to Jönsson's explanation, III should be an auxin like the unchlorinated acid I, whereas II and IV should lack auxin activity owing to steric hindrance caused by the insertion of chlorine in the 1-position.

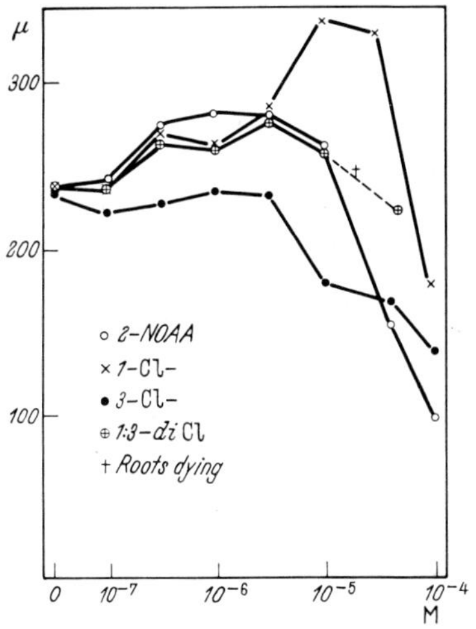

Figure 1. The influence on the root cell elongation of chlorinated 2-naphthoxyacetic acids (2-NOAA). On the ordinate cell length in μ.

The effects on cell elongation are shown in *Figure 1*. It appears that with the exception of the 3-chloro derivative, the acids slightly increase cell elongation up to 3.10^{-6} M, which is a non-auxinic effect shown by the unchlorinated acids (Burström, 1955). Their behaviour, however, differs at higher concentrations; thus, the 1-chlorinated acid gives a considerable increase in elongation, giving an activity curve resembling that of the root auxin 1-naphthoxyacetic acid. The dichloro acid is practically inactive, whereas the 3-chloro compound shows all usual signs of being an auxin.

These observations are in good agreement with Jönsson's rules, under which the 1- and 1 : 3-chlorinated acids should lack auxin activity. However, it is impossible from this or any other rule to predict whether an acid lacking auxin activity should possess some kind of antagonistic activity. In this instance the dichloro acid is inactive and behaves similarly to that of di-*ortho*substituted phenoxyacetic acids, to which acids it bears structural resemblances. This seems to indicate that di*ortho*substitution can annihilate all kinds of root-growth activity in a specific manner.

In order to corroborate the above classification of the acids, they were investigated in the presence of a supposed true anti-auxin, 3-indole*iso*butyric acid.

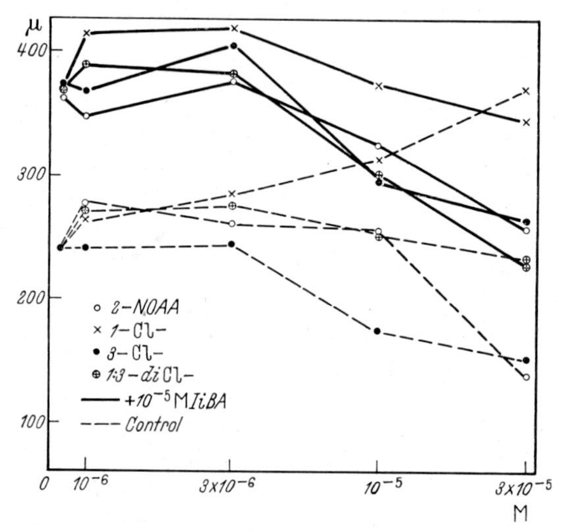

Figure 2. The interaction between chlorinated naphthoxyacetic acids and 3-*indole*iso*butyric acid* (*IiBA*). *Dotted curves controls without IiBA; full-drawn curves with addition of IiBA.*

THE INTERACTION WITH 3-INDOLE*iso*BUTYRIC ACID

The results are shown in *Figure 2* and can be summarized in the following points.

1. Up to 3.10^{-6} M neither of the acids has any effect on the growth increase caused by the *iso*butyric acid; on the contrary, its growth-promoting effect and the weak one of the naphthoxy derivatives are obviously additive. This is in agreement with the earlier conclusion (Burström, 1954) that these effects are of non-auxinic nature.

2. With increasing concentrations of the 1- and 1 : 3-chlorinated acids the effect caused by the addition of the *iso*butyric acid decreases and becomes nil at 3.10^{-5} M.

3. For the unchlorinated and 3-chloro acids, the graphs with and without *iso*butyric acid run parallel within reasonable experimental errors. This means that the activities of these two acids over the whole range of concentrations are additive to that of the anti-auxin as nearly as can be expected from two wholly independent kinds of action. The *iso*butyric acid exerts the same growth-promoting effect in absence of auxin, as when auxin suppresses the elongation by 50 per cent.

These results are surprising and contrary to what had been expected. They imply that the supposed auxins are not antagonists of the supposed anti-auxin, but that the root auxin and the inactive acid are antagonistic.

This prompted an investigation of the interaction between 3-indoleacetic acid and 3-indole*iso*butyric acid, the result of which is presented in *Figure 3.* In the best agreement with the last-mentioned results it shows that the actions of the two acids are strictly additive. The *iso*butyric acid causes a constant promotion of elongation even when the auxin addition has reduced elongation to practically nil.

If any conclusions at all can be drawn on the mode of interaction of the compounds from the shape of activity curves, the logical conclusion in the present instance must be that the root-growth-inhibiting auxins and the root-growth promoters of the *iso*butyric acid type act in two physiologically different systems, and that they do not simply compete in one single reaction

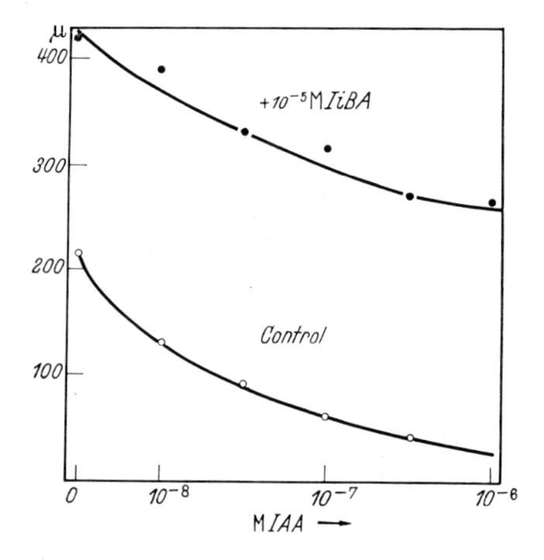

*Figure 3. The interaction between 3-indoleacetic acid (IAA) and 3-indole-*iso*butyric acid (IiBA) on cell elongation.*

mediating the cell elongation. Thus 3-indole*iso*butyric acid should not be an anti-auxin according to the definition, but a root-growth promoter, i.e. a root auxin, with an action of some other kind.

THE LOCATION OF THE ACIDS IN THE CELL-ELONGATION MECHANISM

In order to find an explanation of this unexpected result we must turn to the mechanism of cell elongation itself, and see if it affords some ground for an assumption of independent modes of action of these compounds.

This mechanism has been studied extensively on roots (cf. Burström, 1942; 1954), and the results have led to a hypothesis summarized in *Figure 4.* It implies that the elongation takes place in two steps, the first phase involving a passive, plastic stretching of the cell wall, the second phase an active growth of the wall. The first one may be regarded as a preparatory reaction, necessary for the ensuing active growth. This picture is not founded on preconceived opinions of certain actions of auxins, but on observations of cell wall properties during the elongation, the osmotic conditions in elongating cells, their reaction against calcium ions, and so on. There are some reasons to assume, however, that auxin promotes the first and inhibits the second growth phase, the latter effect usually dominating in roots (Burström, 1942). This picture has also been supported by studies of Rufelt (1954) on the geotropic response of roots.

This model contains the required two sites where auxin and other regulators could influence elongation independently of each other. Attempts should therefore be made to locate the action of the compounds specifically studied, though such efforts must necessarily be very hypothetical.

Assuming that auxin-inhibiting growth acts on phase II, then the physiologically independent promoting action of root auxins should be located to phase I. This leads, however, to the complication that auxin promotes this part, whilst the root auxin promotes the growth too; consequently they should have the same effect in this respect.

This possibility must be seriously considered. A number of observations have been made which indicate a similar action of auxins and root auxins.

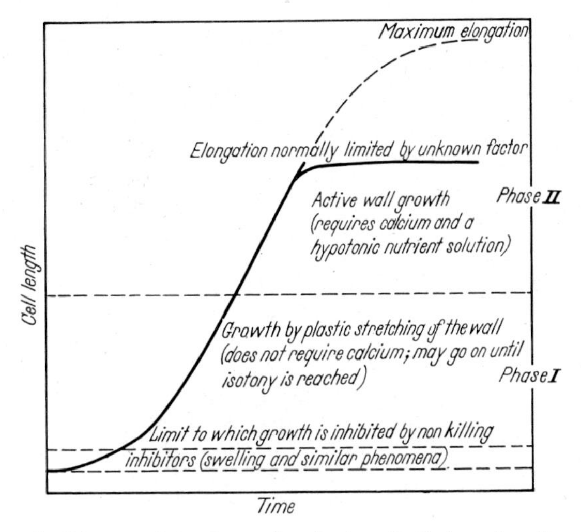

Figure 4. Diagram of the suggested mechanism of cell elongation of roots.

If *iso*butyric acids influence the cell-wall tensibility at all, it is in the same direction as auxin, causing an increase, not a decrease as had been expected (Burström, 1954). One way of locating the action of the compounds is by means of differential elongation. It has been shown that in cells and tissues of many kinds the elongation is not uniformly distributed in the cells (Burström, 1942; Meeuse, 1942). This means that cells elongate only at restricted points, a behaviour which can be demonstrated on roots using the insertion of the root hairs as fixed marking points. Normally, root hair free cells and the basal parts of root hair cells grow at the same rate, but the apical parts much slower or not at all.

Indoleacetic acid in high concentrations causes an accentuation of this differentiation (Burström, 1942). Indole*iso*butyric acid, however, has the surprising effect of increasing the elongation of the basal portions yet relatively retarding the apical parts, as auxin does (*Table 1*). With regard to the elongation in a strict sense, auxin and root auxin have the opposite effects, but with regard to the differentiation both behave as auxins. These are two modes of action which can be simply demonstrated under the microscope. What is observed in recording the average cell elongation, not

Table 1

The influence of 3-indoleacetic acid (IAA) and α-(3-indole) isobutyric acid (IiBA) on the differential elongation in wheat roots

Cell lengths in μ. The concentrations of IAA and IiBA have been chosen so that the combination should give no change in the average elongation.

Additions	*Root hair cells*		*Root hair free cells*	*Average*
	apical part	*basal part*		
Control	60±1	125±3	258±5	222
Action of IAA				
without IiBA	−38	−60	−142	−120
with IiBA	−30	−53	−157	−120
[%	−57	−45	−58]	
Action of IiBA				
without IAA	−2	+58	+163	+109
with IAA	+6	+65	+148	+109
[%	+3	+49	+60]	

to mention the bulk growth of an organ, is, of course, the sum of these two different actions. It is not known, however, how these are related to the elongation mechanisms. The ideal additive effect of the two compounds is well shown in *Table 1*.

That the inhibiting action of auxin is physiologically separated from the positive actions of root auxins has been clearly supported by Rufelt (1954),

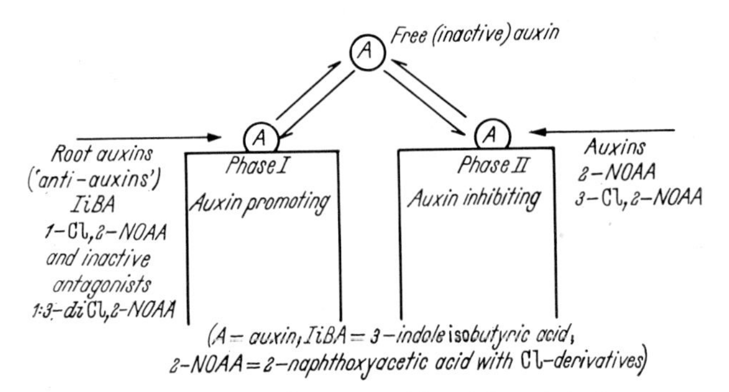

Tentative diagram of the action of 2-naphthoxy derivatives.

Figure 5. Suggested points of action of 3-indole and 2-naphthoxy compounds in the cell elongation process proceeding in two phases (cf. Figure 4).

who has found that auxin and root auxin act on two different, previously known and described geotropic systems in roots, which may or may not be identical with the two modes of elongation.

It can be tentatively assumed, at least as a basis for further discussions, that the actions of the mentioned compounds are located as shown in *Figure 5*. The root auxins of the *iso*butyric acid type exert growth action on the first phase of the elongation, counteracted by their antagonists, which may be inactive in themselves, as is the 1 : 3-dichloronaphthoxyacetic acid, or belong to the same type of growth compounds as the 1-chloro acid. The growth-decreasing effect of auxins should be physiologically independent and located in the second growth phase. This is supported by the observation that the 1-chloronaphthoxyacetic acid does not influence the behaviour of the unchlorinated acid.

On the other hand, it is clear that anti-auxins can be exchanged for the native auxin and act as growth regulators in this way. This has been deduced by means of the kinetic methods introduced by McRae and Bonner (1952), by Ingestad (1953), and shown analytically by Fransson and Ingestad (1955) on coleoptiles. A way out of this dilemma is to make the rather natural assumption that these compounds all act on both phases of the cell elongation, either by competing with the native auxin or by virtue of their own inherent activity. Owing perhaps to minor details in structure, the effect in one or the other system dominates, making one substance an auxin assumed to inhibit predominately growth phase II, another a root auxin when the action on phase I dominates, or a third substance an anti-auxin if it acts mainly by competing with natural auxin.

Such details in the activity do not show up in the net elongation of cells or organs, which is the usual observation recorded, but for correlating structure with activity it may be necessary to pay due regard to the different ways the compounds can act on the growth mechanism.

REFERENCES

Burström, H. (1942). The influence of heteroauxin on cell growth and root development. *Ann. agric. Coll. Sweden*, **10,** 209.

Burström, H. (1954). Studies on growth and metabolism of roots. XI. The influence of auxin and coumarin derivatives on the cell wall. *Physiol. Plant.* **7,** 548.

Burström, H. (1955). Evaluation of the growth activity of naphthalene derivatives. *Physiol. Plant.* **8,** 174.

Fransson, P., and Ingestad, T. (1955). The effect of an antiauxin on the indoleacetic acid content in *Avena* coleoptiles. *Physiol. Plant.* **8,** 336.

Hansen, B. A. M. (1954). A physiological classification of 'shoot auxins' and 'root auxins'. I–II. *Bot. Notiser* 230, 318.

Ingestad, T. (1953). Kinetic aspects on the growth regulating effect of some phenoxy acids. *Physiol. Plant.* **6,** 796.

Jönsson, A. (1955). Synthetic plant hormones. VIII. Relationship between chemical structure and plant growth activity in the arylalkyl, aryloxyalkyl, and indolealkylcarboxylic acid series. *Svensk kem. Tidskr.* **67,** 166.

McRae, D. H., and Bonner, J. (1952). Diortho substituted phenoxyacetic acids as antiauxins. *Plant Physiol.* **27,** 834.

Meeuse, A. D. J. (1942). A study of intercellular relationships among vegetable cells with special reference to sliding growth and to cell shape. *Rec. Trav. bot. nécrl.* **38,** 18.

Rufelt, H. (1954). Influence of growth substances on the geotropic response of roots. *Physiol. Plant.* **7,** 141.

Street, H. E. (1955). Factors controlling meristematic activity in excised roots. VI. Effects of various 'antiauxins' on the growth and survival of *Lycopersicum esculentum, Mill. Physiol. Plant.* **8,** 48.

Tukey, H. B., Went, F. W., Muir, R. M., and Overbeek, J. van (1954). Nomenclature of chemical plant regulators. *Plant. Physiol.* **29,** 307.

CHEMICAL CONFIGURATION AND ACTION OF DIFFERENT GROWTH SUBSTANCES AND GROWTH INHIBITORS:

NEW EXPERIMENTS WITH THE PASTE METHOD

H. Linser

Biologisches Laboratorium der Österreichische Stickstoffwerke A.G., Linz, Austria

In 1953 at Lund, Sweden, I reported on my paste method, and on the difference between the types of concentration–action curves obtained with two types of chemicals, which may be called growth substances and growth inhibitors. Although we commonly use these two words, we are not certain if all the compounds we usually call growth substances would give the typical curve for growth substances in the paste test. There may be some compounds, classed as growth substances, which give a concentration–action curve of the growth-inhibitor type. We could show that every concentration–action curve of a cell-elongating growth substance is composed of two components, one promoting, and one inhibiting. Our paste method, which uses an intact coleoptile, is able to reveal both growth-promoting and growth-inhibiting activity in the same experiment. The two components, the promoting one and the inhibiting one, can be of different magnitudes. In some special cases, the promoting activity of a growth substance can be reduced to zero. Therefore we may say that a growth inhibitor is a growth substance with a promoting component of zero. In the same way we can define a growth substance as a growth inhibitor with a growth-promoting component (larger than zero).

Some experiments with mixtures of a promoting and an inhibiting substance were described at Lund, and I reported in Paris (Linser, 1954a) on further similar experiments. Dr. Kaindl's paper at this Symposium is concerned with the results of these experiments and a mathematical examination of them. Experiments have recently been carried out using mixtures of different growth substances with one another and different inhibitors with one another. The results obtained will be published at a later date. The earlier experiments provided evidence that there is competition between growth substances and growth inhibitors in filling a space, which we call the 'gap', which exists in the living system. The probability of filling this gap is determined by the affinity between the molecule of the active substance and the gap (Linser, 1954b, c). We know that this affinity depends mainly on the chemical nature of the compound, or on the physical properties of the atoms of which the molecule is composed and on its electronic configuration. It also depends, though to a lesser extent, on the size and form of the molecule, i.e. its space-filling capacity.

In view of the above considerations, we compared our results with the chemical structure of the substances we found to be active as growth promoters and inhibitors. Although we know that the form of a molecule is only *one* of the different properties which must be taken into consideration if we want to get a complete knowledge of the relation between activity and chemical structure of different substances, nevertheless, we think that this point of view has so far been too much neglected. It will be seen that there are some surprising similarities in the form of substances of similar physiological action which are very different chemically. We cannot believe that the factor 'form' is of no importance when a molecule enters a living system; indeed, we have good reason to assume that the analogy of key and lock is

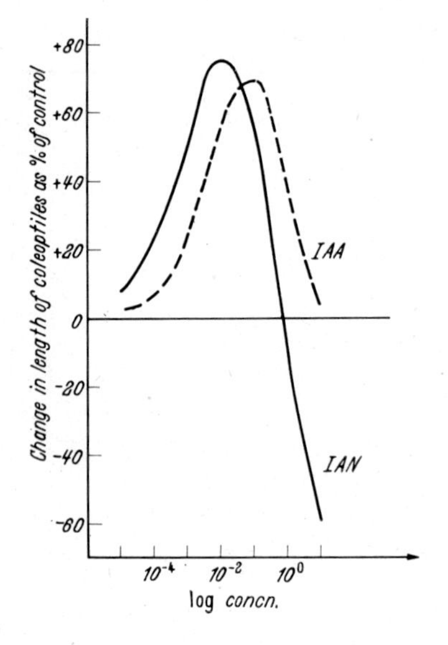

Figure 1. The concentration–action curves of indole-3-acetic acid (IAA) and indole-3-acetonitrile (IAN) in the paste test.

very relevant. We consider that each molecule must be well matched with its corresponding gap by its form, and by its electrical and chemical configuration.

In this communication, I will first present some recent results we obtained by investigating the activity of different synthetic substances using our paste method. Secondly, I will give a comparison of some values for the affinities and other significant constants which we evaluated using Kaindl's formula for the concentration–action curves of growth substances and growth inhibitors (Kaindl, 1954). In addition, photographs are included showing similarities of the molecular form and size of different growth substances and growth inhibitors.

The first important growth substance examined was indole-3-acetonitrile, a compound first isolated from natural sources by Jones and his co-workers (1952). It was tested in comparison with indole-3-acetic acid and showed a similar concentration–action curve, though it was found to be about ten times more active than indole-3-acetic acid (*Figure 1*). I have to thank Prof. Jones of Manchester and Dr. Thoma of Linz for the two samples of nitrile tested, both of which gave the same results. I also wish to thank Dr. J. A. Bentley of Manchester, who sent samples of 2:3:6-trichlorobenzoic acid and 2:3:6-trichlorobenzaldehyde, and, for comparison with these, the

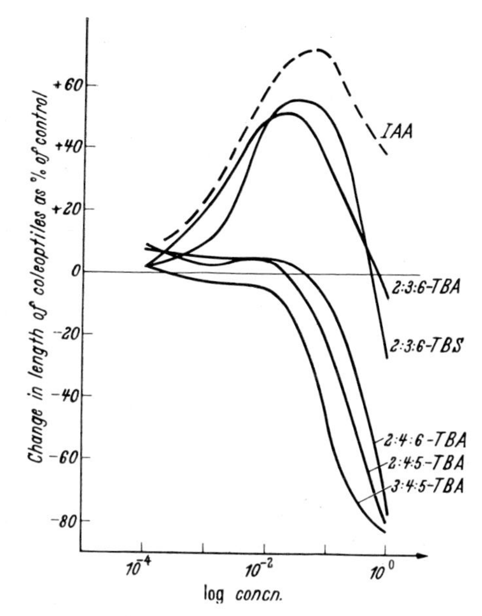

Figure 2. The concentration–action curves of some halogen-substituted benzoic acids and aldehydes in comparison with indole-3-acetic acid.
TBA = trichlorobenzaldehyde;
TBS = trichlorobenzoic acid;
IAA = indole-3-acetic acid.

2:4:6-, the 2:4:5-, and the 3:4:5-trichlorobenzaldehyde. The first two substances, as observed by Bentley (1950) showed growth-promoting activity, but nearly ten times less than indole-3-acetic acid, whereas the other three trichloroaldehydes showed a small activity as growth inhibitors (*Figure 2*).

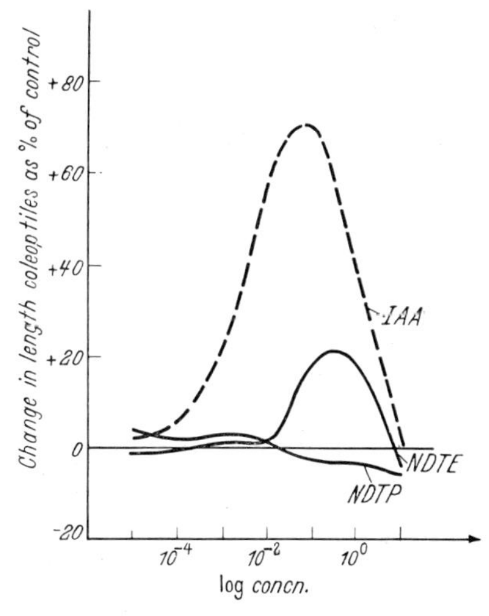

Figure 3. The concentration–action curves of N-*dimethylthiuramacetic acid* (*NDTE*), *NN-dimethylthiurampropionic acid* (*NDTP*), *and indole-3-acetic acid* (*IAA*) *in the paste test.*

The newly discovered growth substance *NN*-dimethylthiuramacetic acid (Kerk, 1955) was kindly provided by Dr. van der Veen of Eindhoven. This gave a small growth-promoting activity in the paste test (*Figure 3*) nearly

1/100 of that of indole-3-acetic acid. Weaver (1952; 1954) observed that benzothiazol-2-oxyacetic acid applied to grape plants at flowering resulted in a high percentage set of rather small fruits. We tested this substance with

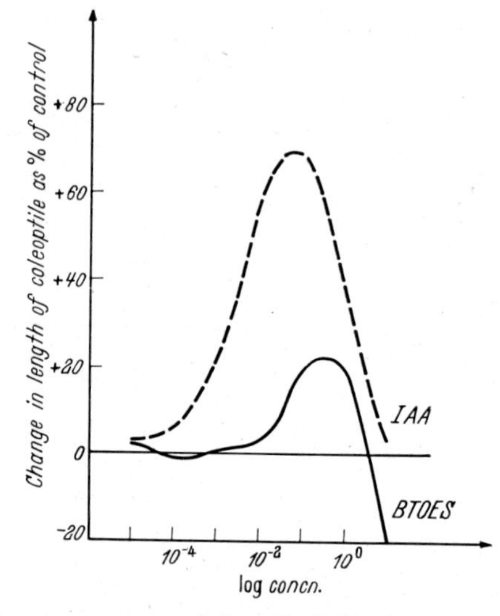

Figure 4. The concentration–action curves of 2*-oxybenzthiazoleacetic acid* (*BTOES*) *and indole-*3*-acetic acid* (*IAA*).

the paste test and found slight growth-promoting activity, about 1/100 that of indole-3-acetic acid (*Figure 4*). In all, we have tested about one hundred different synthetic substances which seemed to be of some interest in comparing the form of the molecule with its activity.

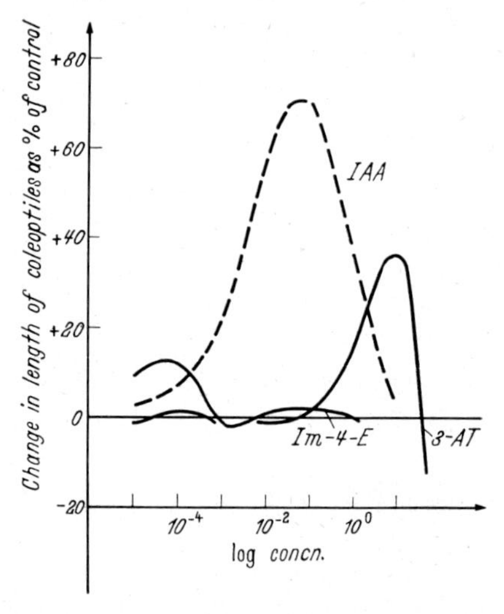

Figure 5. The concentration–action curves of 3*-amino-triazole* (3 *AT*), *imidazole-*4*-acetic acid* (Im-4-*E*); *and indole-*3*-acetic acid* (*IAA*).

In further experiments we found 3-aminotriazole to possess a very small activity not more than 1/1000 of indole-3-acetic acid (*Figure 5*). *NN*-phenylmethylglycine ethyl ester showed a good activity as a growth promoter, whereas that of 2-methylbenzimidazole and 2:4-dichlorophenoxyacetic acid–bisoxyethylamide was slight. In this group of 2:4-D derivatives, in addition to all the different salts and esters of the 2:4-dichlorophenoxy acetic acid, the following substances were active as growth promoters: 2:4-dichlorophenoxyacetamide, 2:4-dichlorophenoxyacetic acid hydrazide, 2:4-dichlorophenoxyacetonitrile, and 2:4-dichlorophenoxymaleic acid hydrazide. The group of 2:4:5-trichlorophenoxy derivatives which showed promoting activity included 2:4:5-trichlorophenoxyacetamide, 2:4:5-trichlorophenoxyacetic acid hydrazide, 2:4:5-trichlorophenoxyacetonitrile, 2:4:5-trichlorophenoxyacetaldehyde, and sodium 2:4:5-trichlorophenoxy-acetamidoethylsulphate showed slight activity. Many other substances showed strong inhibiting activity, like indazole, 3-methylindazole, 1-methyl-benzotriazole, 1-naphthoxyacetic acid, 4-oxycoumarin-3-butyric acid, salts of the 3:6-endoxotetrahydro-*o*-phthalic acid, the *iso*propyl ester of carbamilic acid, cinnamic aldehyde, 3:5-dinitro-2-methylbenzoic acid, 4:5-dinitro-2-methylbenzoic acid, the lactone of the β-oxy-β-*o*-carboxyphenylpropionic acid, $\alpha\alpha$-dichloropropionic acid, allyl cyanoacetate, sodium *iso*propylxan-thogenate, naphthoquinone, sodium 2:5-dichlorophenylacetate, sodium 2:4:5-trichlorophenylacetate, ethyl 2:4:5-trichlorothiophenoxyacetate, pentachlorophenoxyacetic acid and its esters. A tetrachlorophenoxyacetic acid product whose identity is not known exactly showed a small promoting activity with a strong inhibiting component.

It is of some interest, that 4:6-dichlororesorcin-bis(carboxymethyl) ether and phenylimidodiacetic acid (*Figure 6*) were found to be practically inactive, whereas bis-2:4-dichlorophenoxyacetic acid (*Figure 7*) proved to be a strong inhibitor. This latter substance is of special interest, because it is somewhat like a siamese twin, the two 2:4-dichlorophenoxy rings being connected by one acetic acid. In respect of the two-point attachment theory, the assumption could be made that this substance must be active as promoter, because the acid group is free as is an *ortho* position in one or both rings. No promoting activity, however, nor any promoting component within the concentration–action curve could be discovered; indeed, the curve we found was a purely inhibiting one. The two-point attachment theory is here forced to make an additional assumption: a steric hindrance. In other words, it must be assumed that the steric form of other parts of the molecule are as much involved in its activity as the 'two points' which are supposed to be necessary for the growth-promoting action. In our view, it is more useful to consider the form of the molecule in its entirety than only in terms of two separate points. Nevertheless, I do consider it a good idea to nominate two distinct points of the molecular structure as responsible for initiating the growth-promoting action, provided that we assume that the association which takes place between each of these points and the reacting living system occurs by chemical reactions establishing real chemical bonds. But even in the case of chlorinated phenoxyacetic acids, it is not obvious that the free 6-position will give a true chemical reaction with another reacting group of the living system. It therefore seems much better to assume that the 6-position is involved in mode of action in a way other than by chemical reaction.

The terminal group of the side-chain of a growth substance can be changed within a wide range without losing activity. Thus we find the nitrile group to be more active than the acid group, the latter, however, having a higher activity than the aldehyde group. If we assume a chemical reaction to be involved in the mode of action of these substances, it is very improbable that such action can be accomplished by several different chemical reactions; therefore we are forced to conclude that the different active substances are converted within the plant into one certain form. Thus, either the aldehyde

I II III

Figure 6. The chemical formulae of dichloropyrocatechol-acetic acid (I), 4:6-*dichlororesorcin-biscarboxymethyl ether (II), and phenylimidodiacetic acid (III). These substances were found to be practically inactive in the paste test.*

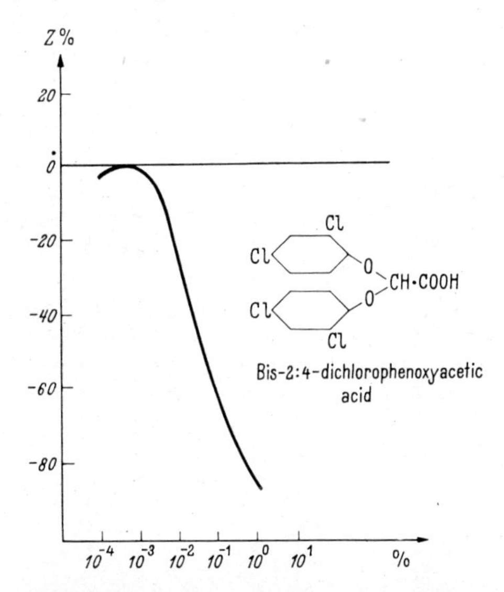

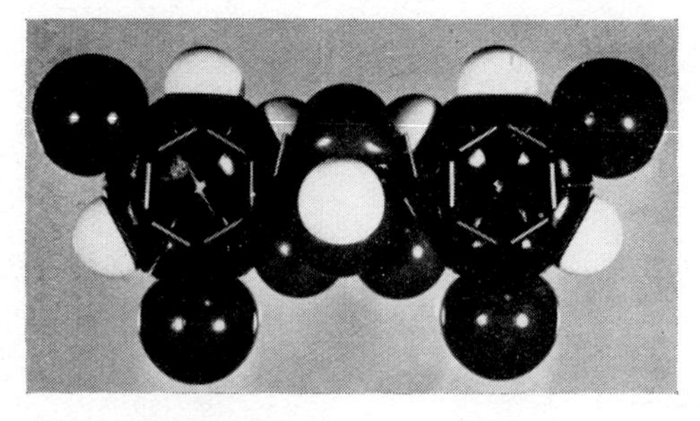

*Figure 7. The molecular model of bis-*2:4-*dichlorophenoxyacetic acid with the concentration–action curve and formula. Abscissa:* log *concn. Ordinate: change in length of coleoptiles as per cent of control.*

and nitrile are converted to the acid, or more probably, the aldehyde goes to the acid and the acid into the nitrile, the latter being the only reacting form which acts directly.

There is, however, another possible explanation of the mode of action; we can assume, as we did in earlier publications, that the action of a growth

Table 1

The λ_W and λ_H values of different growth substances and growth inhibitors

Group	Substance	$\lambda_W \times 10^{15}$	$\lambda_H \times 10^{15}$
Indole derivates	Indole-3-acetic acid	7·9	0·0051
	Indole-3-propionic-acid	0·525	0·0204
	Indole-3-butyric-acid	0·86	0·016
	Indole-3-acetonitrile	70·7	0·042
	Indole	0·0379	0·00226
	α-Methylindole	0·000	0·0414
	β-Methylindole (skatole)	0·0273	0·00291
	Tryptophan	0·000	0·000
Naphthalene derivates	α-Naphthaleneacetic acid	1·36	0·0215
	α-Naphthaleneacetic acid (sodium salt)	2·08	0·0594
	α-Naphthaleneacetic acid methyl ester	2·31	0·0098
Naphthoxy derivates	α-Naphthoxyacetic acid	0·000	0·0342
	β-Naphthoxyacetic acid	0·000	0·144
Phenoxyacetic acid derivates	Phenoxyacetic acid	0·000	0·0948
	*para*Chlorophenoxyacetic acid	0·571	0·0136
	2:4-Dichlorophenoxyacetic acid	2·05	0·102
	2:4-Dichlorophenoxyacetic acid (sodium salt)	3·4	0·00187
	2:4-Dichlorophenoxyacetic acid butyl ester	10·7	0·0940
	2:5-Dichlorophenoxyacetic acid	5·95	0·034
	2:5-Dichlorophenoxyacetic acid (sodium salt)	1·67	0·00169
	2:5-Dichlorophenoxyacetic acid butyl ester	7·03	0·0185
	2:4:5-Trichlorophenoxyacetic acid	23·6	0·0256
	2:4:5-Trichlorophenoxyacetic acid (sodium salt)	9·2	0·199
	2:4:5-Trichlorophenoxyacetic acid butyl ester	9·84	0·144
	2:4:6-Trichlorophenoxyacetic acid	0·000	0·1764
	2:4:6-Trichlorophenoxyacetic acid (sodium salt)	0·000	0·00384
	2:4:6-Trichlorophenoxyacetic acid butyl ester	0·000	0·139
	Tetrachlorophenoxyacetic acid ethyl ester	1·35	0·132
	Pentachlorophenoxyacetic acid	0·000	1·47
	Bis-2:4-dichlorophenoxyacetic acid	0·000	2·49
Other growth promoters	2:3:6-Trichlorobenzaldehyde	7·4	0·0435
	2:3:6-Trichlorobenzoic acid	2·6	0·0139
	N-Dimethylthiuramacetic acid	0·145	0·00542
	Benzthiazole-2-oxy-acetic acid	0·209	0·00322
	3-Amino-triazole	0·00337	0·000
Growth inhibitors	2:3:5-Triiodobenzoic acid	—	3·09
	2:4:6-Trichlorobenzaldehyde	—	0·0290
	2:4:5-Trichlorobenzaldehyde	—	0·0515
	3:4:5-Trichlorobenzaldehyde	—	0·161
	4:6-Dinitro-*o*-cresol	806·0	1·2
	Dinitro-*sec*.butylphenol	—	1·174
	Pentachlorophenol	5·13	0·451
	*iso*Propylphenylcarbamate	—	0·0304
Fluorescein derivates	Sodium fluorescein	0·000	0·000
	Tetrachloro-fluorescein	0·0577	6·13
	Tetrabromo-fluorescein (eosine)	—	49·5
	Tetraiodo-fluorescein (erythrosine)	0·99	23·8

substance occurs by filling in a gap in the structure of the appropriate part of the growing system, not by means of chemical reactions and the formation of new chemical bonds, but only by the action of intermolecular forces. The intensity of these forces, which depends on the gap as well as on the molecule fitting in, is called 'affinity'. This affinity will be high, if the form of the gap agrees with the form of the molecule, or, to be more precise, if the form of the gap agrees with the form of the active group of the molecule with which it is to be filled. The molecule is able to enter into the gap only when its form corresponds to that of the gap. It follows that it must be of some importance to measure the affinity (which we accept as hypothesis for our heuristic purpose) of different growth substances and inhibitors, as well as of different chemically related inactive substances. The mathematical formulation of the concentration–action curves evaluated by Kaindl (1954) enables us to obtain values from the experimental data of these curves, which are called λ and are proportional to the size of the affinity between gap and molecule. These values for λ are designated λ_W for a growth-promoting part of the molecule and as λ_H for the growth-inhibiting part of the same molecule. We do not stipulate that these two parts must be separated. They may be partly or entirely the same. These values λ_W and λ_H have been calculated for the main types of growth substances and growth inhibitors and are shown in *Table 1*.

The most active growth substances show the highest affinities in the order shown in *Table 2*. Apart from the differences in the side chains with the different salts and esters of acid products, which may be altered by the plant metabolism and which lead to differences in ease of penetration into the cells, the most active promoters show the following order:

2:4:5-trichlorophenoxyacetic acid,
indole-3-acetic acid,
2:5-dichlorophenoxyacetic acid,
2:3:6-trichlorobenzoic acid,
2:4-dichlorophenoxyacetic acid,
α-naphthaleneacetic acid,
tetrachlorophenoxyacetic acid.

It is surprising that the 2:5-dichlorophenoxyacetic acid, which has no strong weed-controlling properties, shows a higher affinity λ_W than the very active weed-killer 2:4-D. The same is the case with the inactive weed killer indole-3-acetic acid, which shows a higher λ_W value than 2:4-D.

The most active growth inhibitors can be ranged as shown in *Table 3*. We see that the highest affinity of a growth inhibitor is only about half the highest affinity of a growth promoter. The affinities of the inhibiting group of growth substances (λ_H) range between the affinities of the different growth substances as shown in *Table 4*. This table shows that the most active growth promoters possess λ_H values which are very small, compared with those of most of the inhibitors, but high enough to show effects as the less active inhibitors do. It is not easy to correlate these values for the affinities and the steric forms of different active molecules, because of the difficulties in comparing different molecular shapes. The main difficulty is that the organic molecules with a molecular weight of 100–500 have no fixed form. Free rotation is possible about certain bonds and their actual forms depend on the relative positions

Table 2

The λ_W values of the most active growth promoters in decreasing order

Substance	$\lambda_W \times 10^{15}$
Indole-3-acetonitrile	70·7
2:4:5-Trichlorophenoxyacetic acid ethyl ester	46·3
2:4:5-Trichlorophenoxyacetic acid	23·6
2:4-Dichlorophenoxyacetic acid butyl ester	10·7
2:4:5-Trichlorophenoxyacetic acid butyl ester	9·8
2:4:5-Trichlorophenoxyacetic acid (sodium salt)	9·2
2:4-Dichlorophenoxyacetic acid methyl ester	8·5
Indole-3-acetic acid	7·9
2:3:6-Trichlorobenzaldehyde	7·4
2:5-Dichlorophenoxyacetic acid butyl ester	7·0
2:5-Dichlorophenoxyacetic acid	5·0
2:4-Dichlorophenoxyacetic acid (sodium salt)	3·4
2:3:6-Trichlorobenzoic acid	2·6
2:4-Dichlorophenoxyacetic acid	2·0
α-Naphthalene-acetic acid (sodium salt)	2·0
α-Naphthalene-acetic acid	1·4
Tetrachlorophenoxyacetic acid	1·3
Indole-3-butyric acid	0·9
Indole-3-propionic acid	0·5
2-Oxybenzthiazole-acetic acid	0·2
N-Dimethylthiuramacetic acid	0·1

Table 3

The λ_H values of the most active growth inhibitors in decreasing order

Substance	$\lambda_H \times 10^{15}$
Tetrabromofluorescein (eosine)	49·5
Tetraiodofluorescein (erythrosine)	23·8
Tetrachlorofluorescein	6·13
2:3:5-Triiodobenzoic acid	3·0
Bis-2:4-Dichlorophenoxyacetic acid	2·5
Pentachlorophenoxyacetic acid	1·5
Dinitro-*o-sec*.butylphenol	1·2
Pentachlorophenol	0·45
2:4:6-Trichlorophenoxyacetic acid	0·18
β-Naphthoxyacetic acid	0·15
α-Naphthoxyacetic acid	0·03
Phenoxyacetic acid	0·009

Table 4

The λ_H values of the most active growth promoters between the λ_H values of the most active growth inhibitors

Substance	$\lambda_H \times 10^{15}$
Tetrabromofluorescein	49·5
2:3:5-Triiodobenzoic acid	3·0
β-Naphthoxyacetic acid	0·15
2:4:5-Trichlorophenoxyacetic acid ethyl ester	0·27
2:4:6-Trichlorophenoxyacetic acid	0·18
Indole-3-acetonitrile	0·042
2:4:5-Trichlorophenoxyacetic acid	0·025
α-Naphthalene-acetic acid	0·021
Phenoxyacetic acid	0·009
Indole-3-acetic acid	0·005

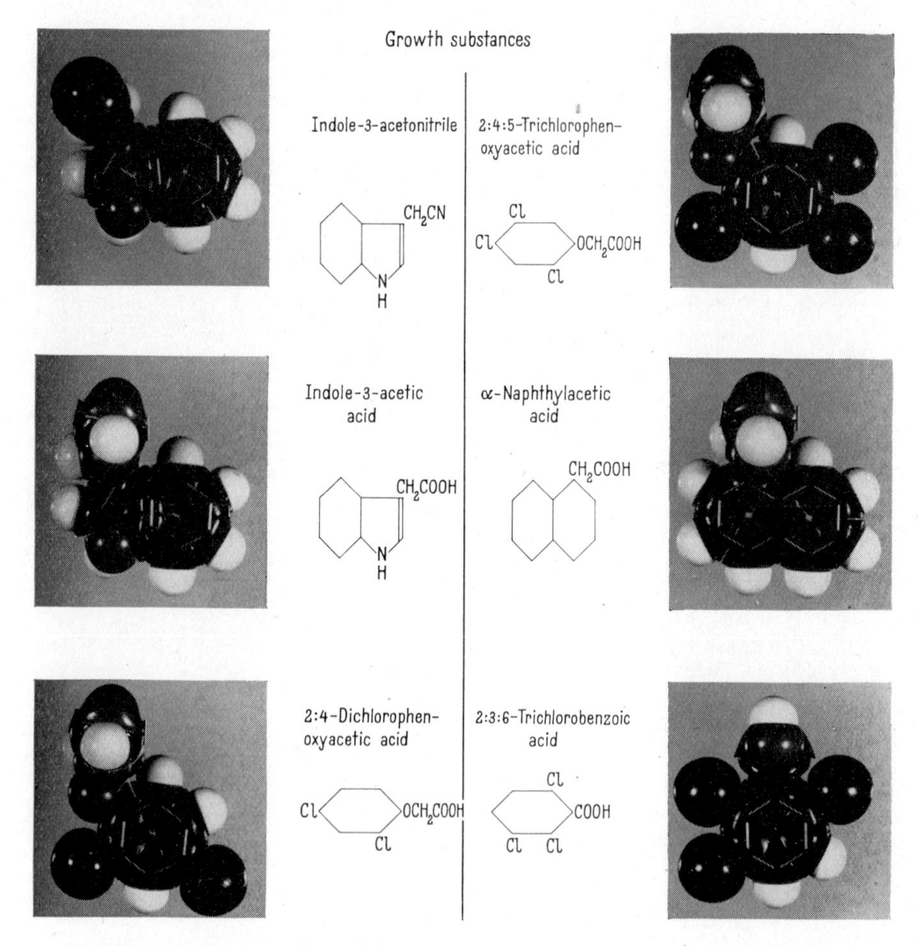

Figure 8. Molecular models of six of the most important growth-promoting substances.

of the revolving groups to one another. These positions, however, are determined by the environs of the molecule, and the nature of these, at site of action, is not known. We also have no information on the required position of the molecule at site of action, nor do we know how to find this active position, which could be supposed to correspond with the gaps of the reacting system. It seems reasonable to assume that different growth substances probably act in the same way on the same cell-elongating system, and must therefore be able to assume the same active form.

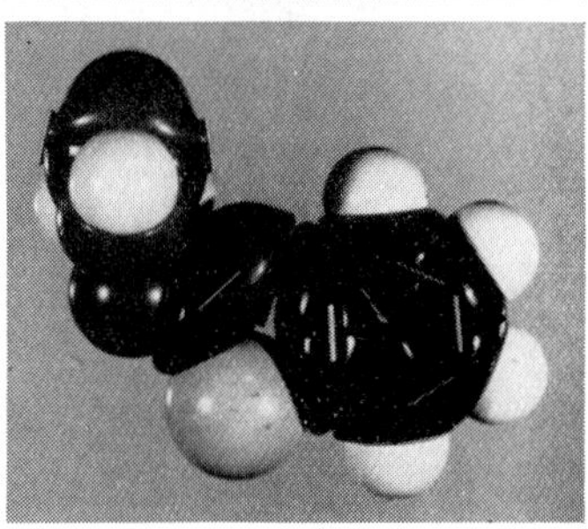

Figure 9. Molecular models of some newly discovered growth promoters. Top: 3-amino-triazole. Middle: N-dimethyl-thiuramacetic acid (van der Veen). Bottom: 2-oxy benzthiazole-acetic acid.

In view of the above considerations, it would seem important to try to find the positions of the more or less free rotating side-chains of different growth substances which show similar activity to one another. A long series of trials with the molecular models constructed by Stuart and Briegleb showing the space occupied by every single atom within the molecule magnified $1:1\cdot 5.10^{8}$, revealed that the main growth substances with acetic acid as a side-chain are able to assume very similar forms. These similarities are shown in *Figure 8*. For the purpose of this comparison, we selected a standard position of the side-chain relative to the ring- (or body-) system of the molecule. The criterion of this position is that the axis of the end group of the side chain lies at an angle of 90° to the longer axis of the ring-system of the molecule (*Figure 13*). In the case of 2:4:5-trichlorophenoxyacetic acid this position is possible and the COOH-group remains free to rotate even in this position; in the case of 2:4:6-trichlorophenoxyacetic acid, however, this is impossible. We do not know if this selected position is the same as that which is necessary for activity and we use it only hypothetically as the standard position for the purpose of comparison. We see (*Figures 8, 9*) that some other growth-promoting substances like 2:3:6-trichlorobenzoic acid or 3-aminotriazole, are not able to fall into this position, yet a chemical substance without any ring system, such as *NN*-dimethylthiuramacetic acid (*Figure 9*), in spite of the completely different chemical

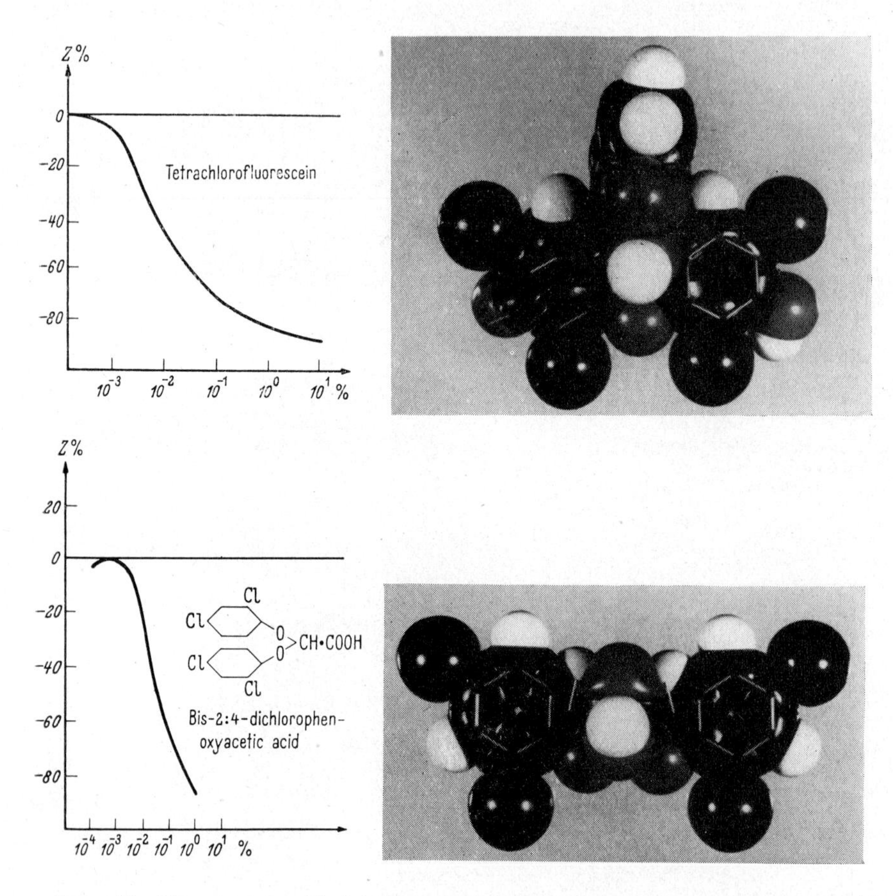

Figure 10. The molecular model of the 'twin' bis-2:4-dichlorophenoxyacetic acid in comparison with the molecular model of tetrachlorofluorescein. Abscissae: log *concn. Ordinates: change in length of coleoptiles as per cent of control.*

structure, is able to fall into the standard position. A molecule like the siamese twin (bis-2:4-dichlorophenoxyacetic acid) is, in spite of its chemically related structure, not able to fall into the standard position and shows no promoting action. On the other hand, this twin molecule is able to fall into another position which is quite similar to that of the substituted fluorescein molecule (*Figure 10*) and we know that substituted fluoresceins, such as tetrachloro-, tetrabromo-, and tetraiodofluorescein, all show growth-inhibiting actions (*Figure 11*) which are stronger than those shown by the twin molecule. Comparing the molecular forms of the unsubstituted and

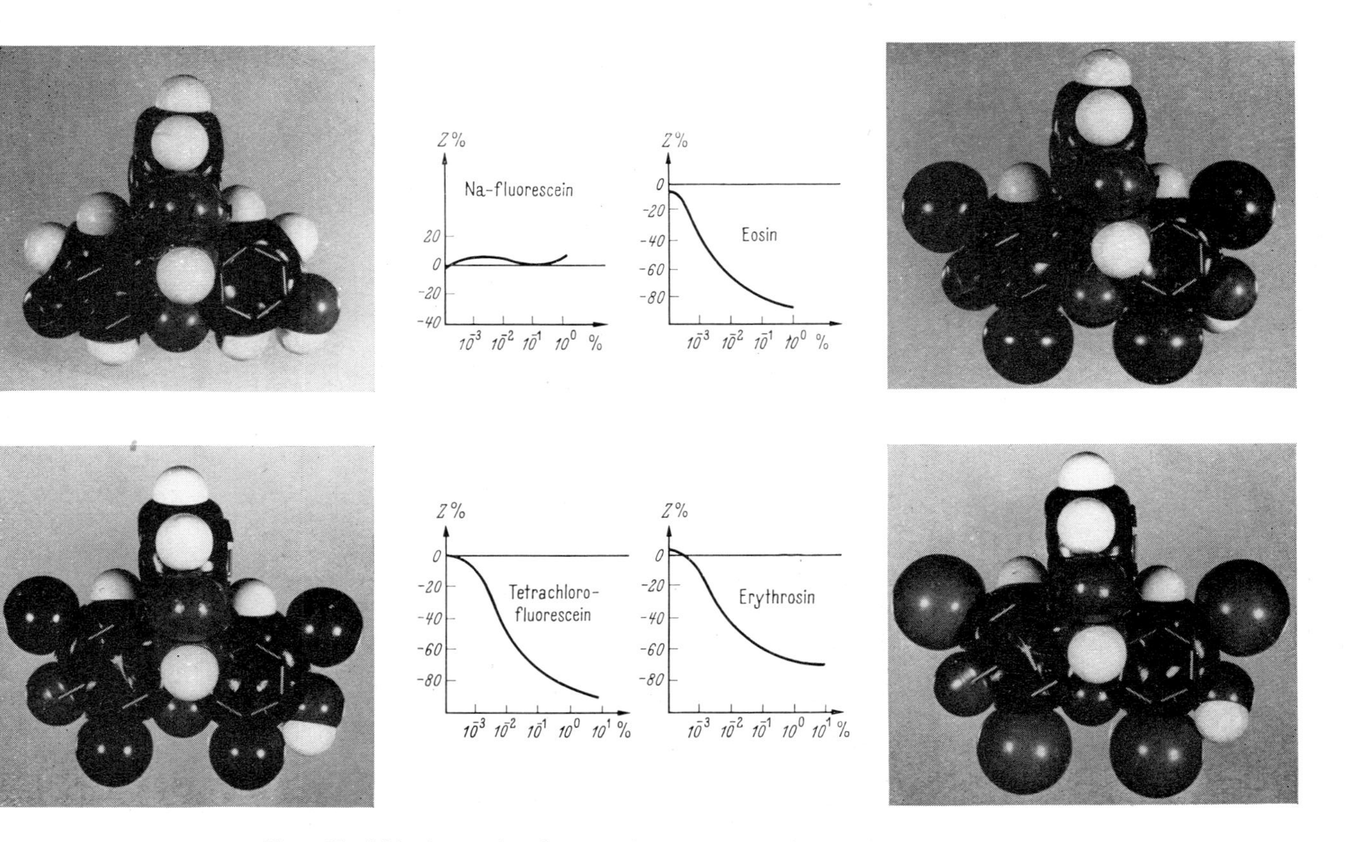

Figure 11. Molecular models and concentration–action curves of some halogen-substituted fluoresceins. Abscissae: log *concn. Ordinates: change in length of coleoptiles as per cent of control.*

substituted fluoresceins, we see that their action as growth inhibitors seems to depend on a specific *W*-form of the molecule (*Figure 11*). This form is due to the substituent halogens and it is immaterial which of the different halogens is substituted. It is not true, however, that all strong inhibitors are

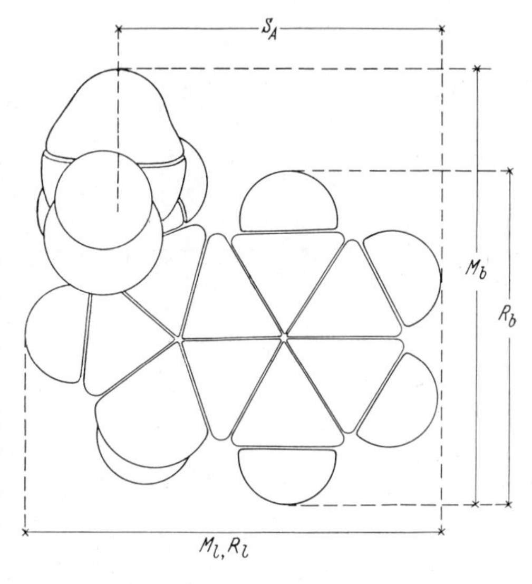

Figure 13. The dimensions of the molecule in projection on the ring-plane in the standard position of the side-chain. M_l = *length of the molecule;* M_b = *breadth of the molecule;* R_l = *length of the ring;* R_b = *breadth of the ring;* S_A = *distance of the side-chain from the opposite side of the ring.*

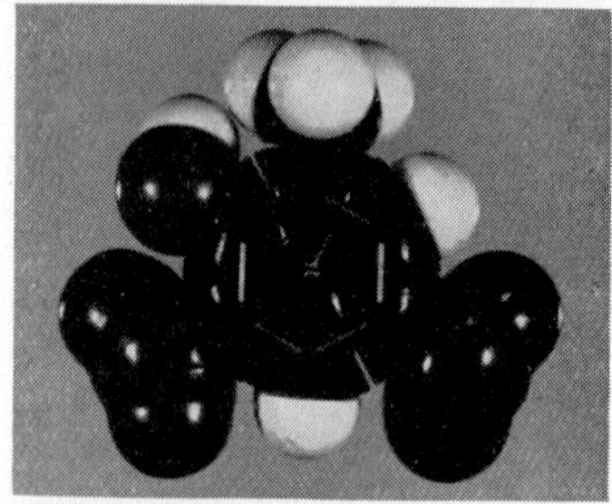

Figure 12. Molecular models of 2:3:5-*tri-iodobenzoic acid (top)*, 4:6-*dinitro*ortho*cresol (middle) and dinitro*-sec.*butylphenol (bottom).*

similar in their form to that of eosine; we know that compounds with one ring-system, like 2:3:5-triiodobenzoic acid, are also strong inhibitors; it is therefore of interest to see that the inhibiting substance 4:6-dinitrocresol is very similar in its form to 2:3:5-triiodobenzoic acid (*Figure 12*).

Our work on the comparison of structural forms and active positions of the molecules of growth substances and growth inhibitors is, as yet, in an early stage and I regret that I cannot give you definitive and conclusive results but only point out some possibilities for proceeding further in the field of our research. In the standard position every molecule shows different measurements (see *Figure 13*). We have carried out measurements in a long series of different molecules, promoting, inhibiting, and inactive ones, and our

Table 5

The dimensions of the molecule and the free rotating power of the side-chain in different growth promoters and growth inhibitors

Group	Substance	Measures of the molecule in Å					Rotating power of the side-chain α°
		M_l	M_b	R_l	R_b	S_A	
A. Promoters	Indole-3-acetonitrile	8·6	8·4	8·6	7·0	6·6	285
	2:4:5-Trichlorophenoxyacetic acid ethyl ester	8·7	9·5	8·7	7·1	6·8	190
	2:4:5-Trichlorophenoxyacetic acid	8·7	9·5	8·7	7·1	6·8	249
	2:4-Dichlorophenoxyacetic acid butyl ester	8·7	9·5	8·7	7·0	6·7	190
	2:4:5-Trichlorophenoxyacetic acid butyl ester	8·7	9·5	8·7	7·1	6·8	190
	2:4:5-Trichlorophenoxyacetic acid (sodium salt)	8·7	9·5	8·7	7·1	6·8	249
	2:4-Dichlorophenoxyacetic acid methyl ester	8·7	9·5	8·7	7·0	6·7	190
	Indole-3-acetic acid	8·6	6·9	8·6	7·0	6·6	92
	2:3:6-Trichlorobenzaldehyde	9·6	8·5	9·7	8·1	4·8	115
	2:5-Dichlorophenoxyacetic acid butyl ester	8·7	9·5	8·7	7·1	6·8	190
	2:5-Dichlorophenoxyacetic acid	8·7	9·5	8·7	7·1	6·8	190
	2:5-Dichlorophenoxyacetic acid ethyl ester	8·7	9·5	8·7	7·1	6·8	190
	2:4-Dichlorophenoxyacetic acid (sodium salt)	8·7	9·5	8·7	7·0	6·7	190
	2:3:6-Trichlorobenzoic acid	8·7	9·5	8·7	7·2	4·8	115
	2:4-Dichlorophenoxyacetic acid	8·7	9·5	8·7	7·0	6·8	190
	α-Naphthalene-acetic acid (sodium salt)	9·0	9·4	9·0	7·0	5·9	73
	α-Naphthalene-acetic acid	9·1	9·4	9·1	7·0	5·9	73
	Tetrachlorophenoxyacetic acid	10·0	13·1	7·6	9·6	7·0	190
	Indole-3-butyric acid	8·6	12·0	8·6	7·0	6·6	360
	Indole-3-propionic acid	8·6	9·5	8·6	7·0	6·6	360
	2-Oxybenzthiazole-acetic acid		8·1	7·8	7·0	9·2	360
	N-Dimethylethiuramacetic acid	8·7	7·7	7·3	6·4	7·0	250
	3-Aminotriazole	5·0	7·0	5·0	5·0	2·5	360
B. Inhibitors	Tetrabromofluorescein (eosine)	14·5	13·2	14·5	8·7	7·2	30
	2:3:5-Triiodobenzoic acid	10·0	9·7	10·5	7·7	5·2	113
	Bis-2:4-dichlorophenoxyacetic acid	7·5	9·5	5·7	8·6	3·6	
		(14·4)	(8·4)	(8·7)	(14·4)	(7·0)	
	Pentachlorophenoxyacetic acid	8·9	11·0	8·9	9·5	7·2	51
	Dinitro-*o-sec*.butylphenol	11·1	9·4	11·1	9·3	5·1	360
	Pentachlorophenol	9·0	9·2	9·0	8·2	5·4	360
	2:4:6-Trichlorophenoxyacetic acid	8·7	9·5	8·7	8·3	6·8	51
	β-Naphthoxyacetic acid	9·9	9·1	8·9	7·0	8·2	360
	α-Naphthoxyacetic acid	9·5	10·9	9·1	7·0	5·9	318
	Phenoxyacetic acid	8·7	9·2	8·7	7·0	6·8	360

results are presented in *Table 5.* We hope that an exact comparison of the affinity values with the measurements of the molecule in respect to electrical and chemical (electronic) configuration, may add to our knowledge of the relations between chemical constitution and activity of growth substances and inhibitors. Without referring to our more recent results which are too extensive to discuss here, we can establish already the following facts: A growth-promoting molecule may not have a ring length (R_l) of more than 9·0 to 9·6 Å, a ring breadth (R_b) of more than 7·1 and 7·6 Å and a side-chain distance (S_A) of more than 7·0 Å (*Table 6*). The general statement that the molecular length may not exceed 9·1 Å could also be made,

Table 6

The differences in dimensions of the most important growth promoters and growth inhibitors

	M_l	R_l	R_b	S_A
Promoters				
Indole-3-acetonitrile	8·6	8·6	7·0	6·6
2:4:5-Trichlorophenoxyacetic acid	8·7	8·7	7·1	6·8
2:5-Dichlorophenoxyacetic acid	8·7	8·7	7·1	6·8
2:3:6-Trichlorobenzoic acid	8·7	8·7	7·2	4·8
2:4-Dichlorophenoxyacetic acid	8·7	8·7	7·0	6·8
α-Naphthalene-acetic acid	9·0	9·0	7·0	5·9
N-Dimethylthiuramacetic acid	8·7	7·3	6·4	7·0
Inhibitors				
Tetrabromofluorescein	*14·5*	*14·5*	*8·7*	*7·2*
2:3:5-Triiodobenzoic acid	*10·0*	*10·5*	*7·7*	5·2
Bis-2:4-dichlorophenoxyacetic acid	7·5	5·7	*8·6*	3·6†
4:6-Dinitro-*o*-cresol	*9·3*	*9·3*	*8·4*	4·7
Pentachlorophenoxyacetic acid	8·9	8·9	*9·5*	*7·2*
2:4:6-Trichlorophenoxyacetic acid	8·7	8·7	*8·3*	6·8
β-Naphthoxyacetic acid	*9·9*	8·9	7·0	*8·2*
Thiophenoxyacetic acid	*9·2*	8·7	7·0	6·7
Phenoxyacetic acid	8·7	8·7	7·0	6·8

† Dimensions of molecule in side by side positions of the rings; when taken as *W*-twin the dimensions are as follows: M_l = *14·4*; R_l = *8·7*; R_b = *14·4*; S_A = 7·0.

with the single exception of 2-oxybenzthiazoleacetic acid. This substance, with a molecular length of about 10 Å, would be expected to be a growth inhibitor like the β-naphthoxyacetic acid, which shows nearly the same measurements, but we found it to be active as a promoter. It is possible that the substance we tested was not really pure and it will be necessary to repeat the tests with extremely pure samples of 2-oxybenzthiazoleacetic acid.

We are not yet able to assume that the growth-promoting molecule must be able to fall into a certain position, called a standard position, because 2:3:6-trichlorobenzoic acid is not able to do so, in spite of its activity as a growth promoter. For this reason, we are forced to suppose that there are two different standard forms of growth-promoting molecules. One group is characterized by the form of indole-3-acetonitrile, and includes indole-3-acetic acid, α-naphthaleneacetic acid, 2:4-D, 2:4:5-trichlorophenoxyacetic acid, 2-oxybenzthiazoleacetic acid, and dimethylthiuramacetic acid.

The other form is characterized by 2:3:6-trichlorobenzoic acid or the corresponding aldehyde; no other growth-promoting substance of this form is yet known. We do not know if there is only one gap in the growing system being filled by each of these two types of molecule, or two different gaps which when occupied show the same growth effect. There is also the possibility that one type of molecule is converted to the other in plant metabolism. It is probable, in the latter case, that the trichlorobenzoic acid would be transformed into the indole-3-acetonitrile type, for this latter type includes a considerable number of chemically different substances which show similarities in form but not so much in chemical behaviour.

Figure 14. The molecular model of tetraiodofluorescein (left) compared with that of 2:3:5-*tri-iodobenzoic acid.*

In the case of growth inhibitors, we can state that the inhibiting action of fluorescein depends on its *W*-like molecular form, which results when halogen substitution is made as in eosine. Another type of inhibitor shows the molecule form of 4:6-dinitro-*o*-cresol. We see, therefore, that there are also two different types of molecular form consistent with growth inhibition. A comparison of the forms of these two inhibitor types showed that the *W*-like structure of substituted fluorescein is composed of two molecules of the form type of 2:3:5-substituted benzoic acid. Eosine looks like a siamese twin, with the two *W*-building molecules very similar in form to 4:6-dinitro-*o*-cresol or to 2:3:5-triiodobenzoic acid respectively (*Figure 14*).

The above results show that our work has led us to some interesting points of view concerning the similarities between active molecules and corresponding similarities between inhibitor molecules. But it also shows that much more has to be done in the future and we hope to find the opportunity to study these problems further.

REFERENCES

BENTLEY, J. A. (1950). Growth regulating effect of certain organic compounds. *Nature*, **165,** 449.

JONES, E. R. H., HENBEST, H. B., SMITH, C. F., and BENTLEY, J. A. (1952). 3-Indolyl-acetonitrile; a natural occurring plant growth hormone. *Nature*, **169,** 485.

KAINDL, K. (1954). Biophysikalische Analyse der Konzentrations-Wirkungskurven von Wirkstoffen insbesondere Zellstreckungswuchsstoffen. *Mh. Chem.* **85,** 985.

KERK, G. J. M. VAN DER, RAALTE, M. H. VAN, KAARS SIJPESTEIJN, A., and VEEN, R. VAN DER (1955). A new type of plant growth-regulating substances. *Nature,* **176,** 308.

LINSER, H. (1954a). Interaction of growth promoters and growth inhibitors. *Huitième congrès int. de. Bot. Paris,* 1954. *Section* 11/12, 174.

LINSER, H. (1954b). Zur Wirkungsweise von Wuchs- und Hemmstoffen. IV. Die Konzentrations-Wirkungskurven einiger synthetischer Zellstreckungswuchsstoffe in Gegenwart verschiedener Mengen von synthetischen Hemmstoffen. *Biochim. biophys. Acta,* **15,** 25.

LINSER, H. (1954c). Chemische Konstitution und Zellstreckungswirkung verschiedener Stoffe. *Mh. Chem.* **85,** 196.

VELDSTRA, H. (1947). Considerations on the interaction of ergons and their substrates. *Biochim. biophys. Acta,* **1,** 364.

WEAVER, R. W. (1952). Response of Black Corinth grapes to applications of 4-chlorophenoxyacetic acid. *Bot. Gaz.* **114,** 107.

WEAVER, R. W. (1954). Effect of benzthiazol-2-oxyacetic acid on development of Black Corinth grapes. *Bot. Gaz.* **115,** 365.

THE ACTION–CONCENTRATION CURVES OF MIXTURES OF GROWTH-PROMOTING AND GROWTH-INHIBITING SUBSTANCES

K. Kaindl
Biologisches Laboratorium der Österreichische Stickstoffwerke A.G., Linz, Austria

As I was trying to show at the Botanical Congress in Paris last year (Kaindl, 1954), it is possible to calculate the action–concentration curves of growth-promoting substances (it is irrelevant in principle by which method they are obtained) by the formula

$$z = A_1(1-e^{-k_w c})+A_2(1-e^{-k'_w c})-B_1(1-e^{-k_h c})-B_2(1-e^{-k'_h c}),$$

wherein z denotes the percentage change of cell elongation, e.g. of an *Avena* coleoptile under the action of an acting substance measured in percentage concentration c. The k-values are a measure of the hit probability with which the correlated sensitive areas, called gaps, of the living system will be hit by the acting molecule entering into the coleoptile. Therefore, the k-values are measures of the affinity between the molecules of the acting substance and the living system.

The first term of the formula describes the extent to which molecules of a growth regulator attach to such gaps (called w-gaps) so that an increase of cell elongation results. A_1 is proportional to the number of open w-gaps (n_{wo}) of the living substance in question and to the effect c_w which one molecule of the growth regulator produces. The expression in brackets gives the probability with which one w-gap will be occupied when a given number of molecules defined by the concentration c enters into the living system.

The second term describes the extent to which molecules of the growth regulator oust the acting molecules of the growth regulators produced by the coleoptile itself. A_2 is proportional, therefore, to the number $\bar{n}_{wo}$ of gaps which are occupied by the natural growth regulators. When the effect of one natural molecule is given by $\bar{c}_w$ on an average, it is evident that the molecular effect produced by one replacement has to be $c_w-\bar{c}_w$. Generally, the molecular effect of a foreign molecule (not produced in the coleoptile) will be lower than that of the average effect of a molecule of the natural growth regulators and therefore A_2 has to be negative. On the other hand, however, if a strong effective component of the natural growth regulators is applied, e.g. indoleacetic acid and indoleacetonitrile, this molecular effect may exceed the average effect of the mixture of natural growth regulators present in the coleoptile, and, in consequence, A_2 will be positive. The expression in brackets shows the probability with which one gap occupied by a natural molecule gets filled by the replacing foreign molecule.

The third term is equivalent to the first and describes the event of molecules of the acting substance attaching to such a gap (h-gap), so that inhibition of cell elongation growth results. B_1 is proportional to the number of open

h-gaps (n_{ho}) and of the molecular effect c_h of a single molecule. The expression in brackets states again the probability with which such an h-gap gets occupied by the entering molecule.

Finally, the fourth term describes the extent to which molecules of the entering growth regulator oust the molecules of the natural growth regulators. Exactly the same considerations as in the case of the second term lead to the conclusion that the molecular effect produced by one replacement has to be $c_h - \bar{c}_h$, and, therefore, B_2 is generally negative. An exception, however, is present when a strong effective component of the natural regulators is applied. In this case, B_2 may be positive. The bracket-term furnishes again the probability with which one h-gap, naturally occupied, gets filled by the replacing foreign molecule.

Figures 1–3 show the agreement of the theoretical function with the experimental data for a strong effective component of the natural growth regulators (indoleacetic acid) promoting cell elongation growth, for a foreign promoting substance (α-naphthylacetic acid) and for an inhibiting substance (eosine). Obviously, the absence of the first term means that the growth regulator is an inhibiting substance, and mathematically it says that either the molecular effect c_w or k_w is equal to zero. In the latter case one has to suppose that the second term has to become zero too, because the probability of replacement k'_w is to be assumed as smaller than the probability of occupation k_w of an empty gap. If the second term is present, A_2 is proportional to $\bar{c}_w$; this consideration makes it possible to set in proportion the c_w and c_h of the different substances, as I showed in my paper last year. Furthermore, one can calculate the proportion between the probabilities k_w and k_h and finally the proportion of the number of gaps n_{wo} and n_{ho}. Subsequently, one can separate the growth-promoting and inhibiting components in regard to the effectiveness of the regulating substances.

Briefly repeating the results referred to last year, I was able to calculate the proportion of the promoting effect (X) and the inhibiting effect (Y) of differently acting substances. The result for the promoting effect was: X_1 (indoleacetic acid) : X_2 (α-naphthylacetic acid) : X_3 (4:6-dinitro-*ortho*-cresol) : X_4 (pentachlorophenol) : X_5 (eosine) : X_6 (dinitro-*ortho-sec*.butylphenol) = 1:0·33:0·97:0·16:0:0;
and for the inhibiting effect:

$$Y_1 : Y_2 : Y_3 : Y_4 : Y_5 : Y_6 = 1 : 32 : 2350 : 794 : 74900 : 1640.$$

The complex effect of growth promotion expressed in terms of $Z_i = X_i / Y_i$ is thus given by the relation

$$Z_1 : Z_2 : Z_3 : Z_4 : Z_5 : Z_6 = 1 : 0{\cdot}01 : 0{\cdot}0004 : 0{\cdot}0002 : 0 : 0.$$

In my opinion, a classification of the different growth regulators is only possible if one analyses the concentration–action curves and compares the different components which yield the complex phenomena one can observe. One might object to this on the ground that the shape of the function derived from the hit-theory will fit in with any experimental results, but I have shown in my previous paper that the different parameters of the function are limited by different rules extracted from the experimental investigations carried out by H. Linser (1954). The only source of unreliability in the calculation of

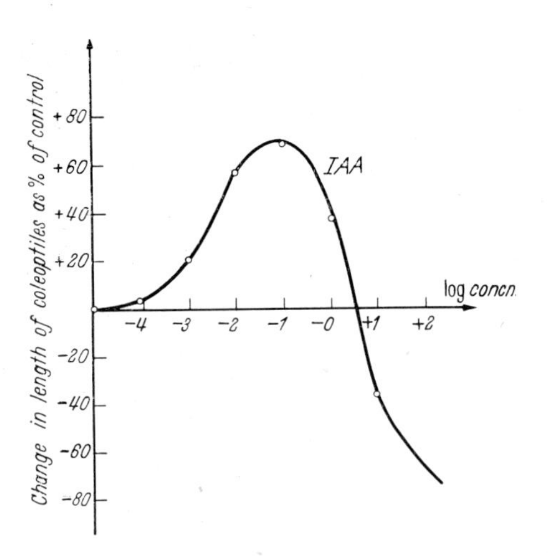

Figure 1. The course of the theoretical concentration–action curve of IAA compared with the experimental data (∘). *Abscissa:* log *of the per cent concentration. Ordinate: percentage change of length of the test plant* (Avena *coleoptile*).

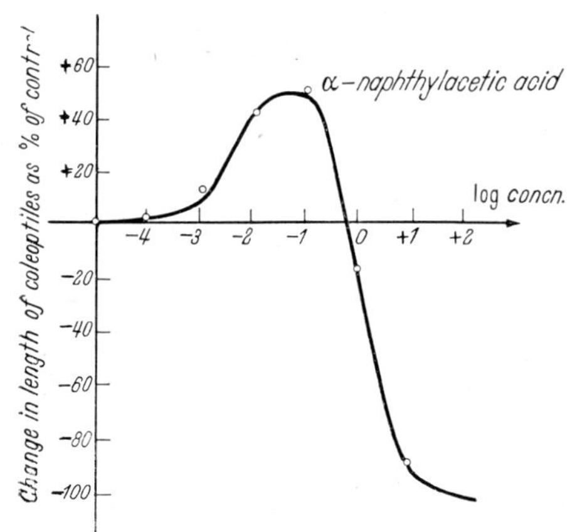

Figure 2. The course of the theoretical concentration–action curve of α-naphthylacetic acid compared with the experimental data (∘). *Abscissa and ordinate as in Figure 1.*

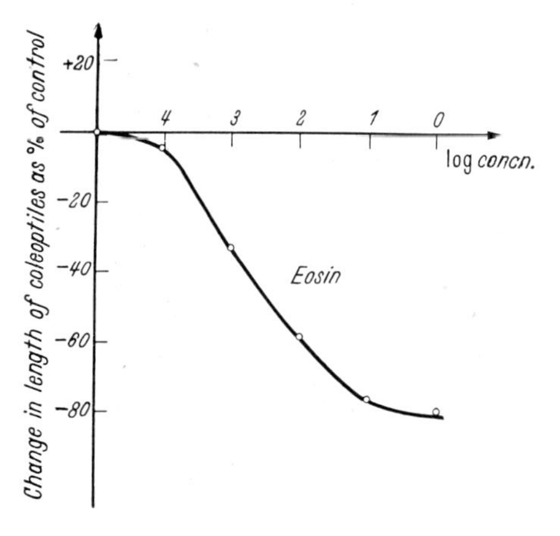

Figure 3. The course of the theoretical concentration–action curve of eosine compared with the experimental data (∘). *Abscissa and ordinate as in Figure 1.*

this function is the comparatively high limits of errors which are inherent in biological experiments. But apart from this, there is no doubt that the theory expounded here would be confirmed if the calculation of action–concentration curves which arise from a mixture of two growth regulators was feasible. It should be possible to calculate the function of the mixture curve providing that the functions of the single acting substances are given and useful considerations of probability are employed. In fact, this idea can already be verified for six different mixture series and the considerations leading to the derivation of the mixture function may be set forth here briefly.

The function of a growth-promoting substance may be given by the formula mentioned above:

$$z_w = A_1(1-e^{-k_w c_1})+A_2(1-e^{-k'_w c_1})-B_1(1-e^{-k_h c_1})-B_2(1-e^{-k'_h c_1}),$$

and

$$z_h = C_2(1-e^{-l'_w c_2})-D_1(1-e^{-l_h c_2})-D_2(1-e^{-l'_h c_2})$$

gives the function of an inhibiting substance. When the two substances are simultaneously applied to the coleoptile the following competing actions take place:

1. The probability that the *W*-molecule enters into a *w*-gap and that an *H*-molecule does not enter into this gap is given by

$$P_1 = (1-e^{-k_w c_1})e^{-l'_w c_2},$$

assuming that the probability of replacement l'_w valid for the ousting process of a natural molecule holds approximately true for this corresponding ousting process too.

2. There is competition between *W*- and *H*-molecules for the ousting of a natural molecule from a *w*-gap. The probability of the occupation of the *w*-gap by a *W*-molecule is given then by

$$P_2 = (1-e^{-k'_w c_1})e^{-l'_w c_2}$$

and for an *H*-molecule by

$${}_2P = (1-e^{-l'_w c_2})e^{-k'_w c_1}.$$

3. For the *W*-molecule competition of the two partners for an *h*-gap leads to the probability

$$P_3 = (1-e^{-k_h c_1})e^{-l_h c_2};$$

for the *H*-molecule to

$${}_3P = (1-e^{-l_h c_2})e^{-k_h c_1}.$$

4. Finally, competition regarding the ousting process of a natural molecule from an *h*-gap leads to the two probabilities

$$P_4 = (1-e^{-k'_h c_1})e^{-l'_h c_2}$$

for the *W*-molecule and

$${}_4P = (1-e^{-l'_h c_2})e^{-k'_h c_1}$$

for the *H*-molecule.

The function of the mixture curve, therefore, has to be

$$z_w+z_h = A_1P_1+A_2P_2-B_1P_3-B_2P_4+C_2 \cdot {}_2P-D_1 \cdot {}_3P-D_2 \cdot {}_4P.$$

The results calculated by this formula show a good agreement with the experimental data obtained in our biological laboratory. For *Figures 4–6*, I have singled out one curve of the mixture series indoleacetic acid (10^{-1})

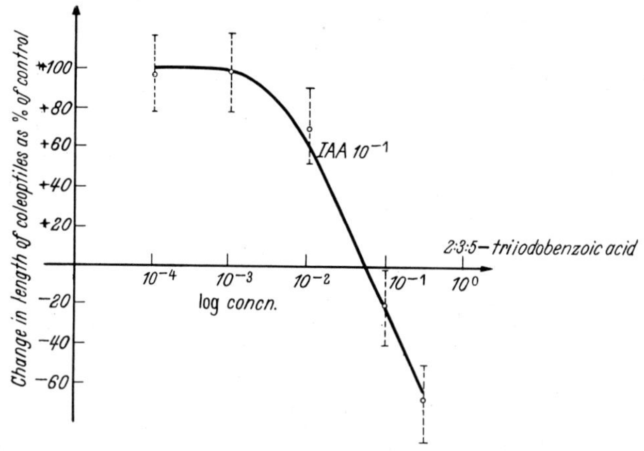

Figure 4. The course of the theoretical concentration–action curve of the mixture of IAA (10^{-1} *per cent concn.) and* 2:3:5-*triiodobenzoic acid compared with the experimental data* (⫯). *Abscissa and ordinate as in Figure 1.*

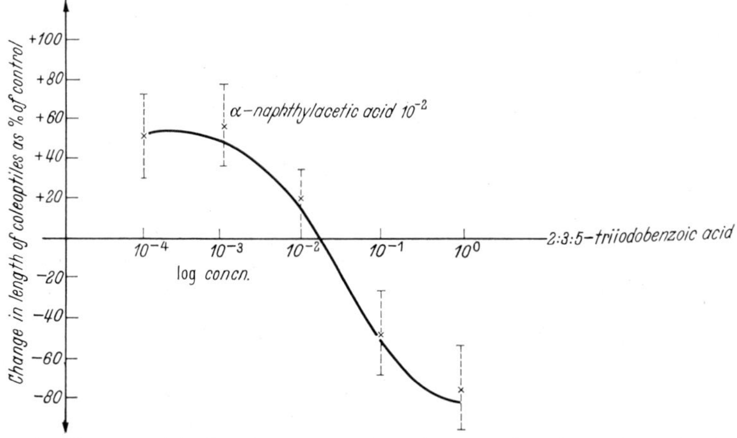

Figure 5. The course of the theoretical concentration–action curve of the mixture of α-naphthylacetic acid (10^{-2} *per cent concn.) and* 2:3:5-*triiodobenzoic acid compared with the experimental data* (⫯). *Abscissa and ordinate as in Figure 1.*

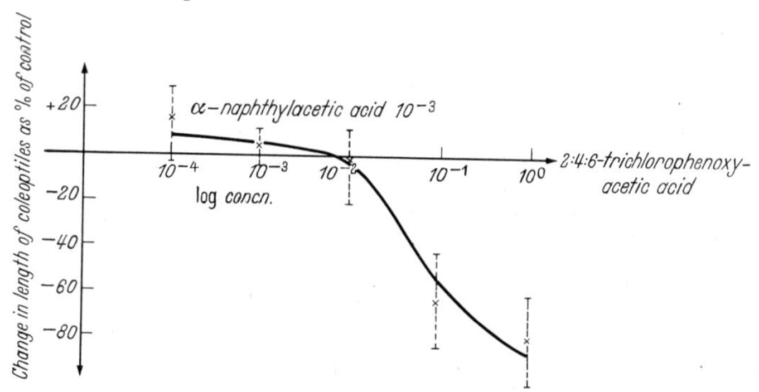

Figure 6. The course of the theoretical concentration–action curve of the mixture of α-naphthylacetic acid (10^{-3} *per cent concn.) and* 2:4:6-*trichlorophenoxyacetic acid compared with the experimental data* (⫯). *Abscissa and ordinate as in Figure 1.*

and 2:3:5-triiodobenzoic acid, one curve of the series α-naphthylacetic acid (10^{-2}) and 2:3:5-triiodobenzoic acid and one curve of the series α-naphthylacetic acid (10^{-3}) and 2:4:6-trichlorophenoxyacetic acid. In spite of the good agreement between the theoretical function and the experimental data, there are few deviations, especially when higher concentrations are applied. *Figure 7* shows such a case (2:4:5-trichlorophenoxyacetic acid (10^0) and 2:4:6-trichlorophenoxyacetic acid). This deviation seems to be based on the fact that either in the mixture itself, or in the interior of the coleoptile, chemical reactions or intermolecular associations take place. The latter may

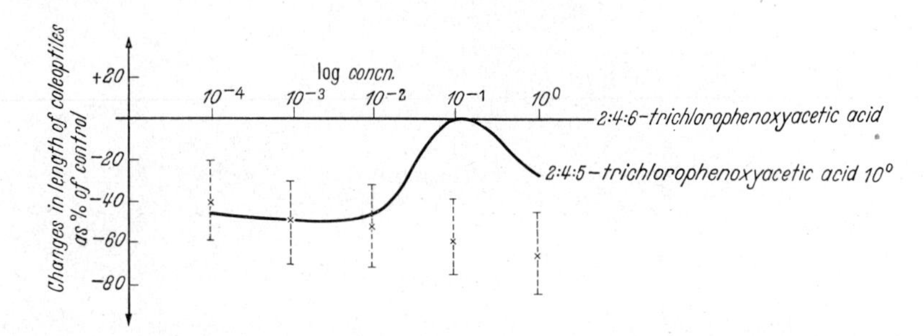

Figure 7. The course of the theoretical concentration–action curve of the mixture of 2:4:5-*trichlorophenoxyacetic acid* (10^0 *per cent concn.*) *and* 2:4:6-*trichlorophenoxyacetic acid compared with the experimental data* (I). *Abscissa and ordinate as in Figure 1.*

be more probable, and means formally that both acting molecules enter into a gap simultaneously. Even in the case shown in *Figure 7* molecular association seems to be present because the two molecules are chemically similar.

The effect brought about by the simultaneous entry is not to be calculated from the fundamental functions of the single partners of the mixture, but one can obtain four correction terms. I will not occupy space here to show this in detail. Further investigations will reveal whether the conclusion is reversible; a deviation from the calculated values would mean that intermolecular powers influence the result. In terms of the probability calculus, the two collectives are not independent of each other when experimental results deviate from theoretical results.

What I want to emphasize, however, is that the instances in which such discrepancies between theory and experiment appear are very few in the cases where I have had the opportunity of calculating mixture series. Further calculations will have to support the considerations of probability applied here, but the results obtained so far indicate the usefulness of the theory based on the fundamental ideas of H. Linser (1954).

REFERENCES

Kaindl, K. (1954). Biophysikalische Analyse der Konzentrations-Wirkungskurven von Wirkstoffen (insbesondere Zellstreckungswuchsstoffen). *Mh. Chem.* **85,** 985.

Linser, H. (1954). Chemische Konstitution und zellstreckungswirkung. Versuch einer allgemeinen Wirkstoffhypothese. *Mh. Chem.* **85,** 196.

THE CHEMICAL INDUCTION OF GROWTH IN PLANT TISSUE CULTURES†

F. C. STEWARD and E. M. SHANTZ
Department of Botany, Cornell University

Part I: Methods of Tissue Culture and the Analysis of Growth

INTRODUCTION: NORMAL PROLIFERATIVE GROWTH IN THE PLANT BODY

BEFORE taking note of various chemical substances and extracts that are capable of inducing rapid, proliferated growth in otherwise mature plant tissues, it is well to take note of a few salient examples in which this occurs normally in the plant body.

The classical example, noted by Fitting (1910), in which pollination in the orchid stimulates the growth of the pistil or ovary wall, is well known. In the development of the coco-nut fruit the embryo is usually immature when the fruit falls to the ground. When the embryo eventually germinates it sends out into the central cavity containing liquid endosperm a cotyledon which acts as an absorbing organ and rapidly produces a cellular tissue capable of filling the entire cavity of the fruit.

The stimulation which pollination and fertilization gives to the development of the fleshy tissue of pome fruits is well known. There are also cases, e.g. the edible banana, in which, under certain genetical situations, a fleshy layer develops without this stimulus and grows parthenocarpically by cell division and proliferation from a well-defined loculus in the fruit. The numerous cases now known of parthenocarpically induced development of fruits give point to the chemical basis of this stimulus to growth.

While the formation of tubers and tuberization and the development of other storage organs, whether roots or bulbs, is often a response to length of day, this stimulus must be communicated to the cells in question by some as yet unknown chemical means.

Galls, whether activated by bacteria, by insects, or by viruses, again induce in otherwise mature cells a return to active growth and proliferation. The formation of nodules, which grow on legumes, is yet another familiar example of chemically induced growth in the tissues of the host.

In other words, although the following account will concentrate upon certain phenomena in which this general type of process may be studied in plant tissue cultures, there are many examples that can be cited in which similar phenomena occur normally in the development of plants.

The *raison d'être* of the investigations to be described was, however, not wholly the attempt to understand the chemical basis for growth induction. It was rather to use the chemical means by which growth may be so induced to contrast the behaviour of rapidly growing and non-growing or resting cells. For this reason attention was turned to the use of tissue culture methods

† This paper was read at the Conference by F. C. Steward.

and these were adapted by means that have been described to experiments that can be carried out in a quantitative manner. The essential outlines of these experiments only will be described here because the methods have been published elsewhere (Caplin and Steward, 1949; Steward, Caplin, and Millar, 1952). In making this summary of the technique, however, an opportunity will be taken to mention certain refinements that have not hitherto been published in full.

TISSUE CULTURE METHODS

The tissue of which the greatest use is made in these investigations is the secondary phloem tissue of the carrot root. Essentially the same methods have, however, been applied to the culture of artichoke tuber tissue and of potato tuber tissue. All of these tissues are essentially secondary in origin but the extent to which they may embark upon rapid, external, proliferative growth is determined by the conditions to be described: these include the use of certain isolated and now-known substances or the use of extracts that contain growth-promoting substances.

The tissue of the storage organ is isolated aseptically in the form of small pieces, or cylindrical 'plugs', which weigh approximately 2 mg. Special steps are taken to ensure that the tissue explants are removed from as closely identical positions in the organ as possible. An essential feature of the technique is that, in given experiments, explants are all removed from the same individual organ, be it root or tuber. In this way variability is kept to a minimum. In our experience there is no method by which already cultured tissues can be subdivided in a random fashion to produce populations of explants that are as uniform in their subsequent growth as the tissues isolated from the intact organ by the means which have been described (Caplin, 1947). It is not necessary to enlarge here upon the accuracy with which these techniques can be performed although one may refer to the discussion that has taken place regarding the use of relatively large, or relatively small, explants (Heller, 1953). The use of small explants is in these experiments essential to exclude those minute centres of growth that would permit the tissue to respond *without* the addition of the particular formative substances that are here under investigation. We can merely say that in our hands the use of small explants, and even transfers of isolated floating cells from a suspension, is capable of giving a greater degree of uniformity than any other means known to us.

The tissue culture procedure which is preferred uses growth of the tissue explants in a liquid medium contained in special tubes arranged around a horizontal shaft revolving about one revolution a minute, so that the tissue spends part of its time in air and part of its time bathed in water. The type of growth curve obtained under these conditions with carrot phloem explants has been described (Caplin and Steward, 1949). The familiar criterion of growth in these experiments has been the change in fresh weight of the individual explant. The medium in which the best growth has occurred has been a standard tissue culture medium (White, 1943), supplemented by whole coco-nut milk, the liquid endosperm from the relatively mature nut (Caplin and Steward, 1948). With suitable modifications of the medium, potato tissue can be successfully cultured in a similar way (Steward and

(*a*) *Culture flask for large numbers of carrot explants: free floating cells in the ambient fluid.*

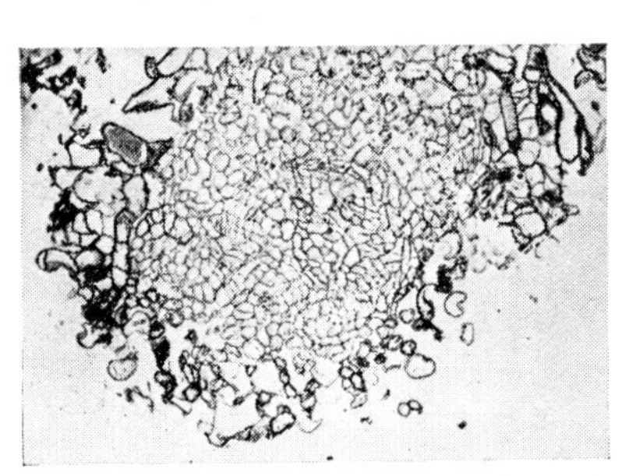

(*b*) *Tissue culture from small explant with organized growing centre.*

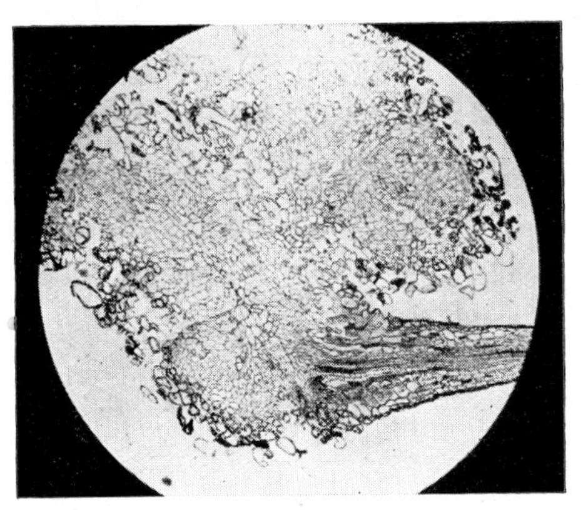

(*c*) *Tissue culture from small explant showing root formation.*

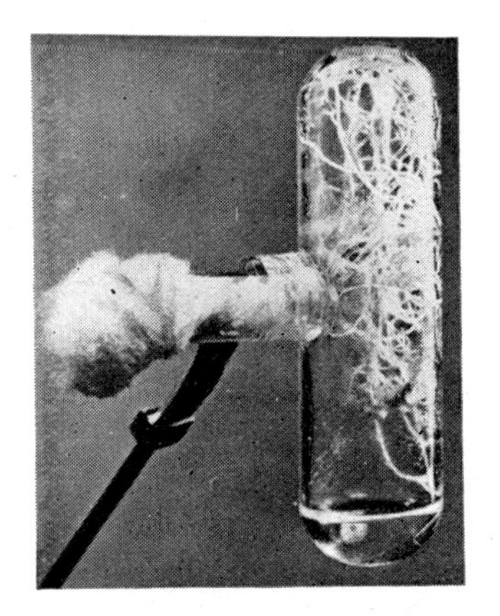

(*d*) *Carrot roots developed in cultures grown from free floating cells.*

Figure 1.

Caplin, 1951), and artichoke tuber tissue can be grown in almost exactly the same fashion as carrot tissue.

Use is now being made of another technique which was devised primarily to permit relatively large amounts of cultured tissue to be obtained for the purposes of biochemical examination. Here the tube, normally containing one or at most two or three individual carrot explants, is replaced by a flask (see *Figure 1(a)*). Around the periphery of the flask, nipples are blown in such a way that the tissue explants distribute themselves in these projections and again are alternately exposed to air and bathed in liquid. 100 explants from an individual carrot root can be successfully grown in a culture of this sort containing 250 ml of nutrient fluid, and in this fashion weights up to 10 g of tissue can be grown in about 28 days. The standard deviation of such a population of explants is very small indeed ($\pm$5–10 per cent of the mean). However, an unexpected sequel to this technique is of interest. Explants taken from the mature carrot root grown by this 'flask technique' grow in much the same fashion as individual explants in a normal culture tube, that is, they produce more or less ellipsoidal masses of a relatively undifferentiated parenchymatous type of tissue. However, when concentrated in the flask the supernatant becomes somewhat turbid, owing to the development of free floating cells which grow in the medium. Such floating cells can be used to make liquid inocula into other flasks. This technique has been in continuous use now for some two years and it has become a common experience that a large number of small tissue cultures can be grown from these liquid inocula which contain only free floating cells, either singly or in very small groups. Also, quite contrary to expectations it was found that cultures grown from these free floating cells are much more prone to organize and form roots than they are when grown in the normal medium from explants newly isolated from the carrot root. Reference is made to this technique here, however, merely to emphasize that it is now quite clear that the tissue culture technique can be extended downward so that inocula can be made, not only from small tissue explants from the whole organ, but also from a stock of free growing cells.

GROWTH REQUIREMENTS OF DIFFERENT TISSUES

Carrot and artichoke tissue grow adequately when a normal basal medium is supplemented by the addition of whole coco-nut milk. The condition, however, is quite different in the case of the potato tuber. Depending somewhat on the individual tuber and the strain from which it was derived, virtually no external growth occurs when minute pieces of potato tissue are exposed to the conditions under which carrot tissue grows apace. To produce an actively growing tissue culture of potato tuber, a synergistic mixture is necessary. This consists of 2 parts: (*a*) the coco-nut milk complex, and (*b*) 2:4-D or an equivalent substance present in minute amount in the solution. For 2:4-D itself, the most effective concentration is of the order of 6 p.p.m. in a medium containing about 10 per cent by volume of whole coco-nut milk (Steward and Caplin, 1951). In this curious twofold requirement for substances that induce proliferative growth in the cells of the potato tuber, it is now clear that both substances are continuously necessary. This can be shown by the experiments illustrated in *Figure 2*, in which the tissue was exposed to coco-nut milk alone after growing for varying lengths of time in the synergistic mixture of coco-nut milk and 2:4-D. The data clearly show that maintained rapid growth requires the continuous presence of *both* the 2:4-D and the coco-nut milk complex. An even greater stimulus to growth can be obtained by further interaction with casein hydrolysate.

As a natural outcome of the development of this technique and its use to assay the naturally occurring growth-promoting substances and growth-inhibiting substances in plant extracts, the following general view has been developed.

Plant cells, fully furnished with nutrients, salts, organic substrates, water, etc., may still fail to grow for different reasons. In some cases there is an

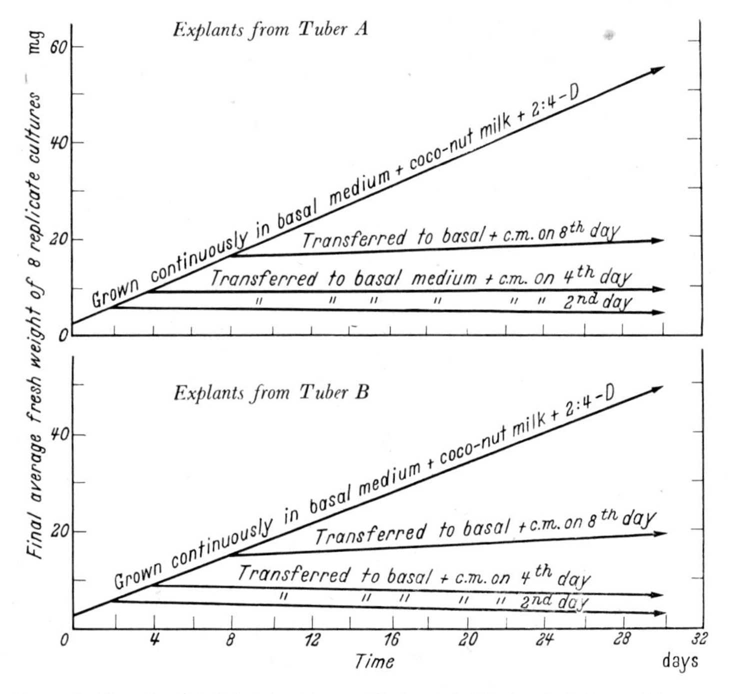

Figure 2. Growth of potato tuber tissue explants started in basal medium with coco-nut milk and 2:4-*D, followed by transfers at varying time intervals to medium without* 2:4-*D.*

evident lack of the factors that will permit the cells actively to divide. This lack may often be met by the use of coco-nut milk or its equivalent. Even so, this may not alone suffice with many plant tissues from which extracts may be shown to contain substances that are inhibitory even when added to the carrot–coco-nut milk system. The potato tissue, shown above to require 2:4-D or its equivalent, is a case in point because it contains a sufficiently strong inhibitory substance, or mechanism, so that small amounts of potato tissue extract will antagonize the normal effect of coco-nut milk on carrot tissue. Various other storage organs, dormant resting buds, and endosperms like those of castor bean, have all been shown to contain such inhibitory substances (Steward and Caplin, 1952). This leads to the general philosophy that in the *organized growth of the plant body* one factor that suppresses the indefinite growth by cell division is the accumulation of inhibitory substances that poison or regulate the system tending to cause cell multiplication. Conversely, it also leads to the idea that examples in which cells indulge in such proliferative growth, where they would otherwise be expected to remain quiescent, furnish instances where these active growth-promoting systems, uninhibited by antagonists, can be detected.

Two prominent examples are furnished by (i) the tumors which may be induced by the crown gall organism on plants such as *Bryophyllum* (Steward, Caplin, and Shantz, 1955) and (ii) the parthenocarpically generated fleshy tissue of the banana fruit (Steward and Simmonds, 1954). In both these cases extracts of the organ in question can be the cause of a growth induction in the carrot tissue explants which is very similar to that normally produced by coco-nut milk. Thus we are led to the idea, not by any means unique to this system, that one of the factors involved in differentiation is that the mechanism which would normally lead to indefinite proliferating growth by cell division is brought under control, either by the entire lack of the growth-promoting substances for this type of growth, or much more probably by the accumulation of inhibitory substances. In short, in the balance between the growth promoters for cell division and their inhibitors lies the clue to the regulatory control of growth in this type of system.

GROWTH BY CELL DIVISION AND CELL EXPANSION

The tissue culture system, therefore, presents a powerful tool in the investigation of growth regulation and of the substances that both induce and antagonize growth of an undifferentiated kind. There is, however, a further development necessary to give the technique its full range and usefulness. In much of the work, previously published, the main criterion of growth was the total increment of weight in the growing culture. For a great many general purposes, this suffices. However, for the understanding of the mechanism and for the full exploitation of the technique, it is necessary to differentiate between growth in cell number and growth in cell size. This has long been recognized but the opportunity only presented itself recently for a full investigation of the growth of these tissues at the cellular level. The basis of this will now be described.

Maceration techniques have been familiar to the plant anatomist for some time. It was, however, Brown and Rickless (1949) who first exploited the maceration technique to trace the course of growth in this way. Following this lead, we have adopted similar procedures to study the growth of these tissue cultures at the cellular level. Since considerable reference will be made to results obtained by this technique, its essential basis is here presented.

The tissue explants, whether the original explants from the whole organ or those grown under the conditions described, are macerated in a suitable volume of a mixture of 5 per cent chromic and 5 per cent hydrochloric acids. This procedure is normally done in small vials. At the appropriate time, which experience indicates is approximately 5–10 hours at room temperature, the tissue is fragmented as much as possible by agitating the liquid. Following Brown's procedure, a hypodermic needle, through which the fluid is taken up and forcibly ejected, is used to reduce the macerate as much as possible to single cells. The total number of cells is calculated from counts made on small aliquots placed in a haemocytometer. In principle this same method is still being used but the following refinements have been added.

The haemocytometer is placed upside down on the stage of a Zeiss Winkel inverted microscope fitted with a camera attachment. A sufficient field (approximately 12 mm^2) on the haemocytometer is viewed with a low power objective (4×). With a suitable eyepiece (6×), photographs are taken of representative fields. The negatives are projected on a screen to count the number of cells per unit area on the haemocytometer, and filed for a permanent record. This method is very much more useful for routine application because a large number of such macerates can be prepared and photographed and the counting done subsequently at leisure, whereas actual microscopical counting is arduous and severely limits the number of observations that are possible on a given day. There is no reason to believe that the photographic technique is any different in its accuracy from the visual technique, whose accuracy is discussed below.

The volume of liquid placed on the haemocytometer slide is a very small part of the total macerate; therefore, the error is largely one of sampling. To reduce this error, several aliquots are counted. By suitable precautions, a relatively accurate estimate can be made of the total number of cells in a tissue explant of this sort.

The method also measures the average cell size. If one records the weight of the tissue explant in milligrams and knows the number of cells per culture, it is readily possible to determine cell size, either in the units micrograms per cell, or cell number per microgram of tissue. Obviously this is a measure of *average* cell size, but nevertheless it permits interesting conclusions to be drawn when the growth passes predominantly from growth by cell division into growth predominantly by cell expansion. With these aids we now know and may summarize much more about the growth of these tissue cultures under controlled conditions than has previously been published.

THE GROWTH CURVE OF TISSUE EXPLANTS UNDER CONTROLLED CONDITIONS

The growth curve in terms of fresh weight follows the familiar sigmoid pattern (Caplin and Steward, 1949). In terms of cell number, growth may be somewhat similarly represented and changes in average cell size as the growth proceeds may also be followed.

In the initial phases of the growth there is first a lag period during which little external growth occurs though preformed cells may enlarge. This is followed by a more or less prolonged period in which cell numbers rise exponentially with time and in which the growth is predominantly by cell division. During this period the average cell size of the culture as a whole steadily decreases so that the effect of any already mature cells is counteracted by the large increment of cell number and of cells that do not conspicuously enlarge. It is worth emphasizing how small are the cells typically produced in coco-nut milk (see *Table 1*). Even so, however, as the culture enlarges, some cells, particularly those internally, do enlarge and some areas occur in the tissue in which relatively large air spaces may be formed. (See Steward,

Caplin, and Shantz, 1955, Plate I). As *Figure 3* shows, it often happens that after about 10 days the average cell size begins to change in a way that clearly indicates that vacuolation and growth by cell enlargement now makes an appreciable contribution to the total growth of the tissue system.

In this system it is found that in the most rapid phase of growth the cell divisions must occur so that successive cell layers are formed approximately every 4 hours. This rapid rate is, however, not inconceivable, and it is quite clear from the large number of cells produced in these cultures that divisions must occur with this order of rapidity.

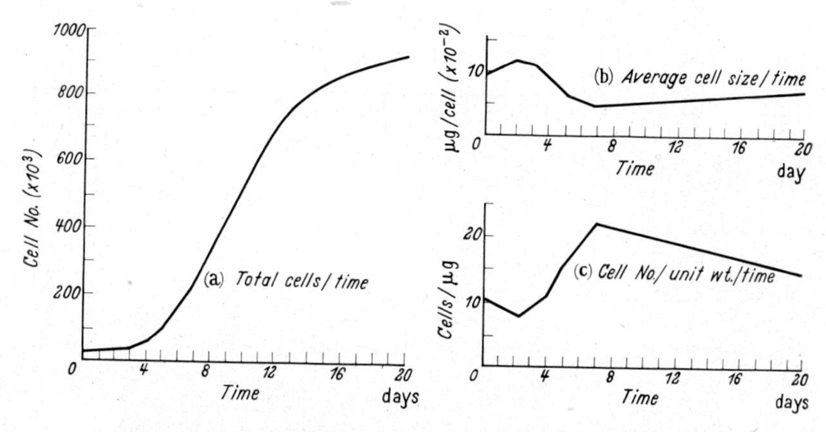

Figure 3. Growth of carrot explants in medium containing coco-nut milk.

It is, however, abundantly clear that the growth surrounding small inocula, producing successive layers at regular intervals of time, cannot proceed indefinitely or even for very long. Vacuolation and the formation of large air spaces certainly occurs in the larger cultures. It may be seen from *Figure 3* that in the example to which this relates, growth by cell enlargement also became evident after 10 days. Visual examination of the anatomy of the cultures clearly shows that as they become larger the familiar local centres of growth, or 'buds', appear on the surface as minute proliferations. Around the familiar lignified elements in these tissue cultures, local centres of growth organize that eventually may lead to roots (*Figure 1*(*b*), (*c*), and (*d*)). Thus, although the concept indicated above is clearly useful for the analysis of the earlier stages of growth, it is quite clear that it cannot be projected into the later periods, in which some parts of the culture may still indulge in random proliferation, while others are growing in a more organized fashion. Most of the work now to be described will, however, have concentrated upon the more early stages in the growth that is capable of more exact analysis in terms of cell number and of cell size.

CHEMICAL FACTORS IN GROWTH INDUCTION

The analysis, by these various means, of chemical factors involved in the induction and regulation of growth in these tissue cultures can best be developed in two parts.

In the first part it will be assumed that the cells are adequately furnished with the media which endow them, to their maximum extent, with the ability to grow by cell division. These media consist either of coco-nut milk or of some equivalent extract obtained from immature corn (*Zea*) or *Aesculus*, etc., supplemented as necessary by casein hydrolysate. The investigations will then concern the extent to which still further added substances either stimulate or depress the ability of the tissue to respond to these materials. In this connection the use of the potato tuber tissue is most effective because it does not grow to any appreciable extent in the basal medium, even though supplemented by the coco-nut milk medium, but it requires the further addition of substances like 2:4-D that are synergistically active with, and enable the tissue to respond to, coco-nut milk. In the second part of this more chemical discussion some observations will be made on the known chemical nature of those fractions of the coco-nut milk or similar extracts that have proved susceptible of isolation and, to some extent, of chemical identification.

Part II: The Chemical Nature of the Growth-Promoting Substances in Coco-nut Milk and Similar Fluids: The Present Position

SUBSTANCES INVOLVED SYNERGISTICALLY WITH COCO-NUT MILK IN A GROWTH RESPONSE OF POTATO TISSUE

MUCH work has been done up to the present time on the effects of 2:4-D or similar compounds in their synergistic effect, with coco-nut milk, on potato tuber tissue. First, to summarize briefly the work that has been published.

A number of other substances have been tested and some of these have been found to possess greater ability than 2:4-D to stimulate the growth of potato tissue which is normally induced by the combination of 2:4-D and coco-nut milk. This investigation was carried out jointly with the laboratory of Dr. R. L. Wain. Though maximum activity occurs at different concentrations for various substances, it is quite clear that some of these substances are more effective than is 2:4-D at its optimum concentration. This was particularly true in the case of 1:2:3:4-tetrahydro-1-naphthoic acid, as shown in Table 1 of the paper on this subject (Shantz, Steward, Smith, and Wain, 1955). However, from the standpoint of the chemistry of this phenomenon, the greatest interest attaches to investigations of those substances which are active in this synergistic combination and which are optically active. It was found in two examples of this kind, namely, α-(2-naphthoxy)propionic acid and α-(2:4:5-trichlorophenoxy)propionic acid, that the (+)-forms of these compounds were active in this growth stimulation, while their respective (—)-forms were not. Furthermore it was found, in striking confirmation of work previously published from Wain's laboratory (Smith, Wain, and Wightman, 1952), that the (—)-form was not merely inactive but tended to suppress the activity of the (+)-form in mixtures of the two. The contrast between the role of the optical enantiomorphs of the same substance clearly indicates that these chemically induced growth phenomena require to be explained by some very subtle properties of the causal molecules.

EFFECT OF ADDED SUBSTANCES ON GROWTH BY CELL DIVISION AND CELL ENLARGEMENT

It will be recalled that Wain and Wightman (1954) had found that the effect of the length of the aliphatic side-chain in a series of aryloxyalkylcarboxylic acids could be interpreted to mean that those substances that were active in certain growth tests also contained an even number of carbon atoms in the side-chain thus permitting the chain to be degraded by progressive *beta*-oxidation to a 2 carbon side-chain. In the attempt to determine the best series of substituted aryloxyalkylcarboxylic acids with which to carry out a similar trial on potato tissue in presence of coco-nut milk as an assay system, a considerable number of variously substituted phenoxyacetic acids were tested. The first result, however, was of a different and somewhat unexpected kind.

Relative increase in:

Fresh wt. = weight of cultures under treatment divided by weight of coco-nut milk controls.

Cell No. = Cell No. of cultures under treatment divided by Cell No. of coco-nut milk controls.

Cell size = Cell size of cultures under treatment divided by cell size of coco-nut milk controls.

Treatment:	R–O, Cl	R–O, Cl, Cl	R–O, Cl, Cl	R–O, Cl, Cl, Cl	R–O, CH_3, Cl	R–O, CH_3, Cl	R–O, Cl, CH_3, Cl	R–O, Cl, Cl
Rel. increase in fresh wt.	×6·9	10·2	5·0	12·0	14·2	4·4	11·4	4·4
Rel. increase in Cell No.	×2·9	2·8	1·8	2·0	2·9	1·8	1·6	0·8
Rel. increase in cell size	×2·3	3·8	2·7	6·0	4·6	2·5	6·7	5·5

Controls	*Weight per culture*	*Cell No. per culture*	*Cell size*	
			Cells per μg	*μg per cell*
Basal medium	2·7 mg	$1{\cdot}9 \times 10^3$	0·70	1·4
Basal medium + coco-nut milk	5·7 mg	$34{\cdot}6 \times 10^3$	6·1	0·16

Figure 4. The effects of various phenoxyacetic acids on growth of potato tuber tissue in media containing coco-nut milk

The tissues in question were submitted to the analysis of growth both in terms of fresh weight and in cell number, and this data furnished the first fairly extensive information relating the effect of chemical constitution to the stimulation by the synergist of growth by cell division and/or by cell enlargement. In *Figure 4* the effect of the various substances, as used at their best concentration of approximately 1–5 p.p.m., is shown in such a way that the structure may be related both to the increment of cell number in the presence of coco-nut milk and also to the change in average cell size, obtained by dividing the weight of the tissue by the number of cells it contained. The comparisons between structure of the added substance and growth are most easily made as follows.

By comparison with the initial tissue, or the controls in a medium free of the added substance, the relative increase due to the substance in either cell number or cell size may be simply calculated. The first important conclusion, evident from an inspection of *Figure 4*, is that the differing structures of the substituted phenoxyacetic acids markedly determine whether the substance acts predominantly on cell number, or on cell size. This is an important result because it immediately establishes the usefulness of this general technique in further work of this sort. It is obviously advantageous to be able to distinguish between the substances that stimulate cells to grow mainly because they stimulate division, and the substances which stimulate cells to grow mainly by causing them to enlarge. Furthermore, some substances, for example 2:4-D itself, have inherent in their molecules the ability to stimulate, in balanced degree, both of these processes.

Figure 4 shows clearly that to a greater or lesser degree all of the substances stimulated growth by cell enlargement when added to potato explants growing in basal medium plus coco-nut milk. However, the ability to cause the tissue to respond by cell division was conspicuously lacking in the case of that compound in which the number 4 ring-position remained unoccupied. Scanning these data, preliminary as they may well appear to be, leads to the following general conclusions:

1. For maximum ability to stimulate the growth of potato cells, which require the presence in the medium of the growth factors present in coco-nut milk, the aryloxyacetic acid used as a synergist should have the number 4 position occupied by chlorine. This being so, other groups may be added in the ring but cell division will still be stimulated. While there may be effects due to the proximity of other groups in the 3 or 5 position, the main effect is clear; namely, that it is the number 4 position that seems to hold the key to the stimulation of growth by cell division in this system.

2. In the absence of the 4 substituent, marked stimulation of growth by cell enlargement may occur, but in all these cases the position that seems to hold the key to the stimulation of growth by cell enlargement is the number 2 position. If the number 2 position is occupied, other groups may be inserted in the nucleus, leaving number 4 unoccupied, and growth by enlargement will still occur.

3. Clearly then, the prevalent role of 2:4-D as a growth-stimulating substance is susceptible to the following interpretation: One may assume that the tissue has inherent factors essential for growth by cell division or indeed cell enlargement, factors which are represented by the chemical substances present in coco-nut milk. The action of such a substance as 2:4-D can be explained through its ability to accentuate markedly the tendency to cell enlargement by virtue of the substituent in the 2-position and it may also accentuate cell division, to which the tissue may itself be somewhat prone, by virtue of substitution in the 4-position. These results are

quoted because they show the pattern of the kind of investigations that can be made, and are being made in this laboratory, rather than that they necessarily represent the ultimate and final conclusion for this type of study.

From this preliminary work, a given substituted aryl nucleus (2-methyl-4-chloro-) was selected so that a series of phenoxy acids could be studied to determine the effect of side chain length, following the type of investigation carried out by Wain and Wightman (1954) using entirely different kinds of assay systems. It must be confessed that there was some prior thought that again it might be found that there were parallels between the potato tuber system and the assay systems of Wain and Wightman. However, as the data show, marked ability of this series of substituted phenoxy acids to function in the potato tuber system by acting synergistically with coco-nut milk was only revealed by the first member of the series. Subsequent members of the series (see *Figure 5*) were but slightly active or actually toxic in their effects. Even here, however, there is some indication that the compounds with 4 and 6-carbon side chains were more effective than those with 3, 5, or 7 carbon atoms. The much greater effectiveness of the substituted caproic acid, with 5 methylene groups, finds a parallel with some recent work at Wye (Wightman, 1955).

		Average final fresh wt. of cultures	
		Tuber A	*Tuber* B
Controls:			
Basal medium + coco-nut milk		3·2 mg	7·8 mg
Basal medium + CM + 2:4-D		21·4 mg	30·9 mg
	n (*number of methylene groups*)		
Treatments:			
Basal medium	1	21·0	31·6
+	2	2·7	4·4
coco-nut milk	3	5·6	8·9
+	4	3·0	5·6
	5	11·8	11·7
$O-(CH_2)_n COOH$ (4-chloro-2-methylphenyl ring; CH_3, Cl)	6	6·6	7·8

Figure 5. Effect of side chain length on the ability of various ω-(4-chloro-2-methylphenoxy)alkyl-carboxylic acids to induce growth in potato tuber explants cultured in a medium containing coco-nut milk.

This type of investigation clearly needs to be extended. As this communication is being written, certain other examples of substituted phenoxy compounds are being tried to obtain further cases in which the 2 position is occupied and the 4 position is vacant. Similarly, investigations are being carried out with a considerable number of substituted aryloxy ethanols. The results of these investigations, which will be recorded in terms of fresh weight, cell number, and cell size, are not yet available but when they are they will add to the evidence documented above. The main point to be made, however, is this: The tissue culture method described is a precise system in which, under controlled conditions, growth may be regulated and subjected to quantitative study. It represents a useful assay tool to be applied in almost all cases where the chemical induction of growth in relation to molecular structure is in question. One of the challenges in this field is that different biological materials respond in different ways. There are few systems that cannot be reduced to a tissue culture type of growth with sufficient perseverance. When supplemented by the analysis of growth in terms of cell number and cell size, the system described is capable of yielding much information of a kind that would otherwise be difficult to obtain.

THE CHEMICAL NATURE OF SOME SUBSTANCES THAT INDUCE GROWTH BY CELL DIVISION

The final question to be asked and answered, so far as possible, is the chemical nature of the stimulus to growth which the coco-nut milk and similar extracts furnish.

It will be recalled that growth in the otherwise mature cells of carrot phloem, artichoke tissue, potato tuber tissue, etc., has been induced by the liquid endosperm that nourishes the immature embryo of the coco-nut; by the endosperm from immature (milk stage) fruits of corn (*Zea*); from such a nutrient material as the female gametophyte of *Ginkgo*; by extracts of the proliferating tissue of tumours induced by the crown gall organism; and by extracts of the loculus of the banana fruit in which, for genetic reasons, the cells do not remain quiescent but grow into a fleshy tissue. Doubtless these various extracts contain variants on the same essential theme. While the type of response induced may be the same, there is no reason to expect *a priori* that identical molecules are the causal agents. In only two types of material has enough investigation proceeded as yet to tell whether the same or different substances may be involved. These materials are the liquid endosperm of the coco-nut (*Cocos*) and the liquid contents of the immature fruit of the horse-chestnut (*Aesculus*). A brief summary will now be given of the present status of these investigations.

SUMMARY OF PREVIOUS WORK

Previous work had shown that the most useful way of isolating the growth-promoting activity of the coco-nut milk from the large number of other unessential constituents was a method based on precipitation by mercuric acetate from alcoholic solution. By this procedure a bulk isolation was carried out from a very large volume of original coco-nut milk. From this concentrate 3 crystalline active substances were obtained which could induce growth, almost as actively as whole coco-nut milk, at concentrations of the order of a few parts per million, though they required the simultaneous presence of casein hydrolysate. Thus the growth-promoting effects of the coco-nut milk consists of at least two essential parts:

(i) A non-specific part replaceable by casein hydrolysate.
(ii) A specific part which is replaceable, wholly or in part, by the isolated materials referred to.

These materials were designated in 1952 as Compounds A, B, and C (Shantz and Steward, 1952). Since then a further compound has been isolated in pure form and its activity similarly demonstrated. This substance is known as Compound F (Steward and Shantz, 1954). It should be mentioned here that a very large number of inactive substances have been fractionated and some of them identified in the coco-nut milk. A variety of amino-acids, including the recently discovered pipecolic acid, were isolated in pure form. None of these functions is the specific response in question.

The main new result to be reported is that Compound A has been re-isolated (Shantz and Steward, 1955) and definitely identified as the quite simple but rather unexpected substance, 1:3-diphenylurea. This has been established beyond any doubt by analysis, mixed melting point, completely matching infra-red (*Figure 6*) and ultra-violet absorption spectra, and all essential criteria for fastidious chemical identification. What is now quite clear is that the response of various strains and varieties of carrot tissue to the

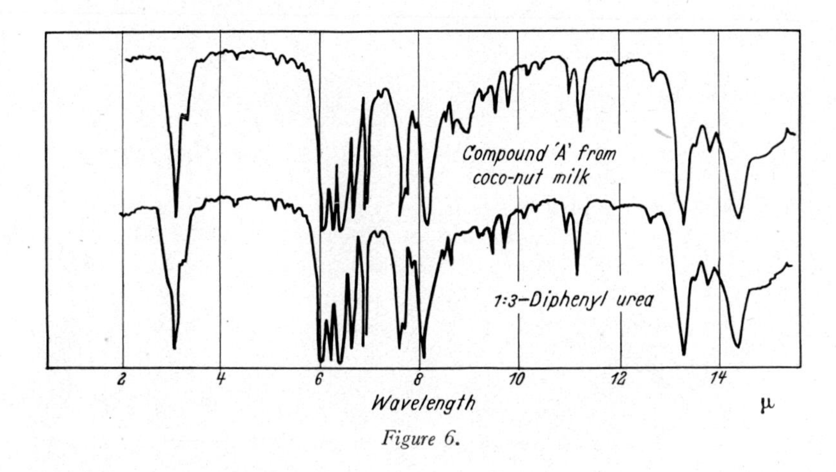

Figure 6.

diphenylurea is very variable. In some cases diphenylurea in presence of casein hydrolysate may replace, in large part, the activity of whole coco-nut milk, approaching at least 50 per cent of that activity. In other cases the activity is small by comparison. The total concentration of diphenylurea that could at its maximum be present in whole coco-nut milk is not large (order of 0·1 p.p.m.) and it is quite clear that the coco-nut milk owes its characteristic properties much more to the other substances that are present therein than to the diphenylurea. In fact the paper in which this new discovery has been communicated still makes cautious reservations because the isolation of a relatively small amount of a substance like diphenylurea from a very large amount of biological material requiring the use of large amounts of reagents does raise the question whether the substance was present as such in the coco-nut milk of the intact nut. While there is every reason to believe that diphenylurea did so occur, the fact still remains that this constitutes the first known case of the isolation from plants of a carbanilide. Be that as it may, it is still a matter of great interest that here we have the first case of the chemical identification of an active substance from coco-nut milk, even though the total growth response produced by that substance may not be as dramatic as that due to the coco-nut milk as a whole.

The remaining substances, Compounds B, C, and F, still await complete chemical identification. It may, however, be stated that they are all cyclic nitrogen compounds though none of them contain the requisite amount of nitrogen to resemble even remotely the substance kinetin, recently described by Skoog and his associates, and which appears to originate when nucleic acids are autoclaved, or aged (Miller *et al.*, 1955a). The structure of kinetin, now known to be 6-furfurylaminopurine (Miller *et al.*, 1955b) does not remotely resemble diphenylurea, nor can it remotely resemble the other substances B, C, and F. The substance kinetin is active in causing cell division in tobacco callus tissue at very great dilutions. Direct comparisons of the activity of kinetin† with coco-nut milk and some fractions thereof and with other substances known to stimulate cell division in the tissue culture system are being made. Preliminary results show that kinetin in presence of indoleacetic acid unquestionably has activity toward carrot tissue under our conditions. However, the growth so induced is much less than that caused by coco-nut milk whether this is measured by fresh weight or cell division. The visible effect of kinetin is accentuated by its ability to form small internal cells in the otherwise large cells of tobacco callus. Though definitely active toward carrot tissue in culture, it has proved almost inactive toward a strain of artichoke tuber tissue. These results are shown by the following extract from the data available.

	Carrot explants (18 *days at* 24·5°*C*)			*Artichoke explants* (19 *days at* 24·5°*C*)		
	Wt. (*mg*)	*Cell No.* (*units* × 10^3)	*Cell size* (μg/*cell*)	*Wt.* (*mg*)	*Cell No.* (*units* × 10^3)	*Cell size* (μg/*cell*)
Basal medium	8·2	33·1	0·25	4·2	11·7	0·36
Basal medium + coco-nut milk	89·6	973	0·09	53·6	290	0·19
Basal medium + IAA + kinetin†	12·5	222	0·06	8·0	32·4	0·24

† Indoleacetic acid and kinetin applied separately do not give this characteristic effect.

There is obviously, therefore, no single molecule that unlocks the door of cell division for all cells. This is hardly to be expected. Many such molecules have this property. Some may be of natural origin and these are of the greatest interest; many more may be found as a result of tests on synthetic substances. Indeed, by chance, a very potent substance capable of inducing growth by cell division in carrot and artichoke tissue has been found in 2-benzthiazolyloxyacetic acid.

The effects of diphenylurea in stimulating growth by cell division in carrot, artichoke, and potato tissue are illustrated in *Tables 1* and *2*. The effect of 2-benzthiazolyloxyacetic acid on both carrot and artichoke tissue are shown in *Figure 7*. It can be seen that the 2-benzthiazolyloxyacetic acid even exceeded the activity of whole coco-nut milk when applied to a given population of artichoke explants grown on agar medium. It is also evident

† The kinetin was kindly supplied by Dr. F. Skoog and his colleagues at the University of Wisconsin.

Table 1

Effect of 1:3-*diphenyl urea* (*DPU*) *on growth of plant tissue cultures*
(*a*) *Carrot tissue—grown* 17 *days at* 24°C

Treatment	*Fresh wt. in mg* B	*Fresh wt. in mg* C	*Cell No.* (×10³) B	*Cell No.* (×10³) C	*Cells per μg* B	*Cells per μg* C
Basal medium	7·2	4·6	45·2	28·8	6·3	6·4
Basal medium+2·0 p.p.m. DPU	9·4	7·5	50·2	49·0	5·4	6·5
Basal medium+casein hydrolysate	29·4	64·8	201·4	536·1	6·8	8·8
Basal medium+casein hydrolysate +2·0 p.p.m. DPU	56·8	108·5	508·6	1042·7	8·9	9·7
Basal medium+casein hydrolysate +10% coco-nut milk	294·4	323·1	2662·8	2692·5	9·1	8·3

(*b*) *Artichoke tissue—grown* 29 *days at* 24°C

Treatment	*Fresh wt. in mg*	*Cell No.* (×10³)	*Cells per μg*
Basal medium+casein hydrolysate	6·0	10·7	1·9
Basal medium+0·08 p.p.m. DPU	12·0	63·2	4·8

Table 2

Effect of 1:3-*diphenyl urea* (*DPU*) *on growth of potato explants in liquid media containing* 2:4-*D and casein hydrolysate*

Explants from potato tuber—33 *days growth at* 24°C

2:4-D applied at 1·0 p.p.m. — Casein hydrolysate applied at 0·05%.
DPU applied at 2·0 p.p.m. — Coco-nut milk (CM) applied at 10% by vol.

Treatment	*Fresh wt. per culture*	
	No casein hydrolysate	*Plus casein hydrolysate*
Basal medium	1·92	2·2
Basal medium+2:4-D	1·72	2·64
Basal medium+2:4-D+DPU	1·80	8·55
Basal medium+2:4-D+CM	20·28	46·80

(*Table 3*) that the predominant effect of this substance is to stimulate cell division with the formation of a very large number of very small cells. By comparison, the effect of the naturally occurring substance diphenylurea is not conspicuously large (*Table 1*) though it is of a similar kind.

The most dramatic development in the current work, however, was the recording of the very first experiment in which an extract from a dicotyledonous fruit proved effective in the carrot assay system. The fluid used was

A *B* *C* *D* *E*

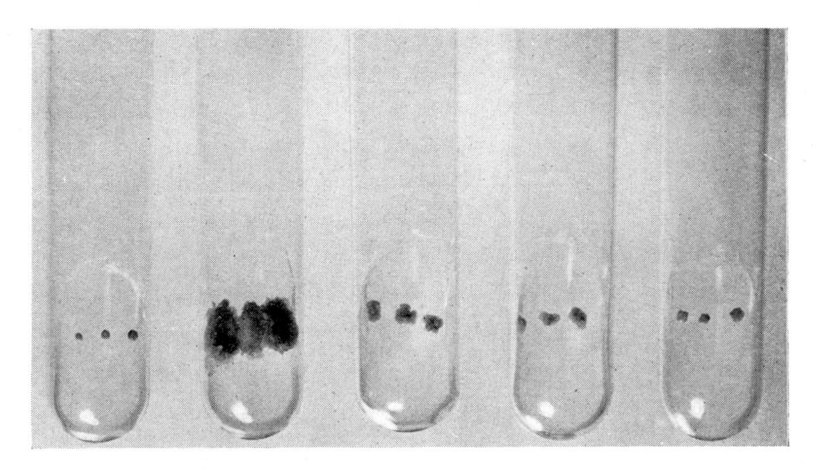

Figure 7(*a*). *Effects of* 2-*benzthiazolyloxyacetic acid* (*BTOA*) *on growth of carrot root explants.*
A = *Basal medium*+*casein hydrolysate* (0·05 *per cent*)
B = *Basal medium*+*casein hydrolysate*+*coco-nut milk* (10 *per cent*)
C = *Basal medium*+*casein hydrolysate*+*BTOA at* 10·0 *p.p.m.*
D = *Basal medium*+*casein hydrolysate*+*BTOA at* 2·0 *p.p.m.*
E = *Basal medium*+*casein hydrolysate*+*BTOA at* 0·4 *p.p.m.*

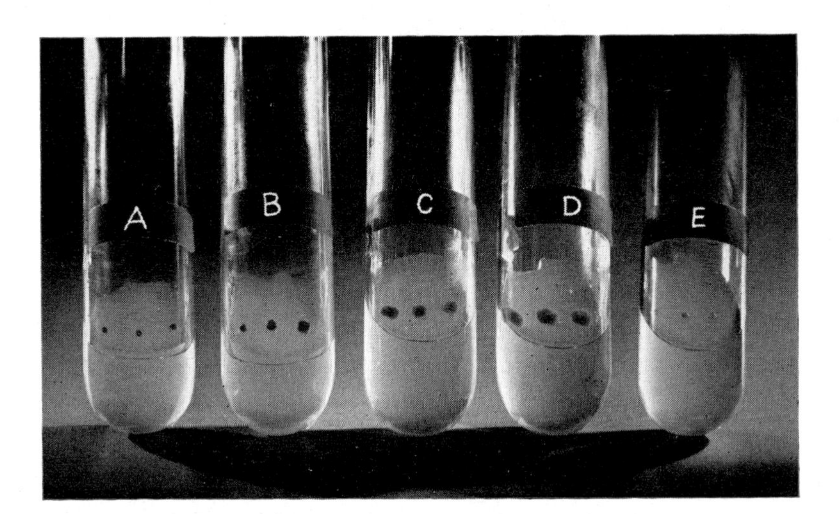

Figure 7(*b*). *Effects of* 2-*benzthiazolyloxyacetic acid* (*BTOA*) *on growth of explants from Jerusalem artichoke tuber.*
A = *Basal medium*+*casein hydrolysate* (0·05 *per cent*).
B = *Basal medium*+*casein hydrolysate*+*coco-nut milk* (10 *per cent*).
C = *Basal medium*+*casein hydrolysate*+*BTOA at* 10·0 *p.p.m.*
D = *Basal medium*+*casein hydrolysate*+*BTOA at* 2·0 *p.p.m.*
E = *Basal medium*+*casein hydrolysate*+*BTOA at* 0·4 *p.p.m.*

Table 3

Effects of 2-benzthiazolyloxyacetic acid (BTOA) on the growth of plant tissue cultures

(*a*) *Carrot root tissue*

Treatment	*Weight per culture in mg*	*Cells per culture* $\times 10^3$	*Cells per* μg
Original explants	3·3	34·7	10·5
Basal medium (BM)+casein hydrolysate (CH)	10·3	33·2	3·2
BM+CH+coco-nut milk (10%)	1046·3	4590·4	4·4
BM+CH+BTOA at 10·0 p.p.m.	81·1	548·2	6·8
BM+CH+BTOA at 2·0 p.p.m.	59·1	225·5	3·8
BM+CH+BTOA at 0·4 p.p.m.	19·5	66·1	3·4

(*b*) *Jerusalem artichoke tuber tissue*

Treatment	*Weight per culture in mg*	*Cells per culture* $\times 10^3$	*Cells per* μg
Original explants	3·2	10·0	3·2
BM+CH	6·5	7·1	1·1
BM+CH+coco-nut milk (10%)	22·1	70·5	3·2
BM+CH+BTOA at 10·0 p.p.m.	52·2	432·7	8·3
BM+CH+BTOA at 2·0 p.p.m.	114·5	1084·1	9·5
BM+CH+BTOA at 0·4 p.p.m.	6·5	16·2	2·5

obtained from the immature fruit of the walnut. By analogy with this system an examination was made of the immature fruit of the horse-chestnut. This data was reported first to the American Society of Plant Physiologists at the Gainesville meeting in 1954. It is now apparent that in the immature fruit of the horse-chestnut there occurs an extremely active growth-promoting effect comparable to that produced by coco-nut milk. *Figure 8* shows that carrot explants can be made to grow in this way in a fashion comparable to that which occurs with coco-nut milk.

This material has been collected on a relatively large scale and has been fractionated by methods somewhat different from the first ones used in the isolations of active substances from coco-nut milk. The present trend in this laboratory has been to use techniques in which heavy metal precipitation could be avoided in the attempt to isolate substances which are active in the carrot tissue assay system and which have some of the ultra-violet absorption properties that were thought, from the examinations of Compounds A, B, C, etc., to be a guide to the active growth-promoting principles. By proceeding in this general way and making use of an automatic Craig–Post liquid–liquid separator, much progress has been made.

The important developments from all this work may be briefly summarized as follows: We now know conclusively that active growth-promoting qualities reside in substances present in coco-nut milk and in *Aesculus* extracts, and presumably occur in all such similar materials, which are *nitrogen free*. This surprising result has led to the recognition that the general class of substances to which some of these materials belong is the leucoanthocyanins.

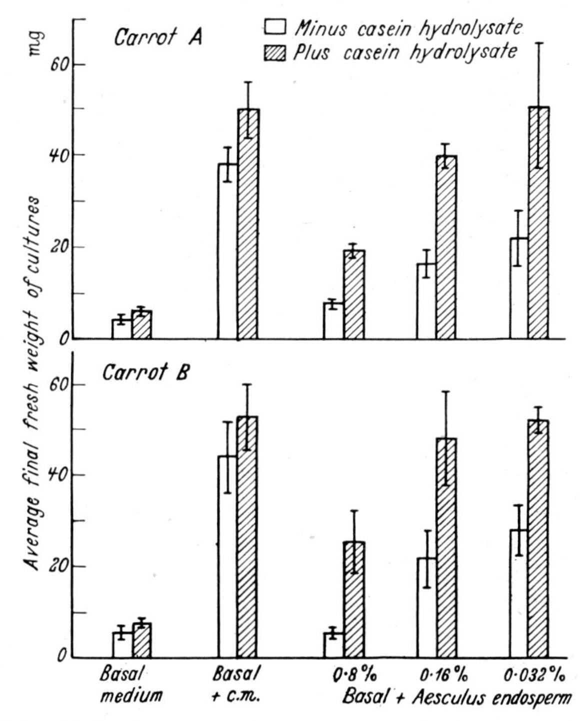

Figure 8. Effect of liquid endosperm from immature fruits of Aesculus woerlitzensis *on the growth of carrot phloem explants, compared with growth in basal medium and in basal medium plus* 10 *per cent coco-nut milk.*

The reasons for arriving at this conclusion are briefly summarized, although the full data cannot be recorded but will be reserved for the time at which one or more of these substances is unequivocally and finally identified. It may, however, be stated clearly that in the immature *Aesculus* fruit a large part of the growth-promoting activity can be ascribed to a leucoanthocyanin which may be a complex monoglucoside with one of the general chemical formulae indicated below, based on structures proposed by (*a*) Robinson and Robinson (1933), and (*b*) Swain

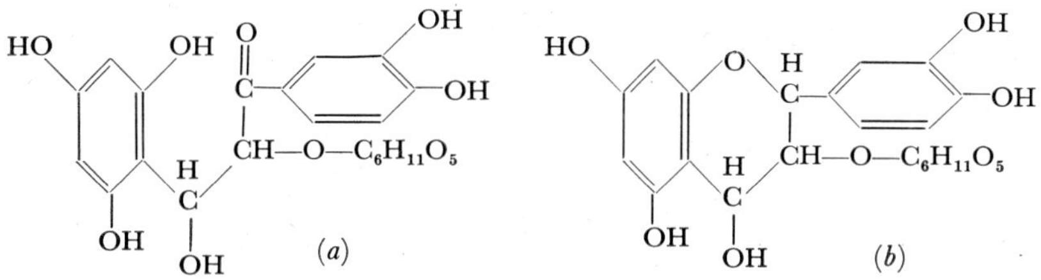

HO OH O OH C OH H CH—O—$C_6H_{11}O_5$ C OH OH (*a*)

HO O H OH C OH H CH—O—$C_6H_{11}O_5$ C OH OH (*b*)

Figure 9. Structure of Leucocyanidin monoglucoside suggested by (*a*) *Robinson and Robinson* (1933) (*b*) *Swain* (1954).

Reliance has to be placed on the known structure of certain related compounds to assign the substituent groups to appropriate positions, but with this latitude one can say definitely that the chemical analysis of the product as isolated, the presence of the monoglucoside group, and the analysis of the pigment which results when the glucose is split off and the cyanidin-like pigment is produced in the form of its oxonium chloride, are all consistent with this type of structure (*Figure 9*).

This general discovery seems to open a new door in the study of the chemical induction of growth. Hitherto, the physiological role of these complex biochemical constituents, the anthocyanins and their precursors the leucoanthocyanins, has been somewhat obscure. When such a function as the ability to induce growth by cell division when added to otherwise complete nutrient media to which mature cells are exposed is attributed to a type of compound such as this, it is obvious that they may have important roles to play. Examinations have therefore been made of a number of other extracted materials (such as anthocyanins and flavanol glucosides) furnished to us by various investigators but having chemical properties somewhat similar to the structural formulae indicated above. Sufficient activity has been detected in compounds of this kind to indicate that we are proceeding along the right general track.

The conclusion of this general account must therefore be as follows:

To undergo growth by cell division and cell enlargement, plant cells obviously require a variety of chemical substances that perform quite different roles: water itself for enlargement, nutrients both inorganic and organic, vitamins and the essential co-factors of vitamin-like systems. Many or all of these may be specified. In addition, however, there still seem to be requirements for additional substances which determine whether the cell can fully exploit its ability to enlarge without division or to divide without enlargement. In balanced degree both processes may occur simultaneously. The presence of one substance may induce one type of growth to the exclusion of another, as for example the predominant effect of indoleacetic acid on cell enlargement. The effect of other types of substances, such as those found in coco-nut milk, may induce cell division to the exclusion of cell enlargement. Almost certainly both types of growth-promoting materials, the auxin-like substances of which indoleacetic acid is the predominant natural example, or the cell division-promoting substances such as those found in coco-nut milk and related materials, represent a group or family of substances rather than single unique individuals. The baffling thing is that the chemical properties which determine the ability of the substance to promote growth by cell division are so obscure that it is difficult to see what substances like diphenylurea, the quite different molecules of Compounds B, C, and F from coco-nut milk, and 2-benzthiazolyloxyacetic acid, with the further addition of the substance kinetin, all may have in common. This becomes even more difficult, however, when this activity is extended in its range by the fact that leucoanthocyanin-like substances, nitrogen-free, are found to be active and even very potent.

It is obviously too soon to state what any or all of these molecules may have in common. The only idea that has already occurred is that, in greater or lesser degree, many of these substances might exert their activity by their ability to chelate or affect chelation of heavy metals. Be that as it may, the main point of this communication is achieved when it is recognized, first of all, that these properties reside in a variety of naturally-occurring substances which may have many synthetic parallels, and, second, that in the further elucidation of the relationship between structure and these functions the use of the tissue culture systems, combined with methods that evaluate growth in terms of both cell division and cell enlargement, offer a most fruitful approach to these interesting problems.

ACKNOWLEDGEMENTS

The authors wish to acknowledge the help of Miss K. Mears with the sterile cultures and of Miss J. Smith with the cell counts.

The work has been supported by grants from the National Cancer Institute of the U.S. Department of Health, Education, and Welfare.

REFERENCES

Brown, R., and Rickless, P. (1949). A new method for the study of cell division and cell extension with some preliminary observations on the effect of temperature and of nutrients. *Proc. Roy. Soc.* **B136,** 110.

Caplin, S. M. (1947). Growth and morphology of tobacco tissue cultures *in vitro. Bot. Gaz.* **108,** 379.

Caplin, S. M., and Steward, F. C. (1948). Effect of coconut milk on the growth of explants from carrot root. *Science,* **108,** 655.

Caplin, S. M., and Steward, F. C. (1949). A technique for the controlled growth of excised plant tissue in liquid media under aseptic conditions. *Nature,* **163,** 920.

Fawcett, C. H., Ingram, J. M. A., and Wain, R. L. (1952). β-oxidation of ω-phenoxyalkylcarboxylic acid in the flax plant. *Nature,* **170,** 887.

Fitting, H. (1910). Weitere entwicklungsphysiologische Untersuchungen an Orchideenblüten. *Z. Bot.* **2,** 225.

Heller, R. (1953). Recherches sur la nutrition minerale des tissus végétaux cultivés *in vitro.* Masson, Paris (Thesis, Faculty of Science, Paris).

Miller, C. O., Skoog, F., Saltza, M. H. von, and Strong, F. M. (1955a). Kinetin, a cell division factor from DNA. *J. Amer. chem. Soc.* **77,** 1392.

Miller, C. O., Skoog, F., Okumura, F. S., Saltza, M. H. von, and Strong, F. M. (1955b). Structure and synthesis of kinetin. *J. Amer. chem. Soc.* **77,** 2662.

Robinson, G. M., and Robinson, R. (1933). A survey of anthocyanins. III. Distribution of leuco-anthocyanins. *Biochem. J.* **27,** 206.

Shantz, E. M., and Steward, F. C. (1952). Coconut milk factor: the growth-promoting substances in coconut milk. *J. Amer. chem. Soc.* **74,** 6133.

Shantz, E. M., and Steward, F. C. (1955). The identification of compound A from coconut milk as 1:3-diphenylurea. *J. Amer. chem. Soc.* **77,** 6351.

Shantz, E. M., Steward, F. C., Smith, M. S., and Wain, R. L. (1955). Investigations on the growth and metabolism of plant cells. VI. Growth of potato tuber tissue in culture: the synergistic action of coconut milk and some synthetic growth-regulating substances. *Ann. Bot., Lond.* (N.S.), **19,** 49.

Smith, M. S., Wain, R. L., and Wightman, F. (1952). Studies on plant growth-regulating substances. V. Steric factors in relation to mode of action of certain aryloxyalkylcarboxylic acids. *Ann. appl. Biol.* **39,** 295.

Steward, F. C., and Caplin, S. M. (1951). A tissue culture from potato tuber: the synergistic action of 2,4-D and coconut milk. *Science,* **113,** 518.

Steward, F. C., and Caplin, S. M. (1952). Investigations on growth and metabolism of plant cells. III. Evidence for growth inhibitors in certain mature tissues. *Ann. Bot., Lond.* (N.S.), **16,** 477.

Steward, F. C., Caplin, S. M., and Millar, F. K. (1952). Investigations on growth and metabolism of plant cells. I. New techniques for the investigation of metabolism, nutrition, and growth in undifferentiated cells. *Ann. Bot., Lond.* (N.S.), **16,** 58.

Steward, F. C., Caplin, S. M., and Shantz, E. M. (1955). Investigations on growth and metabolism of plant cells. V. Tumorous growth in relation to growth factors of the type found in coconut. *Ann. Bot., Lond.* (N.S.), **19,** 29.

Steward, F. C., and Shantz, E. M. (1954). The growth of carrot tissue explants and its relation to the growth factors in coconut milk. II. The growth-promoting properties of coconut milk for plant tissue cultures. *Année biol.* **30,** 399.

Steward, F. C., and Simmonds, N. W. (1954). Growth-promoting substances in the ovary and immature fruit of the banana. *Nature,* **173,** 1083.

Swain, T. (1954). Leucocyanidin. *Chem. & Ind.* 1144.

Wain, R. L. (1953). Plant growth substances. *Roy. Inst. Chem. Monograph No. 2.*

Wain, R. L., and Wightman, F. (1954). The growth-regulating activity of certain ω-substituted alkyl carboxylic acids in relation to their β-oxidation within the plant. *Proc. Roy. Soc.* **B142,** 525.

White, P. R. (1943). *A handbook of plant tissue culture.* Jaques Cattell Press, Lancaster, Pa.

Wightman, F. (1955). Private communication.

THE DEGRADATION OF CERTAIN PHENOXY ACIDS, AMIDES, AND NITRILES WITHIN PLANT TISSUES†

C. H. Fawcett, H. F. Taylor, R. L. Wain, and F. Wightman
Agricultural Research Council Unit on Plant Growth Substances and Systemic Fungicides, Wye College, University of London

Recent work at Wye has been concerned with the β-oxidation of ω-phenoxyalkanecarboxylic acids within plant tissues. It had previously been shown that an alternation in growth-regulating activity might operate in an homologous series of ω-aryl- or ω-aryloxy-alkanecarboxylic acids as the side-chain length increased (Grace, 1939; Synerholm and Zimmerman, 1947). Such behaviour was ascribed by Synerholm and Zimmerman to the degradation of the side-chain by β-oxidation. On this basis, only the acetic derivative and its alternate homologues would be expected to show activity. Further biological evidence for the β-oxidation hypothesis was provided by Fawcett, Ingram, and Wain (1954) and by Wain and Wightman (1954), who showed that only alternate members of the ω-(4-chlorophenoxy)alkanecarboxylic acids were active in the pea curvature and wheat cylinder tests. Again, Luckwill and Woodcock (1955) have recently shown that a similar alternation operates in regard to the capacity of ω-(2-naphthoxy)alkanecarboxylic acids to induce parthenocarpic development of tomato ovaries.

Chemical evidence that β-oxidation can occur within plant tissues has been obtained at Wye. In our first experiments using flax seedlings, members of the homologous series of ω-phenoxyalkanecarboxylic acids, $C_6H_5O(CH_2)_nCOOH$ with $n = 1$ to 10, were supplied to flax seedlings through their roots. After a suitable interval to allow breakdown of the acids to occur, the plants were steam distilled and phenol in the steam distillate estimated colorimetrically. It was found that those acids with an even number of side-chain methylene groups ($n = 2$, 4, 6, 8, and 10) gave rise to appreciable quantities of phenol, e.g.

$$\underset{n=2}{C_6H_5OCH_2CH_2COOH} \rightarrow [C_6H_5OCOCH_2COOH] \rightarrow [C_6H_5OCOOH] \rightarrow \underset{\text{phenol}}{C_6H_5OH}$$

The alternate higher homologues ($n = 4$, 6, 8, 10) could also yield phenol by repeated β-oxidation.

The acids with $n = 1$, 3, 5, and 7, on the other hand, yielded only traces of phenol, which is in agreement with the fact that phenoxyacetic acid is the expected end product from these compounds (Fawcett *et al.*, 1954), e.g.

$$\underset{n=3}{C_6H_5OCH_2CH_2CH_2COOH} \rightarrow [C_6H_5OCH_2COCH_2COOH] \rightarrow \underset{\text{phenoxyacetic acid}}{C_6H_5OCH_2COOH}$$

† This paper was read at the Conference by R. L. Wain.

These results, then, are fully consistent with the view that the side-chain of these acids is degraded within the flax plant by β-oxidation. The 9-phenoxy-nonane-1-carboxylic acid ($n = 9$) showed exceptional behaviour in yielding phenol, a result which can be explained by side-chain degradation involving ω-oxidation as follows:

$$\underset{n=9}{C_6H_5OCH_2(CH_2)_8COOH} \rightarrow [C_6H_5OCO(CH_2)_8COOH] \xrightarrow{H_2O} \underset{\text{phenol}}{C_6H_5OH}$$

This finding for the nonane acid correlates with the results of animal metabolism studies (Verkade and Lee, 1934; Breusch, 1948).

Further chemical evidence that β-oxidation can occur in plants has been provided by recent work on the metabolism of aryloxy-acids in pea-stem tissue. We have found that phenoxyheptanoic acid ($n = 6$) is degraded more readily than phenoxyvaleric acid ($n = 4$) to phenoxypropionic acid ($n = 2$), a result which correlates with the growth-regulating activity shown by these compounds in the pea test (Fawcett *et. al.*, 1954). Furthermore, in these experiments the heptanoic and valeric derivatives were converted to phenol more readily than the propionic analogue.

In another aspect of this work, three homologous series of chloro-substituted phenoxy acids with chlorine substituents in the 4-, 2:4-, and 2:4:5- positions respectively, and each consisting of the first six members, were examined in the wheat cylinder and pea curvature tests (Wain and Wightman, 1954). In the former test, all series showed a typical alternation in activity which was consistent with the β-oxidation hypothesis. In the pea test, however, although this alternation was shown in two series, in the 2:4:5-trichloro-phenoxy series only the acetic derivative was active. Also in this investigation, by using chromatographic and biological methods, clear evidence was obtained that 2:4:5-trichlorophenoxyacetic acid was produced by treating the corresponding butyric and caproic acids with wheat coleoptile tissue. The most important conclusion from this work (Wain and Wightman, 1954) was that whereas different types of plant tissue may all possess β-oxidase enzyme systems, whether or not these are able to degrade the side chain of specific ω-phenoxyalkanecarboxylic acids depends on the nature and position of the nuclear substituents present. Such considerations have led logically to developments in the field of selective toxicity (Wain, 1955).

Evidence that β-oxidation of the side chain of ω-(1-naphthyl)alkanecarboxylic acids can occur in plant tissues has been obtained at Wye. The effect on activity of substituting alkyl groups into the α- or β- positions of the side chain of certain of these compounds was also investigated and found to be consistent with the concept of β-oxidation (Wain and Wightman, 1954).

More recently, a detailed study has been undertaken of the influence of ring substitution in ω-phenoxyalkanecarboxylic acids on the β-oxidation of these compounds in different plant tissues. This work, to which Miss M. B. Pybus and Miss R. M. Pascal have also contributed, has involved the synthesis of the first six members of each of fifteen homologous series of phenoxy acids. The results, which will be published in full elsewhere, provide further evidence that β-oxidase enzyme systems are present in wheat coleoptile and pea stem tissues and that these enzymes can show considerable substrate specificity. In this connection, they confirm and extend earlier findings (Wain, 1955) that substituents in certain positions of the nucleus of ω-phenoxyalkanecarboxylic acids can hinder β-oxidation within specific plant tissues (see *Table 1*).

Table 1

Alternation in activity shown by homologous series of substituted ω-phenoxyalkanecarboxylic acids X–C_6H_4–$O(CH_2)_nCOOH$ *in three biological tests*

Ring substituents	Test		
	Wheat cylinder	*Pea curvature*	*Tomato epinasty*
4-Chloro-	Yes	Yes	Yes
2:4-Dichloro-	Yes	Yes	Yes
2-Methyl-4-chloro-	Yes	Yes	Yes
3:4-Dichloro-	Yes	Yes	Yes
3-Methyl-4-chloro-	Yes	Yes	Yes
2:4:5-Trichloro-	Yes	No	No
2:4-Dichloro-5-methyl-	Yes	No	No
2:5-Dichloro-	Yes	No	No
2-Methyl-5-chloro-	Yes	No	No

In continuing this work on the β-oxidation of ω-phenoxyalkanecarboxylic acid in plants, it was logical to study growth-regulating activity in the corresponding homologous series of amides and nitriles. Accordingly, the ω-(2:4-dichlorophenoxy)-series $Cl_2C_6H_3O(CH_2)_nCONH_2$ and $Cl_2C_6H_3O(CH_2)_nCN$, with $n = 1$ to 6, were synthesized and examined in the wheat cylinder and pea curvature tests, the homologous series of acids being also included. The typical alternation in the acid series which we have already recorded (Wain and Wightman, 1954) was again evident in both tests. The results are recorded in *Figures 1* and *2*. Alternation was also shown in both tests by the amide series (*Figures 3* and *2*) and this is explicable in terms of hydrolysis of amide to acid ($—CONH_2 \rightarrow —COOH$) followed by β-oxidation. The inactivity of all nitriles except the acetonitrile in the pea test (*Figure 4*), however, indicates that a similar hydrolysis of the —CN grouping to —COOH does not readily occur with these higher homologues in pea tissue. Furthermore, whereas such hydrolysis followed by β-oxidation would explain the activity of alternate homologues of 2:4-dichlorophenoxyacetonitrile in the wheat test, no such explanation is valid for the activity shown by other members of this series (*Figure 2*).

To elucidate these problems it was decided to expose solutions of all these acids, amides, and nitriles separately to wheat and pea tissues and then study the compounds present by paper chromatography. As these results will be presented in detail elsewhere, they will be given only briefly here.

The procedure adopted was to run ether extracts of the treated solutions in the descending manner with *n*-butanol/ammonia/water (100:3:18) as solvent for 15 hours at 20°C. After drying, the papers were divided horizontally into ten equal segments representing R_f 0–0·1, 0·1–0·2, 0·2–0·3, etc.

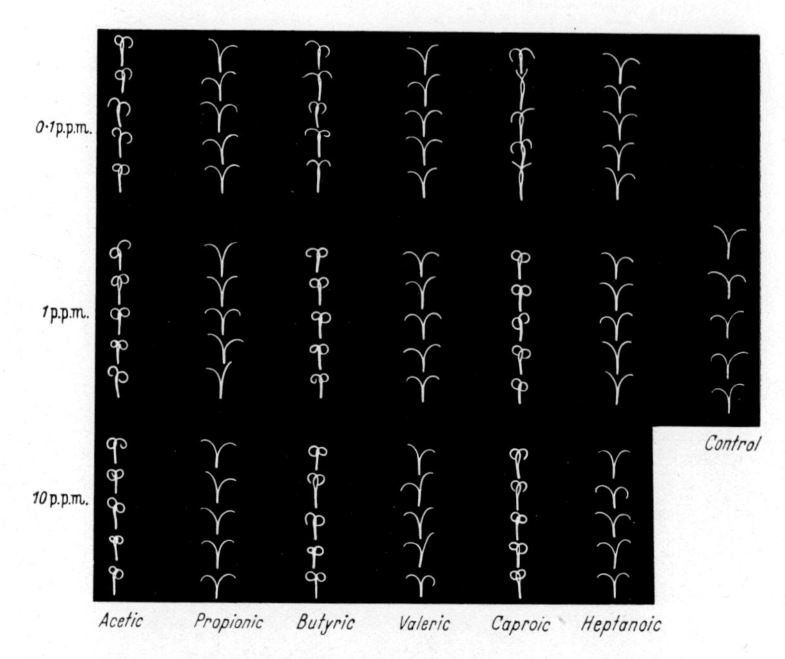

Figure 1. Activities of ω-(2:4-dichlorophenoxy)alkanecarboxylic acids in the pea curvature test.

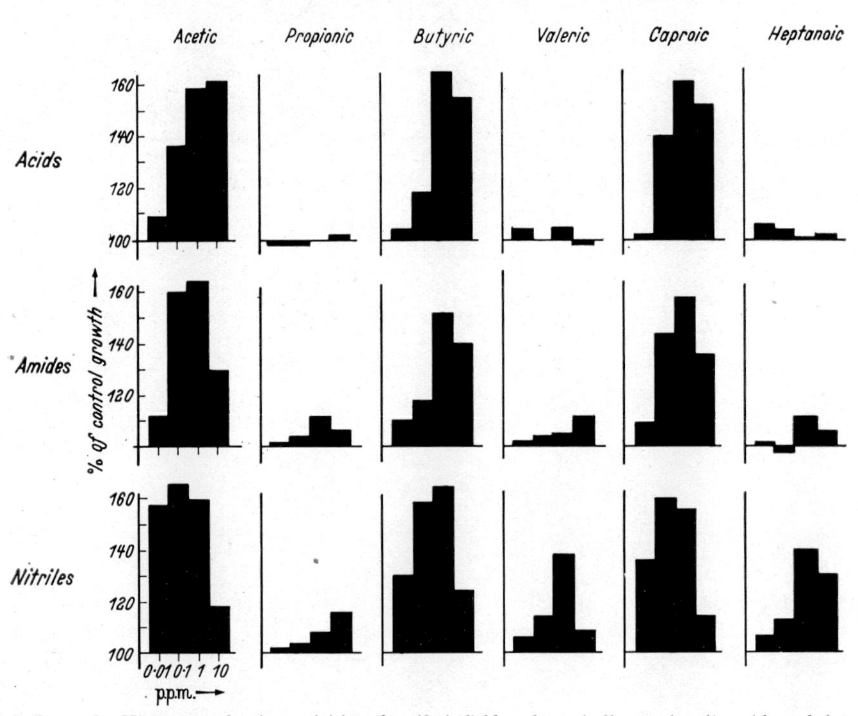

Figure 2. Histograms showing activities of ω-(2:4-dichlorophenoxy)alkanecarboxylic acids and their corresponding amides and nitriles in the wheat cylinder test.

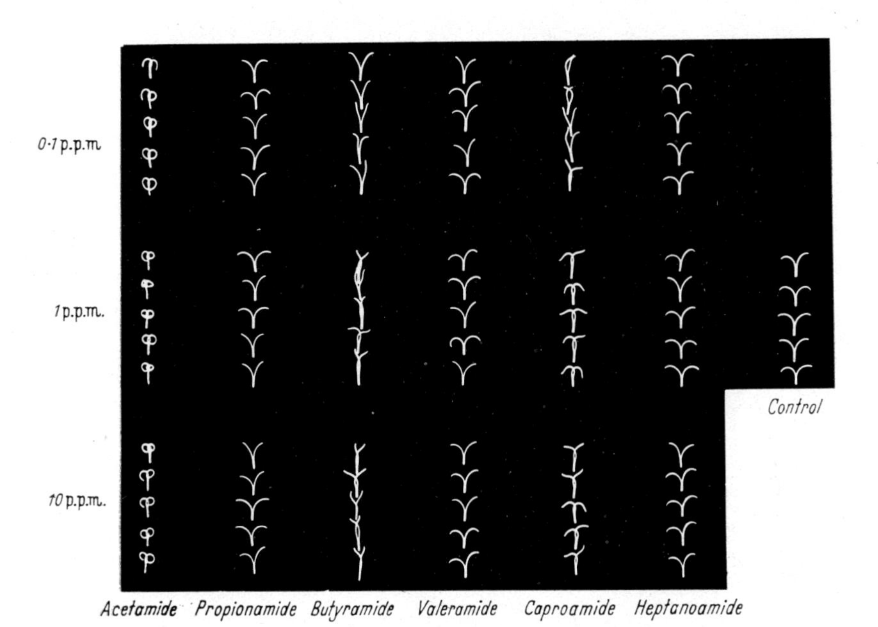

Figure 3. Activities of ω-(2:4-dichlorophenoxy)alkanecarbonamides in the pea curvature test.

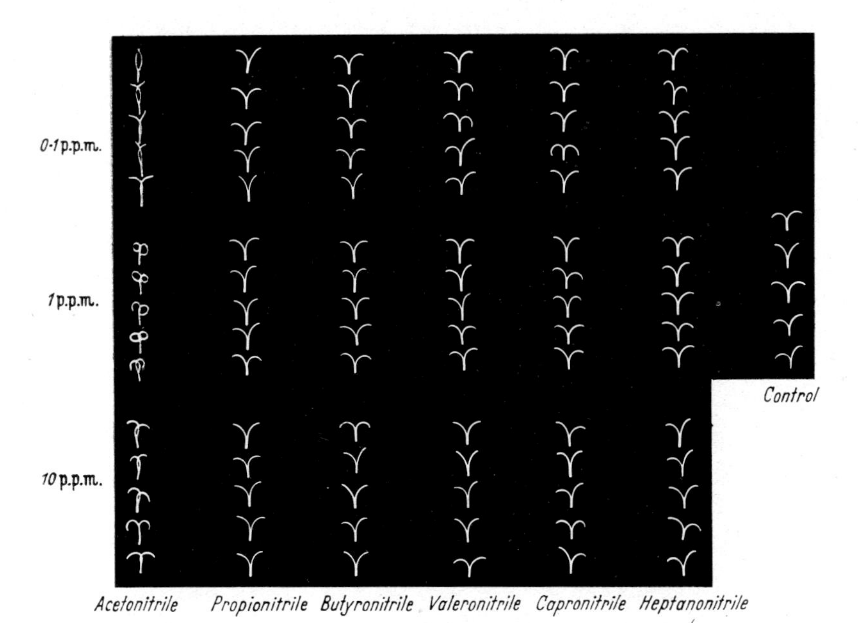

Figure 4. Activities of ω-(2:4-dichlorophenoxy)alkanenitriles in the pea curvature test.

These were placed in water and a biological assay was carried out using either wheat coleoptile sections or split pea stem segments. Authentic compounds were run for comparison in all experiments.

ω-(2:4-dichlorophenoxy)alkanecarboxylic acids

Whether pretreated with wheat or with pea tissue, assessment of the chromatogram segments in both the wheat and pea tests revealed the formation of 2:4-dichlorophenoxyacetic acid (2:4-D) (R_f 0·35–0·45) from the butyric and caproic acids ($n = 3$ and 5), but not from the propionic, valeric, and heptanoic acids ($n = 2$, 4, and 6). These results are readily explicable on the basis of β-oxidation.

ω-(2:4-dichlorophenoxy)alkanecarbonamides

The chromatograms obtained from the first, third, and fifth members of the series ($n = 1, 3, 5$) pretreated with wheat or pea tissue showed two peaks of activity both with the wheat and the pea bio-assay methods. The first of these peaks (R_f 0·35–0·45) represented 2:4-D, and the second, residual amide (R_f 0·75–0·85), present as such on the paper but presumably converted to 2:4-D in the bio-assay. Since other homologues ($n = 2, 4, 6$) yielded no 2:4-D in these experiments, the results indicate strongly that amide to acid hydrolysis can occur in both the wheat and pea tissues and that the acid produced then undergoes β-oxidation.

ω-(2:4-dichlorophenoxy)alkanenitriles

When these compounds were pretreated with pea tissue, only the first member ($n = 1$) yielded 2:4-D. Two peaks of activity were revealed on this chromatogram when both the wheat and pea tests were used for bio-assay and these peaks corresponded with the R_f values of 2:4-D (R_f 0·35–0·45) and 2:4-dichlorophenoxyacetonitrile (R_f 0·8–0·9). With other members of the series, the chromatograms assayed in the pea test showed uniform inactivity over the whole paper, thus confirming that hydrolysis of these higher nitriles to the acids cannot occur in pea tissue. As already noted, all the nitriles showed activity in the wheat test (*Figure 2*). The chromatographic and wheat cylinder bio-assay investigations of nitrile solutions pretreated with wheat tissue showed that all members of the series yielded 2:4-D in amounts which are related to their activity in the wheat cylinder test. In all these chromatograms there was also a second peak of activity representing residual nitrile (R_f 0·8–0·9). With a pea test bio-assay, however, these chromatograms showed no second peak of activity in the higher R_f regions since the higher nitriles are inactive in the pea test.

The methods employed in this work, then, provide a means whereby the growth-regulating activity of compounds can be related to their conversion to known active auxins within the tissues of the biological material employed. It is significant that in all cases where activity is shown the active acetic acid (2:4-D) is produced (cf. Seeley *et al.*, 1956).

One of the most interesting features of this work is the activity of all the nitriles in the wheat cylinder test (*Figure 2*). The greatest activity is again shown by the acetic, butyric, and caproic derivatives ($n = 1, 3, 5$) and this is explicable on the basis of hydrolysis of —CN→ —COOH followed by β-oxidation to yield 2:4-D. The production of 2:4-D from the propionic, valeric, and heptanoic nitriles ($n = 2, 4, 6$), however, is not explicable by this two-stage reaction mechanism. At the same time, there is no reason to suppose that in wheat tissue these three compounds are not subject to hydrolysis followed by β-oxidation, which in their case would lead to 2:4-dichlorophenol as the end product. On the other hand, evidence of their conversion to 2:4-D in wheat tissue indicates that some other type of breakdown must also be involved. To produce 2:4-D from the valeronitrile, for example, it is clear that a single carbon atom must have been lost from the side chain at some stage. This may occur as follows:

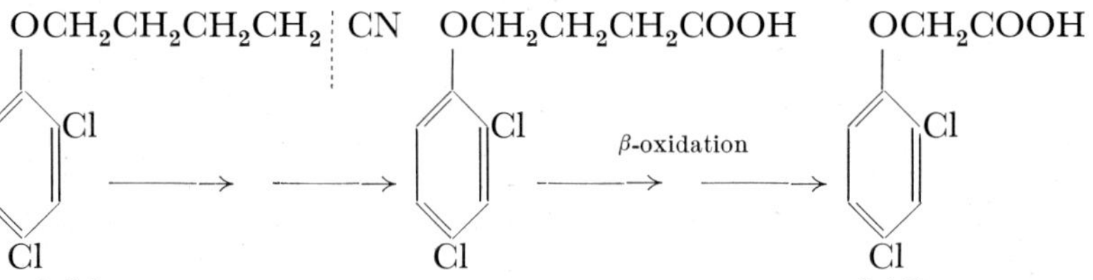

$OCH_2CH_2CH_2CH_2 \vdots CN$ (ring with Cl, Cl) (valeronitrile) $n=4$ ⟶ ⟶ $OCH_2CH_2CH_2COOH$ (ring with Cl, Cl) ⟶ β-oxidation ⟶ OCH_2COOH (ring with Cl, Cl) 2:4-D

Now there is already evidence that the —CH_2CN grouping can be degraded to carboxyl in the animal body. Thus, for example, *p*-chlorobenzylnitrile fed to dogs is excreted in the urine as a derivative of *p*-chlorobenzoic acid (Adeline *et al.*, 1926). Further evidence of the loss of a one-carbon fragment from the —CH_2CN grouping arises from the work of Pattison (1953) in his studies on the toxicity of ω-fluoroalkanenitriles to rats. A similar biochemical degradation would explain our results with ω-(2:4-dichlorophenoxy)alkanenitriles in wheat coleoptile tissue.

In this connection, it is of considerable interest that a separate investigation which was proceeding here with indole compounds has provided strong confirmatory evidence that nitriles can be so degraded in plant tissue with the loss of one carbon atom. In this work, which is referred to in one of our other contributions to this Conference (Seeley *et al.*, 1956), indole-3-acetonitrile has been shown to be converted to indole-3-carboxylic acid in presence of wheat coleoptile or pea stem tissues, i.e.

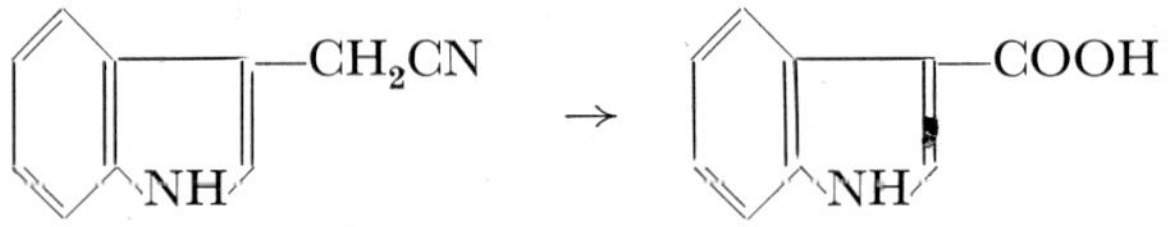

(indole, NH)—CH_2CN → (indole, NH)—COOH

This clearly provides another example of the type of nitrile degradation which we suggest occurs in the phenoxy nitriles. Since, in this breakdown, the α-methylene grouping becomes oxidized, the process may be conveniently referred to as α-oxidation of nitriles.

Finally, since we have shown that pea tissue can convert indole-3-acetonitrile to indole-3-carboxylic acid, and since there is evidence of the presence in germinating peas of a compound with properties similar to that of indole-3-acetonitrile (Cartwright *et al.*, 1956), it was logical to look for the carboxylic acid as a natural constituent of this tissue. Dr. Cartwright has in fact found this acid to occur in young pea plants (Cartwright *et al.*, 1956).

The evidence provided by these separate investigations thus indicates strongly that α-oxidation of nitriles, like β-oxidation of acids, is a degradation mechanism which occurs not only in animal but also in plant biochemistry.

REFERENCES

Adeline, M., Cerecedo, L. R., and Sherwin, C. P. (1926). Detoxication of nitriles. *J. biol. Chem.* **70,** 461.

Breusch, F. L. (1948). The biochemistry of fatty acid metabolism. *Advanc. Enzymol.* **8,** 347.

Cartwright, P. M. (1955). Private communication.

Cartwright, P. M., Sykes, J. T., and Wain, R. L. (1956). The distribution of natural auxins in germinating seeds and seedling plants. This volume, p. 32.

Fawcett, C. H., Ingram, J. M. A., and Wain, R. L. (1954). The β-oxidation of ω-phenoxyalkylcarboxylic acids in the flax plant in relation to their plant growth-regulating activity. *Proc. Roy. Soc.* **B142**, 60.

Grace, N. H. (1939). Physiological activity of a series of naphthyl acids. *Canad. J. Res.* **17,** 247.

Luckwill, L. C., and Woodcock, D. (1955). Plant growth regulators. I. The influence of side-chain length on the activity of ω-(2-naphthyloxy)-*n*-alkylcarboxylic acids for the induction of parthenocarpy in tomatoes. *J. hort. Sci.* **30,** 109.

Pattison, F. L. M. (1953). Toxic fluorine compounds. *Nature,* **172,** 1139.

Seeley, R. C., Fawcett, C. H., Wain, R. L., and Wightman, F. (1956). Chromatographic investigations on the metabolism of certain indole derivatives in plant tissues. This volume, p. 234.

Synerholm, M. E., and Zimmerman, P. W. (1947). Preparation of a series of ω-(2:4-dichlorophenoxy)-aliphatic acids and some related compounds with a consideration of their biochemical role as plant growth-regulators. *Contr. Boyce Thompson Inst.* **14,** 369.

Verkade, P. E., and Lee, J. van der (1934). Researches on fat metabolism. II. *Biochem. J.* **28,** 31.

Wain, R. L. (1955). A new approach to selective weed control. *Ann. appl. Biol.* **42,** 151.

Wain, R. L., and Wightman, F. (1954). The growth-regulating activity of certain ω-substituted alkyl carboxylic acids in relation to their β-oxidation within the plant. *Proc. Roy. Soc.* **B142,** 525.

RELATIONSHIP OF MOLECULAR STRUCTURE OF SOME NAPHTHYLOXY COMPOUNDS AND THEIR BIOLOGICAL ACTIVITY AS PLANT GROWTH REGULATING SUBSTANCES†

L. C. LUCKWILL and D. WOODCOCK
Long Ashton Research Station, University of Bristol.

DURING recent years, despite the considerable amount of work which has been done, particularly with indolyl and phenoxy compounds as growth substances, no systematic investigation of naphthyloxy compounds as growth regulators has yet been reported. One reason for this is doubtless the low activity of this series of compounds in the two tests which have been most widely used for measuring growth substance activity, viz. the *Avena* curvature test and the coleoptile cylinder test. However, 2-naphthyloxyacetic acid is active in delaying the abscission of petioles (e.g. of *Coleus*) and in stimulating parthenocarpy in tomatoes, and in our investigations the latter property was utilized

MEASUREMENT OF BIOLOGICAL ACTIVITY

This was carried out by observing the rate of growth of unpollinated tomato ovaries following treatment with known amounts of each compound. The details of the method have been described in a previous publication by Luckwill (1948). Synthesis of these compounds is represented by James and Woodcock (1951, 1953) and Pope and Woodcock (1954, 1955).

MATERIALS

The compounds discussed in this paper fall into three main groups, viz. those which have involved an alteration in the side-chain of 2-naphthyloxyacetic acid, nuclear substituted acids with an altered side-chain, and nuclear substituted 2-naphthyloxyacetic acids.

ω-(2-NAPHTHYLOXY)-*n*-ALKYLCARBOXYLIC ACIDS

Data for ten members of the homologous series of ω-(2-naphthyloxy)-*n*-alkylcarboxylic acids has appeared in a previous publication by the authors (Luckwill and Woodcock, 1955) and is reproduced in *Table 1* by permission of the Editors.

The outstanding feature of these results is the complete lack of activity of those acids having an odd number of carbon atoms in the side-chain. By contrast γ-(2-naphthyloxy)-*n*-butyric and ε-(2-naphthyloxy)-*n*-caproic acids with four and six carbon atoms respectively in the chain proved as active in this test as 2-naphthyloxyacetic acid itself, whilst η-(2-naphthyloxy)-octanoic acid showed definite though reduced activity. Owing to the very low biological activity and low solubility of the two highest members of the series, ι-(2-naphthyloxy)-decanoic and λ-(2-naphthyloxy)-dodecanoic acids,

† This paper was read at the Conference by Mr. D. L. Abbott.

the ED 50's were well above the highest concentrations of these compounds it was possible to test, and were estimated directly by extrapolation of the probit lines.

This phenomenon of alternation in growth-regulating activity has been previously reported for other homologous series of growth substances. Thus Thimann and Bonner (1938) noticed an alternation in activity (as measured

Table 1

Relative molar activities of a homologous series of ω-(2-naphthyloxy)-n-alkylcarboxylic acids in the tomato ovary test

(All compounds tested as sodium salts)

Name	*Formula* R = (2-naphthyl)—O—	*M.p. of acid*	*Solubility of Na salt in water at 25–27°C p.p.m.*	*Relative molar activity at ED 50*
2-Naphthyloxyacetic acid	$R \cdot CH_2COOH$	155–156°	6,550	1,000
β-(2-Naphthyloxy)-propionic acid	$R(CH_2)_2COOH$	143–144°	7,650	0
γ-(2-Naphthyloxy)-butyric acid	$R(CH_2)_3COOH$	122–123°	5,900	1,000
δ-(2-Naphthyloxy)-valeric acid	$R(CH_2)_4COOH$	111–112°	5,300	0
ε-(2-Naphthyloxy)-caproic acid	$R(CH_2)_5COOH$	126–127°†	3,750	1,000
		94–95°	45	1,000
ζ-(2-Naphthyloxy)-heptanoic acid	$R(CH_2)_6COOH$	96–97°	6,100	0
η-(2-Naphthyloxy)-octanoic acid	$R(CH_2)_7COOH$	91–92°	6,650	180
θ-(2-Naphthyloxy)-nonanoic acid	$R(CH_2)_8COOH$	98–99°	2,250	0
ι-(2-Naphthyloxy)-decanoic acid	$R(CH_2)_9COOH$	114–115°	500	2‡
λ-(2-Naphthyloxy)-dodecanoic acid	$R(CH_2)_{11}COOH$	96–97°	70	1‡

† Two dimorphic forms of this compound were tested.
‡ ED 50 estimated by extrapolation of probit line.

by the *Avena* test) in the indolyl series, $C_8H_6N(CH_2)_nCOOH$ (where *n* varies from 0 to 4) and Grace (1939) investigating the naphthylacetic acids $C_{10}H_7(CH_2)_nCOOH$ found greater root inducing activity with the acids having an even number of carbon atoms in the side-chain, though a general decrease in activity with increasing chain length was apparent. More recently, Synerholm and Zimmerman (1947) reported a similar phenomenon in the first seven members of the ω-(2:4-dichlorophenoxy) aliphatic series. These authors also tested the first three members of the ω-(2-naphthyloxy) series and found β-(2-naphthyloxy)-propionic acid to be inactive for cell elongation in the tomato leaf epinasty test. Synerholm and Zimmerman (1947) put forward an hypothesis to account for these results based on an analogy with the oxidation of fatty acids in animal metabolism, where it is known that oxidation normally occurs at the β-carbon atom, leading to the formation of an acid with two fewer carbon atoms. Thus it was postulated that a compound such as ε-(2:4-dichlorophenoxy)-caproic acid (with 6 carbon atoms in the side-chain) was active as a growth regulator because by successive β-oxidations it could be converted by the plant into the biologically active 2:4-dichlorophenoxy acetic acid, thus:

$$\text{2,4-}Cl_2C_6H_3\cdot OCH_2CH_2CH_2CH_2\overset{\beta\,:\,\alpha}{\vdots}CH_2COOH \rightarrow \text{2,4-}Cl_2C_6H_3\cdot OCH_2CH_2\overset{\beta\,:\,\alpha}{\vdots}CH_2COOH \rightarrow \text{2,4-}Cl_2C_6H_3\cdot OCH_2COOH$$

Those members of the series with an odd number of carbon atoms, on the other hand, would be oxidized *via* the hypothetical carbonate to 2:4-dichlorophenol, which is inactive as a growth regulator.

$$\text{2,4-}Cl_2C_6H_3\cdot OCH_2\overset{\beta\,:\,\alpha}{\vdots}CH_2COOH \rightarrow [\text{2,4-}Cl_2C_6H_3\cdot O\cdot COOH] \rightarrow \text{2,4-}Cl_2C_6H_3\cdot OH$$

This hypothesis has received strong support from the work of Fawcett, Ingram, and Wain (1952), who produced evidence for the production of phenol in flax plants treated with ω-phenoxyalkyl carboxylic acids with an odd number of carbon atoms in the side-chain. Wain and Wightman (1954) have also demonstrated indirectly the β-oxidation within the plant of similar compounds with an even number of carbon atoms in the side-chain.

The results presented in this paper for the ω-(2-naphthyloxy)-*n*-alkyl carboxylic acids are in good agreement with those of Synerholm and Zimmerman (1947) and Wain and Wightman (1954) and it seems likely that a similar mechanism is operative. The reduced activity of the 8, 10, and 12 carbon atom members compared with 2-naphthyloxyacetic acid requires special comment, since if the β-oxidation hypothesis is correct these compounds, like the 4 and 6 carbon members, would be expected to show a relative molar activity of 1000. As can be seen from the table, there is a marked falling off in the water-solubility of the compounds having more than 8 carbon atoms in the side-chain. It seems unlikely, however, that this can be considered as a contributory cause of their lower activity for even at concentrations at which they formed true solutions in water, their activity was much less than would have been expected on the assumption of complete oxidation to 2-naphthyloxyacetic acid. Further confirmation of the fact that biological activity and water solubility are not directly related is provided by the two dimorphic forms of ε-(2-naphthyloxy)-*n*-caproic acid which in spite of a very great difference in solubility both gave an activity of 1000 in the tomato parthenocarpy test (see *Table 1*). The solubility of the lower melting point dimorph of this compound is, in fact, somewhat less than that of the almost inactive dodecanoic acid.

In compounds with eight and ten carbon atoms in the side-chain a certain amount of oxidation may take place at the naphthyloxy end of the chain (i.e. on the ω-carbon atom). This phenomenon of ω-oxidation is known from studies on animal metabolism to occur with those fatty acids having 8 to 11 carbon atoms, and has also been postulated as possibly occurring in plant tissues by Fawcett *et al.* (1952). It would thus be possible, on the assumption of ω-oxidation, to account for the reduced activity of the octanoic, decanoic, and dodecanoic acids. It seems more probable, however, that the falling-off in activity of the 8, 10, and 12 carbon acids is due primarily to restrictions on the penetration of these molecules through the plasma membranes imposed by the length of their fatty side-chains, rather than to any differences in their

Table 2

*Relative molar activities of certain ω-(3-chloro-2-naphthyloxy)-*n*-alkylcarboxylic acids in the tomato ovary test*

(All compounds tested as sodium salts.)

Name	*Formula* R^I = [3-chloro-2-naphthyl]—O—	*M.p. of acid*	*Relative molar activity at* ED 50
3-Chloro-2-naphthyloxyacetic acid	R^ICH_2COOH	182–183°	1,000
β-(3-Chloro-2-naphthyloxy)-propionic acid	$R^I(CH_2)_2COOH$	173–174°	0
γ-(3-Chloro-2-naphthyloxy)-butyric acid	$R^I(CH_2)_3COOH$	174–175°	0
ε-(3-Chloro-2-naphthyloxy)-caproic acid	$R^I(CH_2)_5COOH$	114–115°	0
η-(3-Chloro-2-naphthyloxy)-octanoic acid	$R^I(CH_2)_7COOH$	74–75°	0
ι-(3-Chloro-2-naphthyloxy)-decanoic acid	$R^I(CH_2)_9COOH$	90–91°	0

primary activity at the site of action in the cytoplasm. If this is so, the very sudden drop in activity between the 6 and 8 carbon acids would imply that there is some critical side-chain length below which penetration is not affected and above which it becomes the factor limiting the over-all biological activity of the molecule.

Studies on the effect of nuclear substitution in 2-naphthyloxyacetic acid have shown that the biological activity of this molecule in the tomato parthenocarpy test is unimpaired by the introduction of a chlorine atom in position 3. In the higher homologues of this series, however, the activity of the butyric, caproic, octanoic, and decanoic acids is completely destroyed by a chlorine atom in this position (see *Table 2*), which must presumably block the β-oxidation process. A similar phenomenon has previously been reported, though without comment, by Synerholm and Zimmerman (1947). These authors found that γ-(2:4-dichlorophenoxy)-butyric acid, as would be expected, was active as a growth regulator, as was also 2:4:5-trichlorophenoxy acetic acid, but γ-(2:4:5-trichlorophenoxy)-butyric acid, which should be active, was not.

Wain and Wightman (1954) studying the same compounds also found γ-(2:4:5-trichlorophenoxy)butyric acid and higher homologues to be inactive in the pea and tomato leaf epinasty tests, though the homologues with an even number of carbon atoms in the side-chain were active in the wheat coleoptile cylinder test. This would imply that the β-oxidase capable of degrading the higher homologues of 2:4:5-trichlorophenoxyacetic acid is absent from pea and tomato tissue but present in wheat. The absence of the appropriate β-oxidase from tomato ovaries might therefore provide an alternative explanation for the lack of activity of the homologues of 3-chloro-2-naphthyloxyacetic acid in the present investigation.

α-(2-NAPHTHYLOXY)-*n*-ALKYLCARBOXYLIC ACIDS

The introduction of alkyl groups of gradually increasing chain length on the α-carbon atom of 2-naphthyloxyacetic acid causes a rapid decrease in activity, the first homologue to be completely inactive being α-(2-naphthyloxy)-*n*-valeric acid. In a similar series starting with 3-chloro-2-naphthyloxyacetic acid activity is again rapidly lost (*Table 3*).

Resolution of α-(3-chloro-2-naphthyloxy)-propionic acid using cinchonine (Pope and Woodcock, 1955) has given a highly active (+) form and an inactive optical antipode. Examination of this compound by Matell (1955) has shown that it most probably has the D-configuration, thus supporting the view that optically active plant growth regulators of the α-aryloxyalkyl carboxylic acid type which have greater auxin activity than their respective antipodes belong to the D-series. It is also noteworthy that the (—) form here shows competitive antagonism with the (+) form, resulting in an activity of only 60 for the (±) mixture instead of an expected value of 125. This agrees with the findings of Åberg (1951) with α-(2-naphthyloxy)-propionic acid in root inhibition, and of Smith, Wain and Wightman (1952) with α-(2:4-dichloro-phenoxy)-, α-(2:4:5-trichlorophenoxy)- and α-(2-naphthyloxy)-propionic acids in cell elongation promoting activity.

In general the activity of these α-substituted acids is much lower than the corresponding 2-naphthyloxyacetic acid and the fairly rapid decrease with increasing chain-length would seem to indicate a size or, rather less likely, a solubility effect. The close relationship between activity and the position of nuclear substituents will be more obvious after the results in the next section have been reviewed.

SUBSTITUTED 2-NAPHTHYLOXYACETIC ACIDS

In one of the most recent and critical reviews of structure–activity relationships in the field of plant growth regulating substances, Jönsson (1955) has reformulated the requirements for appreciable auxin activity as follows:

(i) An unsaturated ring nucleus.

(ii) A side-chain carrying a —COOH group which must not be situated at a quaternary carbon atom (or otherwise highly sterically hindered).

(iii) A high interface activity of the extended ring system.

(iv) The side-chain must be able to assume a spatial orientation in which

Table 3

α-(2-*Naphthyloxy*)-n-*alkyl carboxylic acids*

Name	*Formula* R = *Substituted 2-naphthyloxy-*	*M.p.*	*Relative molar activity at* ED 50
α-(2-naphthyloxy)-propionic acid	$R \cdot CH(CH_3)COOH$	114–115°	250
α-(2-naphthyloxy)-*n*-butyric acid	$R \cdot CH(C_2H_5)COOH$	126–127°	9
α-(2-naphthyloxy)-*n*-valeric acid	$R \cdot CH(C_3H_7)COOH$	117–118°	0
α-(2-naphthyloxy)-*n*-caproic acid	$R \cdot CH(C_4H_9)COOH$	107–108°	0
α-(3-chloro-2-naphthyloxy)-propionic acid	$R^{I} \cdot CH(CH_3)COOH$	175–176°	DL- 65 D- 250 L- 0
α-(3-chloro-2-naphthyloxy)-*n*-butyric acid	$R^{I} \cdot CH(C_2H_5)COOH$	149–150°	10
α-(3-chloro-2-naphthyloxy)-*n*-valeric acid	$R^{I} \cdot CH(C_3H_7)COOH$	159–160°	0
α-(3-chloro-2-naphthyloxy)-*n*-caproic acid	$R^{I} \cdot CH(C_4H_9)COOH$	127–128°	0
α-(1-chloro-2-naphthyloxy)-propionic acid	$R \cdot CH(CH_3)COOH$	171–172°	5
α-(8-chloro-2-naphthyloxy)-propionic acid	$R \cdot CH(CH_3)COOH$	132–133°	22
α-(1:3-dichloro-2-naphthyloxy)-propionic acid	$R^{II} \cdot CH(CH_3)COOH$	131–132°	0
α-(1:4-dichloro-2-naphthyloxy)-propionic acid	$R^{III} \cdot CH(CH_3)COOH$	160–161°	0
α-(3:4-dichloro-2-naphthyloxy)-propionic acid	$R^{IV} \cdot CH(CH_3)COOH$	176–177°	5
α-(1:3-dichloro-2-naphthyloxy)-*n*-butyric acid	$R^{II} \cdot CH(C_2H_5)COOH$	81–82°	0
α-(1:3-dichloro-2-naphthyloxy)-*n*-valeric acid	$R^{II} \cdot CH(C_3H_7)COOH$	97–98°	0

the atoms joining the ring and the —COOH group, including the C atom of the latter, are situated almost in the plane of the ring forming a pseudo-ring with the —COOH group close to the original ring and near the centre of the extended ring system thus formed.

(v) At least one side of the plane of the extended ring system must be free of atoms other than hydrogen and one of the O atoms of the —COOH group projecting out from it.

(vi) An optical configuration corresponding to the D-series of the amino-acids.

This formulation is essentially an elaboration of the views of Veldstra (1944a,b) in which his 'certain spatial relationship' between the ring and the side-chain now appears as an 'extended ring system.' It will be convenient to view the results given in *Tables 3* and *4* against this background.

Table 4

Substituted 2-naphthyloxyacetic acids

Substituent	*M.p.*	*Relative molar activity at* ED 50
1-chloro	169–170°	1
3-chloro	182–183°	1,000
4-chloro	168–169°	2
5-chloro	202–203°	0
6-chloro	208–209°	72
7-chloro	168–169°	19
8-chloro	131–132°	280
5-nitro	211–212°	0
8-nitro	179–180°	29
1:3-dichloro	179–180°	0
1:4-dichloro	188–189°	0
3:4-dichloro	182–184°	20
1:3:4-trichloro	207–208°	0

In general it may be said that nuclear chlorine substitution increases the activity of phenoxyacetic and benzoic acid growth substances and in certain positions, especially 4, 5, and 6, with 3-indolylacetic acid activity is only slightly diminished or is even enhanced (Veldstra, 1953). By contrast no increase in activity of 2-naphthyloxyacetic acid can be obtained by nuclear substitution of chlorine. On Veldstra's hypothesis (Veldstra and Booij, 1949) this could be explained by assuming that in 2-naphthyloxyacetic acid the lipophilic/hydrophilic character (L/H ratio) of the molecule is at its optimum for biological activity, chlorination merely serving to increase the L/H ratio beyond the optimum, resulting in a reduction in activity. The same argument would apply to the effect of lengthening the side-chain in the α-acids, but not to the ω-acids where the side-chain can be broken by β-oxidation.

Considering the effect of chlorine substitution at specific positions in the ring (see *Table 4*) it is immediately obvious that the important ring positions are 1, 4, and 5. When any of these are blocked with Cl there is a complete or almost complete loss of activity, both in mono and in poly-substituted compounds. Matell (1953) has also reported that the activity of (+)-α-(2-naphthyloxy)propionic acid in the flax root growth test is lowered about 600 times when chlorinated in position 1. He also makes the significant comment that the strong antagonistic action of the (—) form is very little affected by chlorination. Positions 6, 7, and 8 are also important for activity, though blocking of these points with chlorine causes a reduction but not complete loss of activity. It is interesting to note that replacement of the chlorine in position 8 by a nitro-group causes a further ten-fold reduction in activity. In the first results of substitution in the 3-position which we now report, it is seen that a chlorine atom here has no detrimental effect on the activity in the acetic acid series, though some reduction in the α-propionic acid series takes place, being part of the gradual decrease in the activity of α-substituted acids already mentioned.

An examination of Fischer–Hirschfelder molecular models of chlorinated 2-naphthyloxyacetic acids shows that chlorine atoms in positions 1 and 3 interfere to some extent with the free rotation of the $—O \cdot CH_2COOH$ side-chain, and thus influence the final spatial arrangement of atoms. Although the naphthalene nucleus is planar, large substituent groups such as chlorine may cause a buckling effect to relieve strain, which would destroy planarity, and in certain cases possibly affect the compactness of the molecule. It is unfortunate that the models give little help on this point. Jönsson (1955) does however stress that a planar structure is not the *only* requirement for bicyclic molecules to possess high activity.

The electronic effects of nuclear chlorine atoms may also be important. Reaction with other molecules such as coenzyme *A* forming an acetyl–thiol ester as has been suggested by Leopold and Guernsey (1953) would appear to be encouraged by chlorine atoms in positions 1, 3, 6, and 8 but not in positions 4, 5, and 7 as shown in the following diagrams:

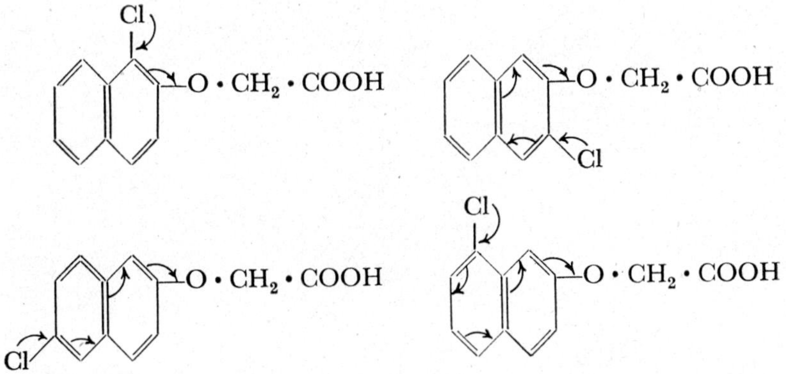

The inactivity of the 1-chloro-compound would then have to be explained by a superimposed steric effect involving the side-chain (Jönsson's activity requirements (iv) and (v)).

Two other hypotheses concerning mode of action have suggested interaction of growth substances with a hypothetical plant protein. The papers of

Hansch and Muir (1950) who postulated a two-point attachment involving the carboxyl group and one *ortho*-position, and Wain (1953) who presented much evidence in favour of a three-point attachment, an essential feature of which was a hydrogen atom on the α-carbon atom, are well known.

In order to explain the importance of certain positions in 2-naphthyloxy-acetic acid for growth substance activity, it is necessary to postulate a four-point, or in order to meet Wain's α-hydrogen requirement, a five-point attachment theory. This would involve in addition to one hydrogen atom on the α-carbon atom of the side-chain, and the carboxyl group, positions 1, 4, and 5 in the nucleus. Substitution in these positions leads to inactivity, whilst substitution in positions 6, 7, and 8 could reduce activity by hindering close interlocking with the substrate molecule. This hindrance would be greater the larger the substituent atom or group of atoms. Thus 8-nitro-2-naphthyloxyacetic acid would be expected to be less active than the corresponding 8-chloro compound, a fact which has already been noted. Although it is possible on the basis of such a five-point attachment theory, to explain all the known results so far obtained relating to 2-naphthyloxy-acetic acid, several criticisms may be made not least of which is the fact that an entirely hypothetical substrate, different from that postulated by Muir and others for phenoxy growth substances is involved. Although different types of growth substances may each have their own substrates, this seems unlikely in view of the great similarity in the growth responses they produce.

REFERENCES

ÅBERG, B. (1951). On the growth substance activity of enantiomorphic α-(naphthoxy)-propionic acids. *Ark. Kemi.* **3,** 549.

FAWCETT, C. H., INGRAM, J. M. A., and WAIN, R. L. (1952). β-oxidation of ω-phenoxyalkylcarboxylic acids in the flax plant. *Nature*, **170,** 887.

GRACE, N. H. (1939). Physiological activity of a series of naphthylacetic acids. *Canad. J. Res. (C)* **17,** 247.

HANSCH, C., and MUIR, R. M. (1950). The ortho effect in plant growth regulators. *Plant Physiol.* **25,** 389.

JAMES, P. M., and WOODCOCK, D. (1951). Synthesis of plant growth regulators. Part I. Substituted β-naphthyloxyacetic acids. *J. chem. Soc.* 3418.

JAMES, P. M., and WOODCOCK, D. (1953). Synthesis of plant growth regulators. Part II. Dichloro-β-naphthyloxyacetic acids. *J. chem. Soc.* 2089.

JÖNSSON, Å. (1955). Synthetic plant hormones. VIII. Relationship between chemical structure and plant growth activity in the arylalkyl-, aryloxyalkyl-, and indole-alkylcarboxylic acid series. *Svensk. kem. Tidskr.* **67,** 166.

LEOPOLD, A. C., and GUERNSEY, F. S. (1953). A theory of auxin action involving coenzyme *A. Proc. nat. Acad. Sci. Wash.*, **39,** 1105.

LUCKWILL, L. C. (1948). A method for the quantitative estimation of growth substances based on the response of tomato ovaries to known amounts of 2-naphthoxy-acetic acid. *J. hort. Sci.* **24,** 19.

LUCKWILL, L. C., and WOODCOCK, D. (1955). Plant growth regulators. I. The influence of side-chain length on the activity of ω-(2-naphthyloxy)-*n*-alkylcarboxylic acids for the induction of parthenocarpy in tomatoes. *J. hort. Sci.* **30,** 109.

MATELL, M. (1953). Stereochemical studies on plant growth substances. *LantbrHögsk. Ann.* **20,** 233.

MATELL, M. (1955). Private communication.

POPE, P. M., and WOODCOCK, D. (1954). Synthesis of plant growth regulators. Part III. ω-2-naphthyloxyalkanecarboxylic acids. *J. Chem. Soc.* 1721.

POPE, P. M., and WOODCOCK, D. (1955). Synthesis of plant growth regulators. Part IV. Substituted 2-naphthyloxy propionic acids. *J. chem. Soc.* 577–579.

SMITH, M. S., WAIN, R. L., and WIGHTMAN, F. (1952). Studies on plant growth regulating substances. V. Steric factors in relation to mode of action of certain aryloxyalkylcarboxylic acids. *Ann. appl. Biol.* **39,** 295.

SYNERHOLM, M. E., and ZIMMERMAN, P. W. (1947). Preparation of a series of ω-(2:4-dichlorophenoxy)-aliphatic acids and some related compounds with a consideration of their biochemical role as plant growth regulators. *Contr. Boyce Thompson Inst.* **14,** 369.

THIMANN, K. V., and BONNER, J. (1938). Plant growth hormones. *Physiol. Rev.* **18,** 524.

VELDSTRA, H. (1944a). Researches on plant growth substances. IV. Relation between chemical structure and physiological activity. I. *Enzymologia,* **11,** 97.

VELDSTRA, H. (1944b). Researches on plant growth substances. V. Relation between chemical structure and physiological activity. II. *Enzymologia,* **11,** 137.

VELDSTRA, H. (1953). The relation of chemical structure to biological activity in growth substances. *Ann. Rev. Pl. Physiol.* **4,** 164.

VELDSTRA, H., and BOOIJ, H. L. (1949). Researches on plant growth regulators. XVII. Structure and activity. On the mechanism of the action. III. *Biochem. biophys. Acta,* **3,** 278.

WAIN, R. L. (1953). Plant growth substances. *Royal Inst. Chem. Monograph, No. 2.*

WAIN, R. L., and WIGHTMAN, F. (1954). The growth-regulating activity of certain ω-substituted alkylcarboxylic acids in relation to their β-oxidation within the plant. *Proc. Roy. Soc.* **B142,** 525.

STUDIES ON THE RELATION BETWEEN MOLECULAR STRUCTURE AND PENETRATION OF GROWTH REGULATORS INTO PLANTS

J. VAN OVERBEEK

Agricultural Research Division, Shell Development Company, Modesto, California

INTRODUCTION

THE penetration of auxins into plants is a property which so far has not been given much attention. One generally accepted reason for this is that it has not been possible to locate a specific site in the molecule which can be held responsible for auxin activity. It is therefore impossible to distinguish between those properties of the auxin molecule which cause it to penetrate and those which cause it to react inside the cell as an auxin.

It thus becomes necessary to reason by analogy, that is to study the relation between physiological activity and molecular structure in compounds which possess something that resembles an active grouping in the molecule, even though this activity is not auxin activity.

An example of a compound of this type is maleimide. There is actually a whole group of maleimides (all having the maleimide ring in common), differing from one another by the substituent on the nitrogen atom. It is reasonably certain that the anti-auxin properties of the maleimides reside in the maleimide ring (more precisely in the sulphydryl reactivity of its double bond) and that the substituents on the nitrogen atom merely function as a 'lipophilic tail' to carry the molecule into the cell.

THE PROBLEM

In *Figure 1* has been presented a number of comparisons in which the increased auxin activity was caused by a modification of the molecular structure. In the writer's opinion the resulting increases in physiological activity of these compounds can be satisfactorily explained by increased penetration into the cells. One can distinguish three types: (1) *alpha* substitution of phenyl- and phenoxyacetic acids, (2) phenyl- versus phenoxyacetic acids, and (3) chlorination of the benzene ring. The relatively more active member of each pair of compounds appears on the right, and is indicated by +. We will now scrutinize the evidence for this contention on the basis of the study of the maleimides and later also on another pertinent example, that of the amino phosphine oxides.

The maleimides

The maleimides are anti-auxins in the sense that they inhibit the growth rate of coleoptile sections growing under the influence of applied indoleacetic acid. The inhibition of the growth rate is restored by increasing the concentration of the auxin. These relations are shown on maize coleoptile sections in *Figure 2*.

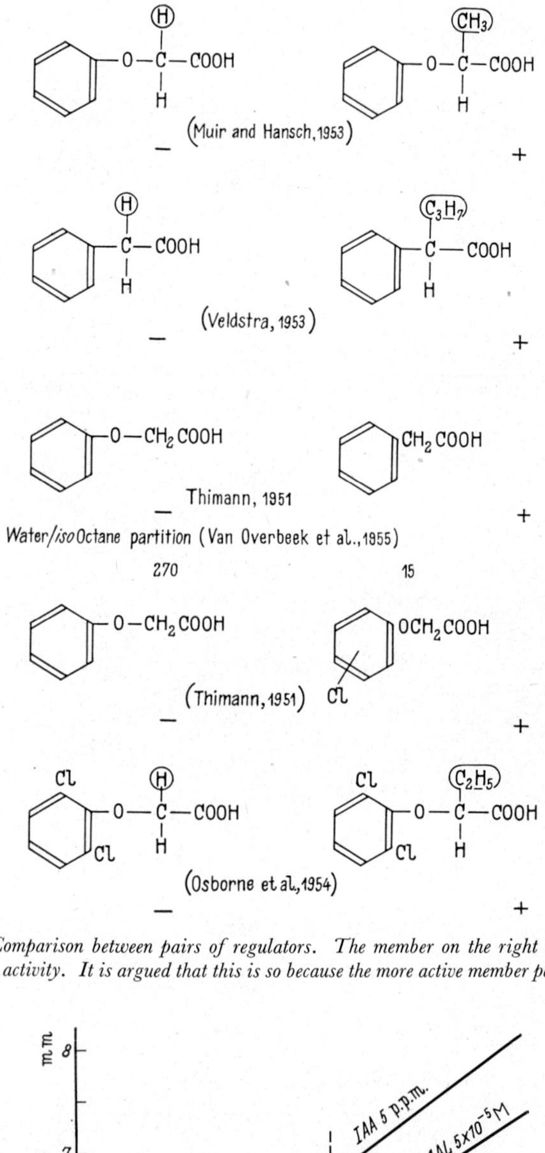

(H) — O—C—COOH — H (phenyl) | (CH3) — O—C—COOH — H (phenyl)

(Muir and Hansch, 1953)

– | +

(H) — C—COOH — H (phenyl) | (C_3H_7) — C—COOH — H (phenyl)

(Veldstra, 1953)

– | +

O—CH_2COOH (phenyl) | CH_2COOH (phenyl)

Thimann, 1951

– | +

Water/*iso*Octane partition (Van Overbeek et al., 1955)

270 | 15

O—CH_2COOH (phenyl) | OCH_2COOH (Cl-phenyl)

(Thimann, 1951) Cl

– | +

Cl, Cl — O—C(H)—COOH — H | Cl, Cl — O—C(C_2H_5)—COOH — H

(Osborne et al., 1954)

– | +

Figure 1. Comparison between pairs of regulators. The member on the right has the higher physiological (auxin) activity. It is argued that this is so because the more active member penetrates the cell better.

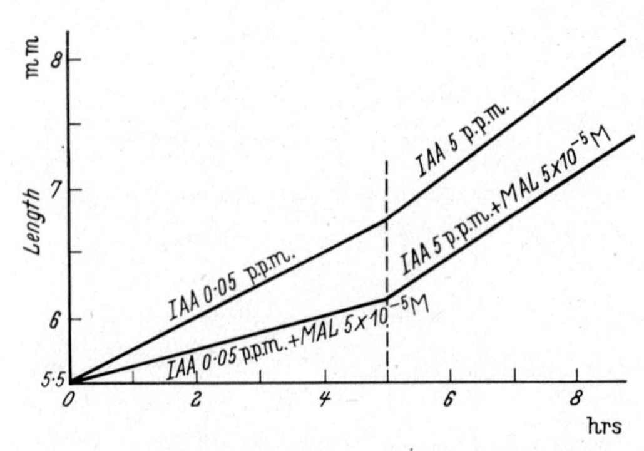

Figure 2. Reversible inhibition of indoleacetic acid (IAA) induced growth of maize coleoptile sections by 2:4-dichlorophenylmaleimide (MAL). (After van Overbeek et al., 1955.)

One of the more striking manifestations of the anti-auxin reaction is defoliation. A quantity of *N*-1-naphthylmaleimide as small as 0·35 gamma per cm² leaf area will cause the complete defoliation of peach branches in three days. The leaves drop entirely green, without any evidence of chemical burn. Simultaneous application of the auxin naphthalene acetic acid (at 0·1 of the concentration of the maleimide) prevents defoliation completely (*Figure 3*). This again shows the anti-auxin nature of the maleimides.

Since the maleimides react with SH compounds, and in addition lose their anti-auxin activity when the double bond is saturated, it is reasonably certain that the biochemical activity of the maleimide molecule resides in the

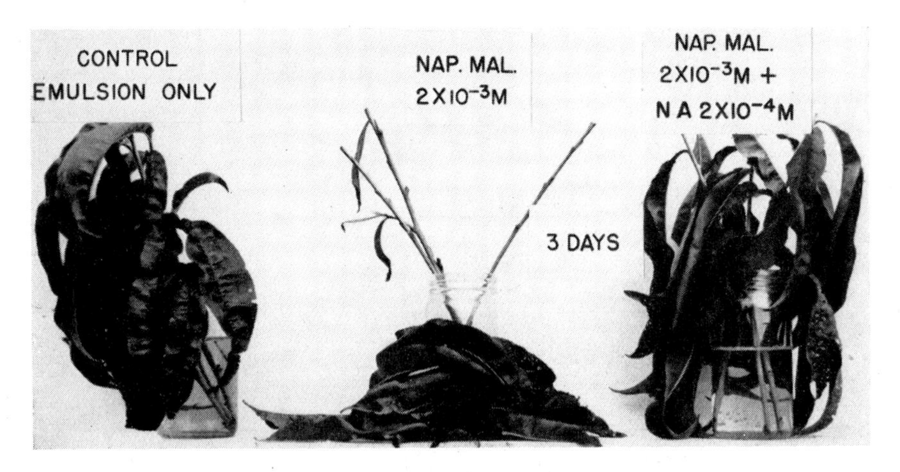

Figure 3. Defoliation of peach branches by naphthylmaleimide. When naphthalene acetic acid was applied simultaneously with the maleimide, the defoliant effect of the latter was prevented. (From van Overbeek et al., 1955, *by courtesy of the American Journal of Botany.)*

maleimide ring rather than in the substituents on the nitrogen atom. Therefore, if there was no penetration factor involved, all maleimides could be expected to give equal defoliation on the peach branches. This is clearly not so. In fact, *iso*propylmaleimide was not active at all within the range of concentrations used in these tests (*Figure 4*). Phenylmaleimide has intermediate activity, while 2:4-dichlorophenylmaleimide has high activity. Naphthylmaleimide has an equally high activity.

Originally we were inclined to conclude that high anti-auxin activity is obtained when the maleimide possesses an 'auxin ring' from a highly active auxin. We soon learned, however, that no ring is necessary for anti-auxin activity and that the substitution on the nitrogen atom may be an ordinary aliphatic radical. Thus it was found that octylmaleimide has considerable activity (*Figure 4*).

It appears, therefore, that the degree of physiological activity of the maleimides is determined by the character of their 'lipophilic tail'. The latter serves to carry the molecule into and perhaps through the lipoidal plasma membrane into other lipophilic bodies of the cytoplasm. The water solubilities of the maleimides (*Figure 4*) are low in the physiologically active materials and high in the inactive compounds of the group. From this and the structure of the compounds it follows that the active materials have a greater tendency to go into an oil phase than the physiologically inactive ones. Especially striking is the difference between chlorinated and unchlorinated phenylmaleimides. This points to the conclusion that one large factor in the increased physiological effect of benzene chlorination is the increased fat solubility that goes with this type of chlorination.

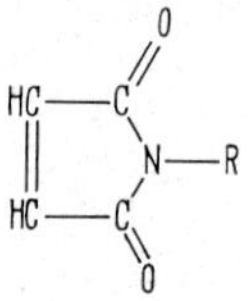

R	Water solubility p.p.m.	% defoliation
$-CH(CH_3)_2$	5000	5
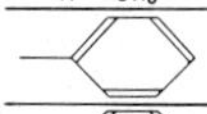	100	20
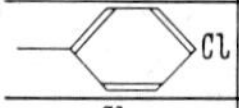 Cl	10	55
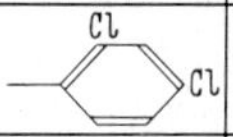 Cl, Cl	5	70
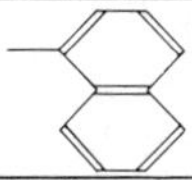	5	75
$-C_8H_{17}$ (n)	10	35

Figure 4. Structures, water solubility, and physiological activity of maleimides. (After van Overbeek et al., 1955.)

The amino phosphine oxides

While in the maleimides we can identify the reactive grouping in the molecule, we do not know with what active site in the cell this grouping reacts. In the amino phosphine oxides, on the other hand, we have a rare example in which we can identify both the active grouping in the molecule and the site in the cell with which it interacts. The structure of a reactive amino phosphine oxide is shown in *Figure 5.* The reactive grouping in the molecule is the amino phosphine oxide grouping, while the butyl radicals serve to give the molecule the proper lipophilic characteristics. The reactive site in the cell is the chloroplast, and more specifically chlorophyll molecules.

When a benzene solution of chlorophyll is exposed to light, or exposed to the action of other destructive agents such as acids, its colour will soon turn from green to brown because the Mg atom is lost. The presence of equimolar quantities of amino phosphine oxides will greatly retard this chlorophyll degradation. Chromatographic studies have shown that chlorophyll and amino phosphine oxides form a complex. Polar solvents such as alcohols separate the components again.

In the test tube all amino phosphine oxides of the type considered here are capable of complexing with chlorophyll, whether the radicals on the P atom are methyl, ethyl, propyl, allyl, butyl, or amyl. Biochemically speaking, all these compounds are active, and if there were no penetration problem all these materials should be equally active when applied to living cells. This is not so.

When the amino phosphine oxides of this series are put in aqueous solutions in which *Elodea* leaves are present, only the higher homologues show evidence of physiological activity. This is manifested under 1000 × magnification by blue green droplets in the chloroplasts. These droplets are quite characteristic for the presence of amino phosphine oxides in the chloroplasts, and thus serve as an index for penetration. The lower homologues of the series, by contrast, do not penetrate into the cell and the chloroplasts, or only do so when supplied at a much higher concentration.

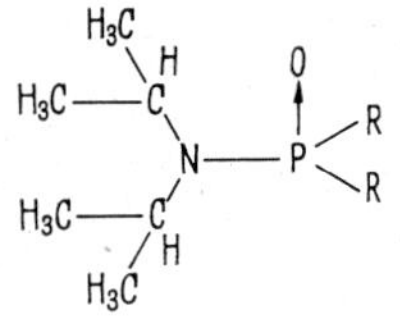

R	Water/oil part. coeff.	Relative penetration into cell
$-CH_3$	4	10
$-C_2H_5$	>0·1	25
$-C_3H_7$	0·1	90
$-C_4H_9$	0·006	100
$-C_5H_{11}$	0·0007	110

Figure 5. Structures, partition coefficient, and physiological activity of diisopropylamino phosphine oxides.

When partition coefficients (water/olive oil) were made for this series of amino phosphine oxides, it was found that the more the compound partitions into the oil phase the more it penetrated into the chloroplasts. This is not surprising because chloroplasts are highly fatty bodies (Chibnall, 1939).

CONCLUSION

It has thus been demonstrated on these two examples, maleimides and amino phosphine oxides, that *physiological* activity of the molecule (as contrasted with *biochemical* activity inside the cell) depends on the presence of a lipoid radical whose function it is to carry the molecule into the lipoid phases of the cell. It has further been shown that simple aliphatic chains will often perform this function. By analogy it is thus concluded that the increased auxin activity of the *alpha* substituted growth regulators of *Figure 1* is also due to increased oil solubility.

It has further been shown that chlorination of the benzene ring caused increased lipophilic properties in the maleimide molecule. By analogy it is concluded that at least part of the increased auxin activity caused by a similar chlorination in phenyl- and phenoxy acetic acids is simply due to increased lipoid solubility.

We compared the water/oil partition coefficients of phenoxy- and phenylacetic acids and found that the phenyl partitioned far more into the oil (*Figure 1*). It would seem, therefore, that the long-known difference in auxin activity between these two acids is also a logical result of their difference in capacity to penetrate into the lipoid phases of the plant.

R. C. Brian substantiated this conclusion (during the discussion of another paper in this Symposium) from his studies on the adsorption and penetration of regulators on and into monolayers of plant lipoids. He found that two chlorinated phenylacetic acids penetrated the film up to 5 times as much as the corresponding phenoxyacetic acids.

REFERENCES

CHIBNALL, A. C. (1939). *Protein Metabolism in the Plant.* Yale University Press.

MUIR, R. M., and HANSCH, C. (1953). On the mechanism of action of growth regulators. *Plant Physiol.* **28,** 218.

OSBORNE, D. J., BLACKMAN, G. E., POWELL, R. G., SUDZUKI, F., and NOVOA, S. (1954). Growth regulating activity of certain 2:6-substituted phenoxyacetic acids. *Nature,* **174,** 742.

OVERBEEK, J. VAN, BLONDEAU, R., and HORNE, V. (1955). Maleimides as auxin antagonists. *Amer. J. Bot.* **42,** 205.

THIMANN, K. V. (1951). The synthetic auxins: relation between structure and activity. *Plant Growth Substances,* ed. F. Skoog, University of Wisconsin Press, p. 21.

VELDSTRA, H. (1953). The relation of chemical structure to biological activity in growth substances. *Ann. Rev. Pl. Physiol.* **4,** 151.

THE RESOLUTION OF PHYTO-HORMONE ACIDS BY MEANS OF THEIR OPTICALLY ACTIVE PHENYL*ISO*PROPYLAMIDES. RESOLUTION OF α-(1-NAPHTHYL)PROPIONIC ACID†

J. M. F. Leaper and J. R. Bishop
American Chemical Paint Company, Ambler, Pa.

HISTORY OF THE RESOLUTION OF PHYTO-HORMONE ACIDS

The term 'hormone acids' will be used here to include two main groups:

(*a*) Acids actually derived from plant sources, or closely related chemically to these; e.g. indole-3-acetic acid, α-(indole-3)propionic acid, and α-(indole-3)*n*-butyric acid.

(*b*) Acids not related to these and arising solely from synthetic sources, e.g. the substituted and unsubstituted phenoxy- and naphthoxyacetic acids and homologues and their related imino and thio derivatives. Also in this category will be the α- and β- naphthylacetic acids and their homologues.

Some of both these classes have an asymmetric carbon atom and are capable of being resolved into their optically active enantiomorphs.

It was fairly obvious from the start and in fact might be considered axiomatic that when such resolutions were brought about, the resulting two isomers would produce different physiological responses in the appropriate plant tissue. I say appropriate advisedly since some plant response can often be found that does not differentiate between the two isomers, e.g. the variations observed by Kögl (1944) in the pea test and the *Avena* test using indole-α-propionic acid isomers. However, these are comparatively rare exceptions.

As has often been pointed out, the parallel cases in animal physiology involving the optical isomers of such compounds, both naturally occurring and synthetic, as thyroxine, hyocyamine, adrenaline, ascorbic acid, amphetamine, and many others, where very striking differences in biological reactions are found as between the isomers, would seem to make it obvious that similar differentiations would be the case with compounds having phytobiological activity.

Actually, the first resolution of what we are calling 'hormone acids' was made as far back as 1925 by Fourneau and his co-workers (Fourneau and Balaceano, 1925) at the Pasteur Institute, who resolved α-(2-naphthoxy)-propionic acid. However, this was many years before the phytobiological activity of 2-naphthoxyacetic acid was disclosed by Irvine (1938) and the relative activity of the isomers of α-(2-naphthoxy)propionic acids studied by Smith and Wain (1951). Fourneau was primarily interested in producing a cheap and readily available optically active acid for use in resolving synthetic adrenaline and related vasoconstrictors.

It is worthy of note that whereas most of the useful medicinal compounds found naturally are optically active, the only well-defined phyto-hormone

†This paper was read at the Conference by J. M. F. Leaper.

acid so far isolated is the, of course, optically inactive indoleacetic acid. It seems to me a reasonable speculation that the latter is perhaps the biological ultimate result of breakdown in the plant of similar acids of longer and partially branched side chains, just as in the explanation of the breakdown in the carbon pairs of the simpler ω-acids, postulated by Synerholm and Zimmerman (1947), except that in the latter case the starting acids were not potentially optically active.

The first conscious effort then to resolve any hormone acid with the idea of finding out something of the contrasted activities of the enantiomorphs was made by Kögl and Verkaaik in 1944 in synthetic α-(indole-3)propionic acid (1944). It is notable, as pointed out above, that they found that the (+) isomer had thirty times the activity of the (—) in one test and that in another test the differences were negligible.

At about the same time our group in the Agricultural Chemicals Division of the American Chemical Paint Company in Ambler, after launching the 2:4-D type of compounds for the use of American agriculture, turned our attention to homologues of this substance and particularly to α-(2:4-dichlorophenoxy)propionic acid. We had already found that the corresponding β-substituted propionic acid had practically no potential applications, the ω-series being later expanded by Synerholm and Zimmerman (1947) and by Wain and Wightman (1954), who discovered the β-oxidation series of activities referred to above.

The asymmetric carbon atom, of course, was a magnet, and we shortly obtained by the methods described below the (+) isomer of α-(2:4-dichlorophenoxy)propionic acid which was tested at Harvard for us in 1947 by Professor Thimann in comparison with the racemic form (Thimann, 1947). His report stated that the (+) form in the pea test showed about 2·5 times the activity of the racemic, indicating that the (—) isomer has very low activity. These results were further discussed by Thimann at the Madison, Wisconsin, meeting on Plant Growth Substances in 1949 and finally in book form as edited by Skoog (1951), this being the official account of the papers given at this meeting. Results were confirmed by Matell (1952). For various reasons the work on optical resolutions which we had initiated as above was shelved. Later on, Åberg, Fredga, and Matell at Uppsala, Veldstra at Amsterdam, and Wain and others at Wye College carried out very many resolutions of hormone acids, so that today we have upwards of twenty such acids which have been completely resolved and tested and which work has led to some very interesting conclusions by Wain and others on the physiological action of such compounds.

METHOD FIRST USED FOR RESOLUTION OF α-(2:4-DICHLOROPHENOXY)PROPIONIC ACID

Since the time of Pasteur very little in the way of new methods of optical resolution have been put forward. The three standard methods: (*i*) hand picking of large crystals of the appropriate enantiomorph salts, (*ii*) use of biological means such as moulds, fungi, etc. which will preferably grow at the expense of one of the isomers leaving the other, and (*iii*) separation by fractional crystallization in a suitable solvent of the mixture of enantiomorph salts with a suitable optically active base. The last method is the one generally used and, in fact, all the optically active acids so far produced have been made by this method.

The range of active bases available is not very large, comprising first the naturally occurring alkaloids mainly from the quinine, morphine, and strychnine groups. All of these are tertiary amines and are readily available. A somewhat rarer alkaloid, yohimbine, which is a secondary amine has been useful in one or two instances. A later development is the use by Matell (1953) of two synthetic optically active primary amines, phenylethylamine and phenyl*iso*propylamine. Both of these can be obtained in(+) and (—) forms, the (—) form of the latter being a by-product of the manufacture of *dextro*-amphetamine, a widely used sympathomimetic drug.

In our first work on the resolutions of α-(2:4-dichlorophenoxy)propionic acid, following the above procedure, we got very poor results with the alkaloids which were then available and using *dextro*-amphetamine we also could not get a crystalline salt. This was later confirmed by Matell (1953).

However, it occurred to us that since organic salts of primary amines usually lose water on heating to form substituted amides, we might find that these amides could be more readily separated into their optical components than the too soluble salts themselves.

Using in this way (+) amphetamine and racemic α-(2:4-dichlorophenoxy)-propionic acid and heating a molecular mixture of these to about 170°C until one molecule of water was eliminated, the melt then being diluted with methanol, we obtained a crystalline mass of the compound, later identified as

$$\mathrm{(+)\text{-}2,4\text{-}Cl_2C_6H_3\text{—}O\text{—}CH(CH_3)\text{—}CO\text{—}NH\text{—}CH(CH_3)\text{—}CH_2\text{—}C_6H_5(+)}$$

(m.p. 164–5°; $[\alpha]_D^{25}$ —39·5 (c = 2·00-in toluene)),

the compound

$$\mathrm{(-)\text{-}2,4\text{-}Cl_2C_6H_3\text{—}O\text{—}CH(CH_3)\text{—}CO\text{—}NH\text{—}CH(CH_3)\text{—}CH_2\text{—}C_6H_5(+)}$$

(m.p. 106–7°; $[\alpha]_D^{25}$ +31·7 (c = 1·5 in toluene))

remaining for the most part in solution.

The (+)-(+) amphetamide is readily purified completely by one or two recrystallizations and is then optically pure.

Its constitution was definitely established by hydrolysis, giving one molecule each of (+) α-(2:4-dichlorophenoxy)propionic acid and (+) amphetamine. Neither the acid nor the base was racemized in this hydrolysis.

If (—) amphetamine is used in the same way with the racemic acid, the product which crystallizes out is

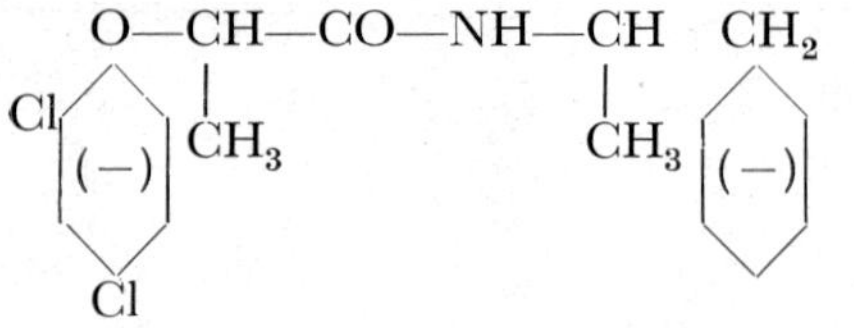

O—CH—CO—NH—CH CH_2 (m.p. 164–5°; $[\alpha]_D^{25}$ +39·0 (c = 2·00 in toluene)),

Cl, (−) ring, CH_3, CH_3, (−) ring, Cl

and the (+)-(—) remains in solution.

The (—)-(—) product is again readily purified by recrystallization from methanol and on hydrolysis gives the pure (—) α-(2:4-dichlorophenoxy)-propionic acid and (—) amphetamine.

These phenyl *iso*propylamides of hormone acids in general have been the subject of considerable biological study in our greenhouse apart from the acids themselves and represent an entirely new hormone-type product which has great possibilities in practical application. They can be made from any hormone acid whether potentially optically active or not but, of course, should have their major usefulness in connection with the more active one of a potentially optically active pair of acids. In this connection they would have the following advantages:

(*i*) they are readily obtained pure without tedious recrystallizations;

(*ii*) they are made from a readily available base which is easily recoverable if desired;

(*iii*) they are made from the racemic acid directly without having to use the pure (+) or (—) acid at all;

(*iv*) they contain the most active half of the hormone acid;

(*v*) they have a low molecular weight;

(*vi*) they have extremely low solubility in water.

The last property may seem to be a disadvantage, but our experience, for instance in apple blossom thinning, has led us to the conclusion that a spray of a comparatively insoluble compound formulated in a wettable form such as for instance 1-naphthylacetamide has at least the advantage over the corresponding acid or salt, that it will not cause damage to the trees when used carelessly, since its maximum solubility is not very far from the concentration needed for blossom thinning. Even apart from this advantage, it also does a consistently superior job and is today being widely used. The amphetamides of (+) α-(2:4:5-trichlorophenoxy)propionic acid, α-(2-naphthoxy)propionic acid, and α-(1-naphthyl)propionic acid (see below) are expected to be particularly useful.

RESOLUTION OF α-(1-NAPHTHYL)PROPIONIC ACID

Since we have been prominent in the manufacture and uses of 1-naphthylacetic acid and its derivatives since the early days of plant hormone application, it was natural that we should look into the possibilities of the homologues. The activity of the ω-homologues of 1-naphthylacetic acid was studied by Grace (1939), who found a similar alternate spacing of activity with length of side-chain as was found in the substituted phenoxy series by Synerholm and

Zimmerman. However, no similar report has appeared on the branched or α-series.

Racemic α-(1-naphthyl)propionic acid was first described by Blicke. The method we used was to react naphthalene with α-bromopropionyl bromide in the presence of a catalyst and extract the product from the mainly unreacted naphthalene remaining.

There are several other methods of arriving at α-(1-naphthyl)propionic acid but after attempting the production by such strictly laboratory scale methods as those involving the Knoevenagel reaction and those including Grignard and Friedel Craft techniques, we found our method more convenient:

$$\left.\begin{array}{l} CH_3{-}CH_2{-}CO \\ CH_3{-}CH_2{-}CO \end{array}\right\rangle O \xrightarrow{Br_4} 2(CH_3 \cdot CH\,Br \cdot CO\,Br) \xrightarrow{C_{10}H_8} \begin{array}{c} CH_3 \\ | \\ CH \cdot COOH \end{array}$$

(attached to naphthalene ring)

The product is readily dissolved out from the reaction mixture with bicarbonate solution and best purified from the crude acid by esterification and distillation *in vacuo* of the ethyl ester followed by saponification. It has m.p. 149·3–150·0°. To resolve the racemic acid we naturally first attempted to accomplish this by the means of the (+) and (—) amphetamides as above outlined. There was no difficulty in this reaction, but it was found that the hydrolysis was extremely difficult in this case as compared with α-(2:4-dichlorophenoxy)propionic amphetamide. In the latter case although the alkaline saponification was impossible, the acid method as employed by Manske in his work on α-naphthylacetonitrile gave good results. However, with the amphetamides of naphthylpropionic acid it was found that the only way to hydrolyse them was by heating at 180°C for 48 hours with syrupy phosphoric acid and acetic acid. As might have been expected, this drastic treatment racemized the compound almost completely so that nothing was accomplished.

We reverted to the older methods and found that a good separation could be obtained using the cinchonine salt in an aequeous methanol medium. The cinchonine salt of the (—) acid crystallizes out first and is pure after three recrystallizations. The (+) acid is obtained without any difficulty from the mother liquors in the usual way.

The (—) acid has the following characteristics:

m.p. 68–9°, $[\alpha]_{D}^{25} = -118{\cdot}1$ ($c = 3{\cdot}168$ in methanol)
$-141{\cdot}3$ ($c = 3{\cdot}87$ in acetone)
$-131{\cdot}7$ ($c = 3{\cdot}863$ in chloroform)
$-172{\cdot}0$ ($c = 2{\cdot}419$ in benzene)
$-35{\cdot}3$ ($c = 2{\cdot}25$ in NaOH sol.)

The (+)-acid has m.p. 67·5–68° and $[\alpha]_{D}^{25}$ $+117{\cdot}5$ ($c = 2{\cdot}00$ in methanol).

BIOLOGICAL REACTIONS OF THE ISOMERS

As we had found in our work on the series of chlorinated phenoxyacetic acids (Leaper and Bishop, 1951) and on the isomeric monochloro orthocresoxy acetic acid (Leaper and Bishop, 1955) that the inhibition of root growth of 4-day-old seedlings of *Lupinus albus* served as a good method for differentiation of hormone acids, we used the same method here for preliminary biological tests. The results so far have shown that there is not such a wide difference in the inhibitive action of the isomers as there is in the 2-naphthoxy series, the slight increase in inhibition obtained with the (+) isomer in this case being parallel to that obtained with the 1-naphthoxy series. However, other important differential specificities are showing up with further biological tests and these will be reported later in a more comprehensive assessment.

The experimental details of the chemical work described above will also be reported elsewhere.

REFERENCES

BLICKE, F. F., and FELDKAMP, R. F. (1944). Antispasmodics. VI. *J. Amer. chem. Soc.* **66,** 1087.

FOURNEAU, E., and BALACEANO, F. (1925). α- and β-naphthoxypropionic acids, their mononitro-derivatives and optical isomerides. *Bull. Soc. chim.* **37,** 602.

GRACE, N. H. (1939). Physiological activity of a series of naphthyl acids. *Canad. J. Res.* **17,** 247.

IRVINE, V. C. (1938). Studies on growth-promoting properties as related to X-radiation and photoperiodism. *Univ. Colo. Stud.* **26,** 69.

KÖGL, F., and VERKAAIK, B. (1944). Über die Antipoden der α-(β′Indolyl)-propionsäure und ihre verschieden starke physiologische Wirksamkeit. *Hoppe-Seyl. Z.* **280,** 167.

LEAPER, J. M. F., and BISHOP, J. R. (1951). Relation of halogen position to physiological properties in the mono-, di-, and trichlorophenoxyacetic acids. *Bot. Gaz.* **112,** 250.

LEAPER, J. M. F., and BISHOP, J. R. (1955). *Proc. Northeastern Weed Conference.*

MATELL, M. (1952). Stereochemical studies on plant growth regulators. III. The steric relations of some chloro-substituted α-phenoxypropionic acids. *Ark. Kemi,* **5,** 341.

MATELL, M. (1953). α-N-Arylaminocarboxylic acids as plant growth-regulators. *Acta chem. Scand.* **7,** 228.

OGATA, Y., ISHIGURO, J., and KITAMURA, Y. (1951). Condensation of naphthalenes with α-halo fatty acids and related reactions. *J. org. Chem.* **16,** 239.

SKOOG, F. (1951). *Plant Growth Substances,* p. 29. University of Wisconsin Press.

SMITH, M. S., and WAIN, R. L. (1951). The plant growth-regulating activity of *dextro-* and *laevo-α-*(2-naphthoxy)propionic acid. *Proc. Roy. Soc.* **B139,** 118.

SYNERHOLM, M. E., and ZIMMERMAN, P. W. (1947). Preparation of a series of ω-(2:4-dichlorophenoxy)-aliphatic acids and some related compounds with a consideration of their biochemical role as plant growth regulators. *Contr. Boyce Thompson Inst.* **14,** 369.

THIMANN, K. V. (1947). Private communication.

WAIN, R. L., and WIGHTMAN, F. (1954). The growth-regulating activity of certain ω-substituted alkyl carboxylic acids in relation to their β-oxidation within the plant. *Proc. Roy. Soc.* **B142,** 525.

III

METABOLISM AND MODE OF ACTION

SOME METABOLIC CONSEQUENCES OF THE ADMINISTRATION OF INDOLEACETIC ACID TO PLANT CELLS

A. W. GALSTON†

Kerckhoff Biological Laboratories, California Institute of Technology, Pasadena, California‡

OUR knowledge of the mode of action of auxin in promoting the extension growth of plant cells is at present so primitive and fragmentary that almost any biochemical fact which can be related to auxin is of interest. No man can predict which of the numerous leads now being explored will result in a final elucidation of this problem. This permits us, with a clear conscience, to devote ourselves to pursuits which, at least at present, do not seem to be aimed at the heart of the problem, but which are none the less of considerable interest.

It is now well known that 3-indoleacetic acid (IAA) is a naturally occurring auxin of wide occurrence in the plant world, and of great quantitative significance in the auxin economy of the plant (Larsen, 1951). Indeed, in many instances, it appears that all of the auxin in the plant is either IAA or closely-related compounds, such as indoleacetonitrile or indoleacetaldehyde, which can be metabolized to IAA. For this reason it seems to be of interest, in investigating the mode of action of auxin, to analyse in detail the metabolic consequences of the administration of IAA to tissues which can respond to this compound.

In such a biochemical analysis, we may note at least two separate categories of events:

(1) The IAA itself undergoes certain alterations:

(*a*) A small portion is firmly bound to protein, apparently *via* peptide and other linkages, as IAA.

(*b*) A much larger portion suffers oxidative degradation to a physiologically inactive compound tentatively designated as a phenolic aminoacetophenone.

(2) The biochemistry of the cell is altered, in at least the following ways:

(*a*) The ability of cells to destroy IAA (hereafter referred to as IAA oxidase activity) may be increased by pretreatment with physiological concentrations of IAA.

(*b*) Both of the functional moieties of the IAA-oxidase complex of etiolated peas, i.e. the peroxide-producing system and the peroxidase which actually destroys IAA, may similarly be increased in activity by pretreatment with IAA.

† I wish to acknowledge generous financial aid provided by the National Science Foundation and the American Cancer Society. I am greatly indebted to the following colleagues for their contributions to this work: Miss L. Dalberg, Dr. P. L. Goldacre, Dr. W. A. Jensen, Dr. D. T. Manning, Dr. I. B. Perlis, Dr. P. E. Pilet, Dr. S. M. Siegel, and Dr. R. L. Weintraub.

‡ Address after 1 September, 1955: Plant Science Department, Yale University, New Haven, Connecticut, U.S.A.

(*c*) The cells may acquire the capacity for lignin synthesis, probably by virtue of the induced formation of a peroxidase involved in the conversion of hydroxyphenylpropane-type precursors into lignin.

I propose during the remainder of my paper to discuss in some detail each of the above-mentioned consequences of IAA-administration to plant cells.

THE EXPERIMENTAL COUPLING OF IAA TO PROTEIN

Several years ago, Dr. S. M. Siegel and I were examining the proteins of pea root apices which had been exposed for several hours to extremely high (10^{-3} M) concentrations of IAA (Siegel and Galston, 1953). We noticed that the trichloroacetic-acid (TCA) precipitates of the *brei* of roots previously exposed to IAA had a faint but distinctly pink colour when compared with that of roots incubated in buffer alone as a control. After demonstrating to ourselves that TCA applied to IAA on filter paper gave a pink colour, we naturally suspected that the colour of the protein might be a consequence of IAA bound to it. This conclusion was borne out by the application of the Salkowski reagent (Tang and Bonner, 1947) which gives a characteristic pink colour with IAA and some related compounds. This reagent turned the protein a bright pink to red. Unlike free IAA, which turns pink gradually and then fades when treated with Salkowski reagent, the IAA-protein became coloured quickly and retained the same colour intensity for at least several days under refrigeration. This fact permitted the quantitative estimation of the IAA on the protein.

The major conclusions which Dr. Siegel and I derived from our study (Siegel and Galston, 1953) of this IAA protein formed in pea root apices are:

(*a*) IAA placed in the medium may be detected in the tissues in the free form within 2–3 minutes. Significant quantities of protein-bound IAA may be noted within 5–10 minutes, the amount of the material increasing rapidly for 30 minutes and less rapidly for several hours after that (*Figure 1*).

(*b*) The higher the concentration of IAA supplied, the greater is the amount of IAA bound to protein. Under the most favourable conditions, however, only 10 per cent as much IAA is coupled to protein as is destroyed by the oxidase. Assuming a molecular weight for the protein of 100,000, then it appears that of the order of 0·1 to 1·0 mole of IAA is bound per mole of protein.

(*c*) The IAA-protein appears to be localized in the 'non-particulate' phase of the cytoplasm.

(*d*) The binding of IAA to protein occurs only under conditions of active aerobic respiration linked to the synthesis of energy-rich compounds such as ATP. It is prevented by oxygen deprivation, or by the inhibitors cyanide, azide, iodacetate, and 2:4-dinitrophenol (*Figure 2*).

(*e*) Prior treatment of the roots with some other auxin, such as 2:4-dichlorophenoxyacetic acid or α-naphthalene-acetic acid, interferes with IAA binding to the protein. The greater the concentration of analogue, the less IAA is bound (*Figure 3*). This implies some general affinity of the protein for auxin-type molecules.

(*f*) *In vitro*, IAA may be coupled to the proteins in an acetone-powder of pea roots with the aid of ATP. Coenzyme A, which we expected might aid

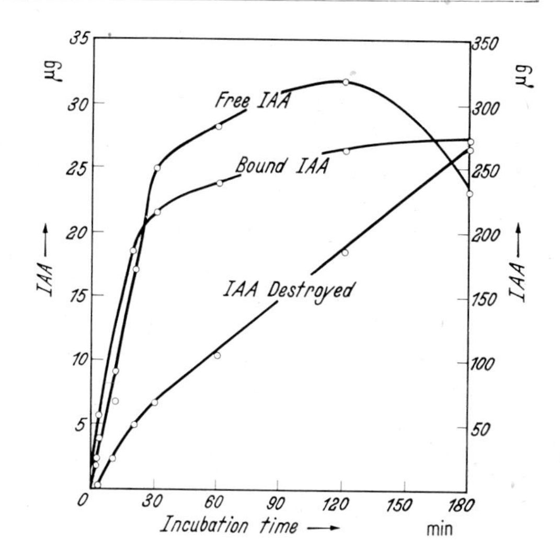

Figure 1. The fate of IAA fed to excised pea root apices. The left ordinate refers to 'free IAA' and 'bound IAA'; the right ordinate to 'IAA destroyed'.

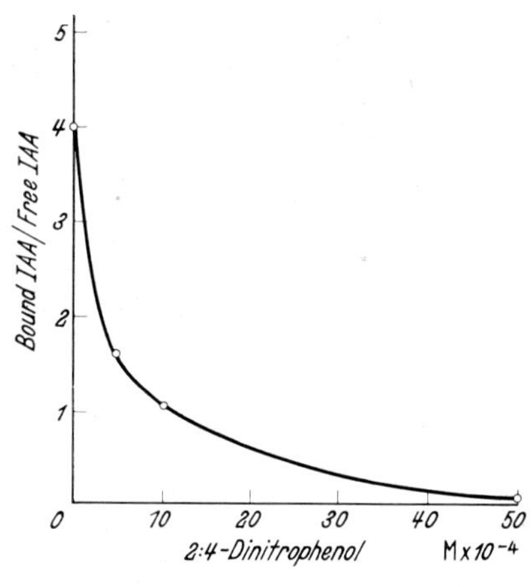

Figure 2. The inhibition of IAA coupling to pea root protein in vivo *by* 2:4-*dinitrophenol.*

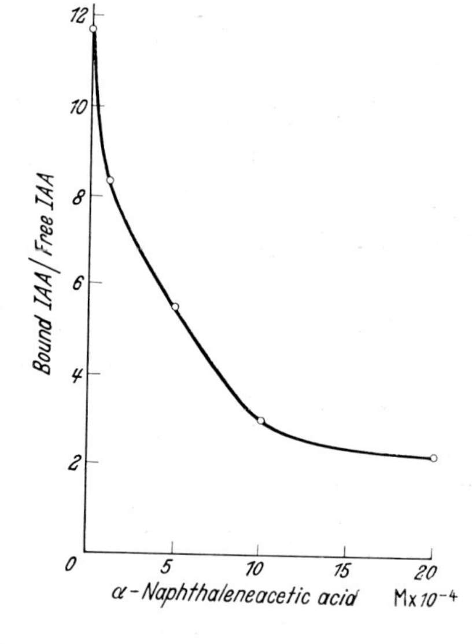

Figure 3. The inhibition of IAA coupling to pea root protein in vivo *by another auxin, α-naphthalene acetic acid.*

in the coupling reaction, actually interferes with it by favouring the dissociation of the IAA protein into protein plus unbound IAA. This 'unbound IAA' seems not to be free IAA, since much of it is not extractable into diethyl ether at pH 3·0. We consider that it is either IAA linked to CoA or IAA bound to a small peptide. We have, however, not had sufficient time to investigate this problem properly.

Since these investigations, the IAA-protein has been investigated further by Dr. I. B. Perlis. He has found the IAA-protein to be formed in all portions of the etiolated pea seedling, even in those incapable of growth. He has also been able to purify the protein several-fold by means of ammonium sulphate and KH_2PO_4 fractionation.

What is the physiological significance, if any, of this IAA-protein? Unfortunately, we do not yet know. It is tempting, of course, to suppose that the catalytic effect of IAA on growth is a consequence of its coupling to some protein, the whole then forming an enzyme somehow critically involved in the growth process. If this supposition is true, then the IAA-protein we have discovered may function in this important way. However, we have not yet been able to localize any enzymatic activity within this protein. This situation is also true of other auxin-proteins of natural occurrence (Larsen, 1951).

Another possibility is that the IAA-protein constitutes a stored, but physiologically inactive form of IAA. In support of this hypothesis is the fact that the IAA bound to protein can apparently not be destroyed by the IAA oxidase system. The release of IAA from such a stored state may, in the cell, be mediated by CoA, which could either release it from protein entirely, or effect its transfer from storage to catalytically active protein.

THE OXIDATION PRODUCT OF IAA IN PLANT *BREIS*

If IAA is added to a *brei* prepared from roots or etiolated aerial portions of certain plants, it is rapidly inactivated (Tang and Bonner, 1947; Wagenknecht and Burris, 1950). This inactivation may be followed either by bioassay procedure such as the *Avena* coleoptile curvature test, or by chemical procedures such as the Salkowski colorimetric reagent. Results with both techniques are essentially the same, so that the colorimetric technique is generally employed because of its greater convenience.

It is known that in the inactivation of IAA, one mole of O_2 is absorbed and one mole of CO_2 is released per mole of IAA inactivated. This simple relation has prompted the conjecture (Tang and Bonner, 1947; Wagenknecht and Burris, 1950) that a simple oxidative decarboxylation of IAA to 3-indolealdehyde is involved. This conclusion is supported by the fact that the oxidation product gives a colour with Ehrlich's reagent (and therefore may have an indole ring), and also forms an insoluble 2:4-dinitrophenylhydrazone (implying the presence of a carbonyl group). Despite this evidence, we are now convinced that the oxidation product is not 3-indolealdehyde, but is rather of the nature of a hydroxyaminoacetophenone.

Dr. D. T. Manning investigated this problem in our laboratories by the use of paper chromatography. He added large amounts of pure IAA to active IAA oxidase preparations from etiolated pea seedlings. After a major portion of the IAA had been destroyed, as shown by Salkowski-reagent assay of an aliquot of the *brei*, he extracted the reaction products from the medium with chloroform. The chloroform extract was concentrated, applied to paper, and an analysis of the nature of the product attempted by the combined use of R_f, spray reagents, and the preparation of derivatives.

Using the *iso*propanol–ammonia–water developer in a 10 : 1 : 1 ratio and later in a 2 : 1 : 1 ratio, Dr. Manning was able to show the presence of at least two principal products which accumulated concurrently with the disappearance of IAA. These products moved with R_f's of 0·94 and 0·91, and had a faint yellow colour before the application of any spray reagent. Upon spraying with Ehrlich's reagent (1 per cent *p*-dimethylaminobenzaldehyde in 1 N HCl), both spots immediately turned orange. With standing,

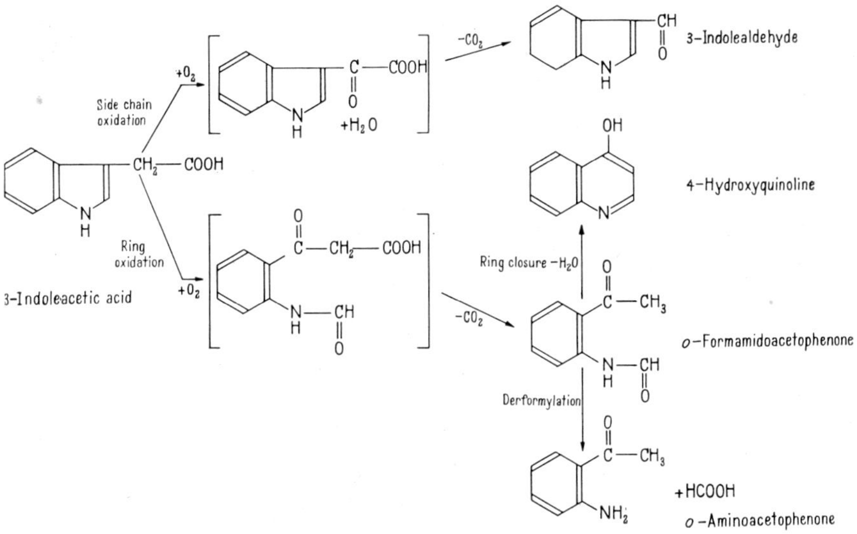

Figure 4. Four possible oxidation products of IAA, resulting from oxidation of either side-chain or ring.

the R_f 0·94 spot developed red tinges, and finally became uniformly pink. The spot at R_f 0·91 behaved similarly, finally becoming red. Both spots gave a rose colour in 3–5 minutes with 1 per cent aqueous $FeCl_3$, which deepened with time, assuming an especially deep colour at the R_f 0·94 spot. Since 3-indolealdehyde differs from both of the observed reaction products in R_f and colour reactions, we have concluded that it is not a major product of the oxidation (Manning and Galston, 1955).

On the basis of analogy with the conversion of tryptophan to kynurenine (Beadle, Mitchell, and Nyc, 1947), we had supposed that the indole ring of IAA could be cleaved (*Figure 4*) to yield *o*-formamidoacetophenone (OFA), or secondarily *o*-aminoacetophenone (OAA) or dihydroxyquinoline (DHQ). Unfortunately, none of these compounds has properties which exactly match the behaviour of either of the two unknowns, nor are they acted upon by the enzyme to yield the authentic products. Nevertheless, the mobilities and and colour reactions of OFA and OAA are close enough to the products to warrant the assumption that they are in fact related to the products. The main difference lies in their failure to give a proper colour with $FeCl_3$, which is generally considered to be a phenol reagent. Thus, we have tentatively concluded that the product may be a phenolic aminoacetophenone. Since neither OFA nor OAA is converted to the product, the hydroxylation step (presumably at the No. 5 or 6 position on the indole ring) must precede the ring cleavage between the No. 2 and 3 carbons (*Figure 5*).

Our understanding of the physiological significance of this conversion is limited to the observation that neither OAA, OFA, nor the authentic oxidation products appear to have any marked effects on growth in the pea epicotyl section test. Thus, IAA oxidase, if it is operative in tissue, results in the diminution of growth by the lowering of the effective auxin level.

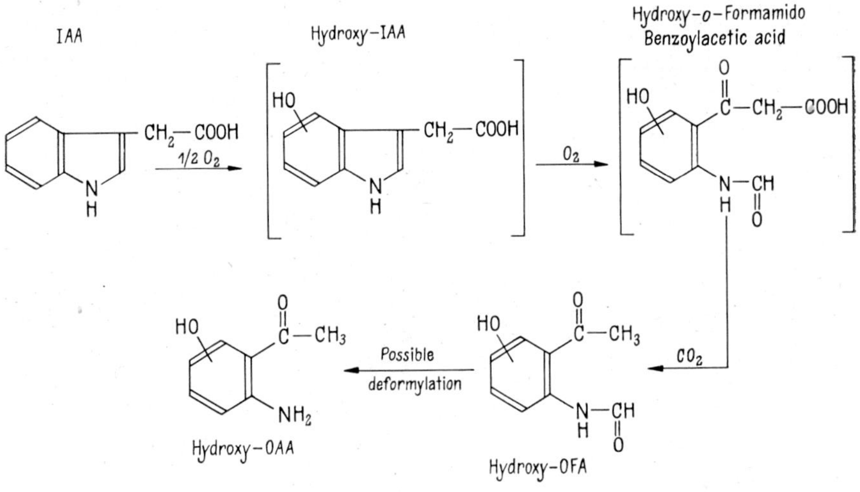

Figure 5. A possible scheme of oxidation of IAA and a possible product satisfying all experimental data.

THE NATURE OF INDOLEACETIC ACID OXIDASE AND ITS INDUCTION BY IAA

The enzyme complex which we refer to as indoleacetic acid oxidase was discovered by Tang and Bonner (1947) in etiolated peas and has since been shown to exist in other higher plants (Wagenknecht and Burris, 1950; Gortner and Kent, 1953; Jensen, 1955; Pilet and Galston, 1955) and in fungi (Sequeira and Steeves, 1954; Tonhazy and Pelczar, 1954). It appears certain that the enzyme differs from plant to plant and is absent from some tissues (Platt, 1954); but we have limited ourselves to an attempt to understand its make-up in one plant, *Pisum sativum*, and in some closely related legumes.

The essential facts which need to be considered in understanding the nature of the IAA oxidase system in peas, and the principal deductions to be drawn from them are:

(*a*) The enzymatic activity is inhibited by crystalline catalase (Goldacre, 1951), implying the intervention of H_2O_2 somewhere in the system (*Figure 6*).

(*b*) The inhibition conferred by catalase can be reversed by light (Galston and Baker, 1951), the action spectrum for such a light activation resembling the absorption spectrum of flavoproteins. Since reduced flavin enzymes are known to give rise to H_2O_2 upon reoxidation by molecular oxygen, we have inferred that the oxygen known to be required for the oxidation of IAA by the oxidase is involved in such a reaction.

(*c*) The enzymatic activity is inhibited by cyanide, azide, and other heavy-metal inhibitors (Tang and Bonner, 1947; Wagenknecht and Burris, 1950). This fact, together with the apparent requirement for H_2O_2, led us to conjecture that the oxidase was in fact composed of two moieties, a peroxide-generating system (presumably flavo-protein) and a peroxidase (Galston, Bonner, and Baker, 1953).

This conjecture has been supported by the construction of an analogous system consisting of xanthine oxidase and horseradish root peroxidase, which will oxidize IAA when some substrate for the flavo-protein moiety is

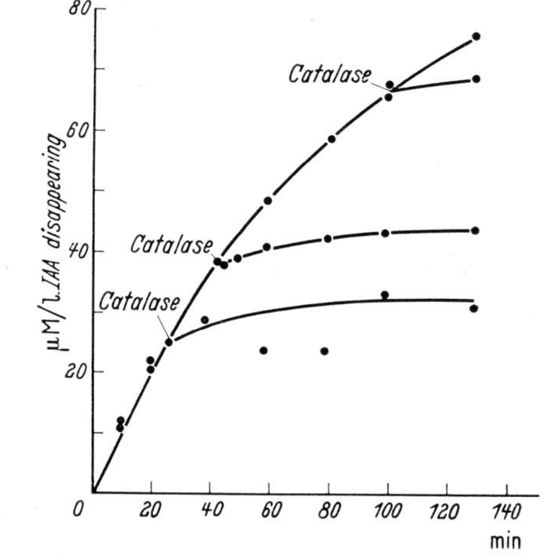

Figure 6. The inhibition of IAA-oxidase activity by crystalline catalase. At each arrow, the reaction mixture was divided, and catalase added to one aliquot.

supplied to the system (Galston *et al.*, 1953). Since, in the IAA oxidase, no such additional substrate is required, we have further postulated that IAA, like dioxymaleic acid (Swedin and Theorell, 1940), is capable of giving rise to a peroxide used in its own peroxidation. This conjectured peroxigenic action of IAA was first directly demonstrated by Andreae and Andreae (1953) and later confirmed in our own laboratory (Siegel and Galston, 1955; Pilet and Galston, 1955).

(*d*) One final fact concerning the enzyme needs to be recorded here, though its full significance is not yet completely appreciated. The action of the oxidase is greatly enhanced by certain cofactors, among which 2:4-dichlorophenol (DCP) (Goldacre, Galston, and Weintraub, 1953) and the manganous ion (Wagenknecht and Burris, 1950) are most effective. We have obtained direct evidence that both of these cofactors operate by increasing the effective peroxide level (Siegel and Galston, 1955), though Lockhart (1955) believes the effect of DCP to be directly on the peroxidase.

With this picture of the chemical nature of IAA-oxidase in mind, let us return to the etiolated pea seedling and inquire as to the functional significance, if any, of this auxin-destroying system. Miss Dalberg and I discovered two facts which seemed to us highly interesting (Galston and Dalberg, 1954). In the first place, roots, which are known to be much more sensitive to auxins than the aerial portions of the plant, have a tenfold higher oxidase activity than stems. Secondly, in both roots and stems, it is true that young, actively growing regions are very low in oxidase activity, while progressively older and older regions have successively higher and higher oxidase activity (*Figure 7*). This suggested that destruction of auxin by the oxidase system is actually a growth-regulatory mechanism.

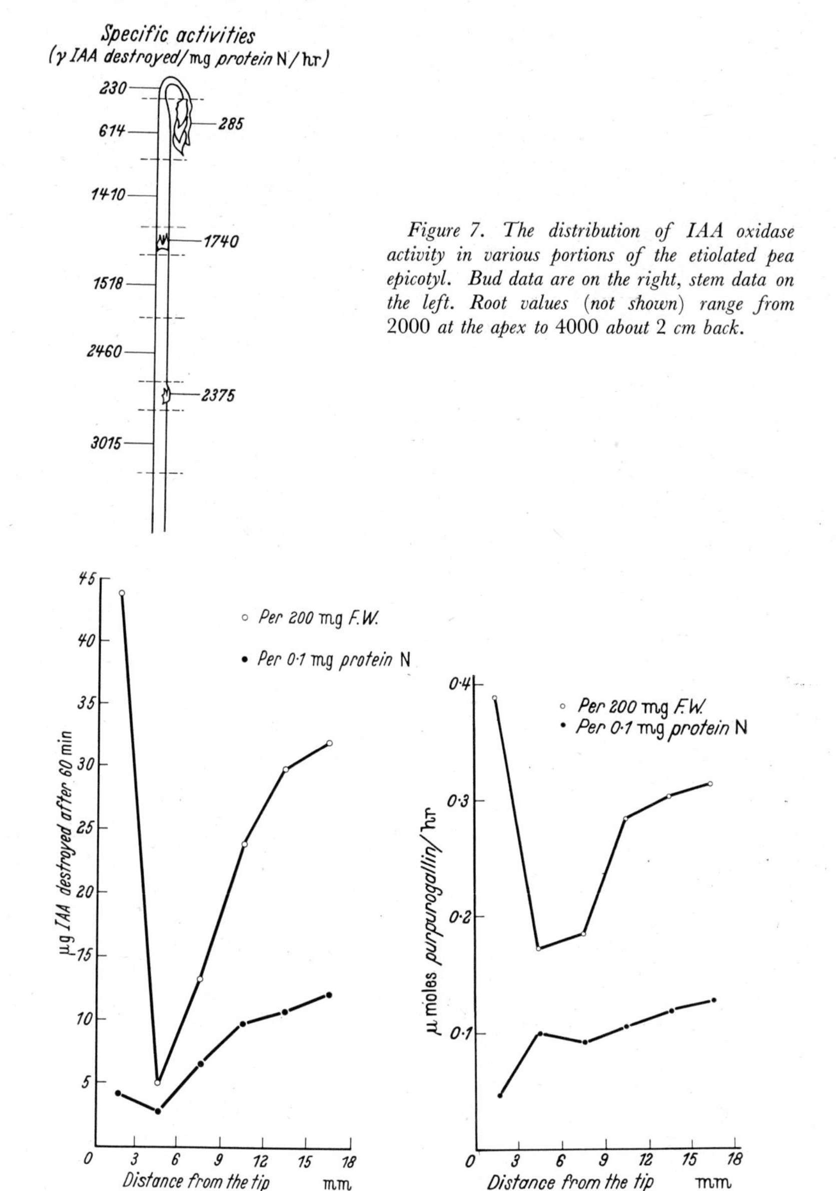

Figure 7. The distribution of IAA oxidase activity in various portions of the etiolated pea epicotyl. Bud data are on the right, stem data on the left. Root values (not shown) range from 2000 *at the apex to* 4000 *about* 2 *cm back.*

Figures 8, 9. The distribution of IAA-oxidase activity (Figure 8) and peroxide generating capacity (Figure 9) in successive 3 *mm sections of the primary root of* Lens culinaris.

If the oxidase activity increases as cells age, at least two major questions may be asked: (*a*) which of the two functional moieties of the enzyme manifest the increase in activity, and (*b*) by what mechanism is the increase in activity accomplished?

The answer to the first question seems to have been obtained by Dr. Pilet in the root of *Lens culinaris* (Pilet and Galston, 1955). He has found that the peroxide-generating capacity of the tissue closely parallels its IAA-oxidase activity, rising as the cells age (*Figures 8* and *9*). Peroxidase activity, on the other hand, shows no such increase, and may actually show a decline with age of the cell (*Figure 10*). Furthermore, the addition of the peroxigenic cofactor DCP raises peroxide genesis and IAA oxidase activity of the meristematic region tremendously, but has little or no effect on the older regions (*Figure 11*). This leads us to the conclusion that auxin destruction is normally limited by the peroxide-generating capacity of the tissue, which in turn is controlled by some naturally-occurring DCP-like substance. The mode of action of DCP is, as I have indicated, open to several interpretations (Siegel and Galston, 1955; Lockhart, 1955), but this subject cannot be further discussed here.

As for the second question, regarding the mechanism by which IAA oxidase activity is increased in older cells, the answer appears to be that this is somehow controlled by the IAA itself. We have found that if the young tissues, low in IAA-oxidase activity, are pretreated with physiological concentrations of IAA, then their capacity for IAA destruction increases (Galston and Dalberg, 1954). This phenomenon appears to be a case of induced enzyme formation, similar to those frequently described for micro-organisms. Maximal induction results from the administration of *ca.* 10^{-7} M IAA, a concentration which is certainly in the physiological range for stems though a little high for roots. Synthetic analogues of IAA, as well as certain compounds of the anti-auxin type, are capable of inducing greater IAA-oxidase activity, though they are not themselves substrates for the oxidase. This again resembles the situation in certain micro-organisms, where inductive activity has been demonstrated for molecules known not to be attacked by the induced enzyme.

The significance of the auxin-induced formation of an IAA-destroying system can only be conjectured about, but certain attractive possibilities present themselves. It seems possible that the decreased sensitivity to auxin of older cells is a consequence of their higher IAA oxidase activity, which in turn is a consequence of prior induction by IAA. According to this scheme, the administration of IAA to a young cell not only initiates growth, but also sets in motion a chain of events leading to the diminution and eventual culmination of growth. This, if true, is a neat example of the 'feed-back' required in all cybernetic systems. As I shall point out later, such an increased oxidase level may also be of morphogenetic significance for the cell.

The concept of the induced formation of an IAA-destroying system under certain auxin levels, and its possible 'de-inductive' disappearance under lower levels of auxin, permits the formulation of hypotheses to explain endogenous rhythms of auxin, lateral bud inhibition, and certain types of auxin interactions (Galston and Dalberg, 1954). These will not be further discussed here.

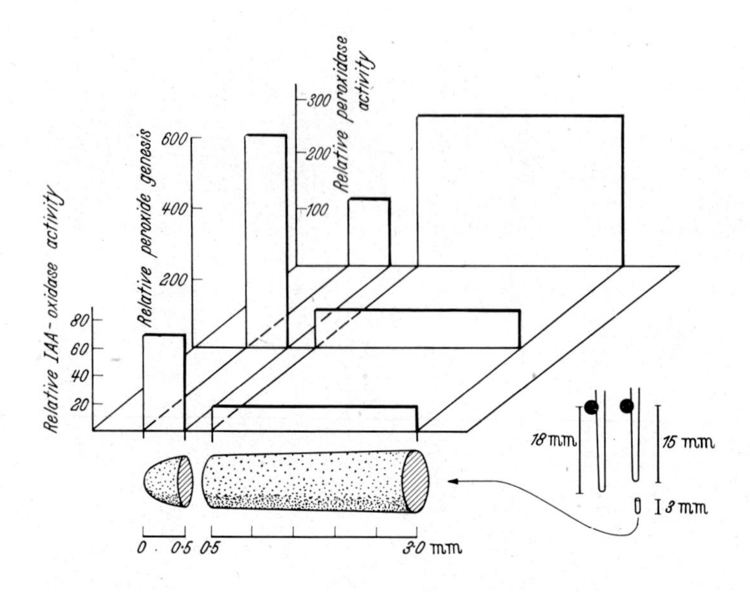

Figure 10. IAA oxidase and peroxidase activities and peroxide generating capacity in the apical 0·5 *mm (root cap) and subjacent region (growing area) of the* Lens *root.*

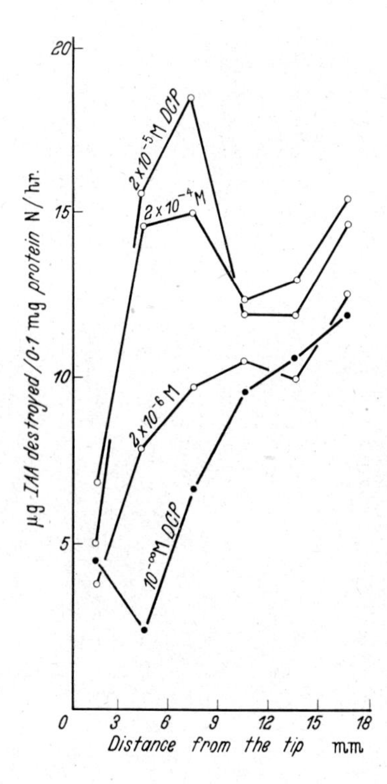

Figure 11. The effect of various levels of DCP on the IAA-oxidase activity of successive 3 *mm sections of the* Lens *root.*

THE INDUCTION OF PEROXIDASE ACTIVITY BY IAA AND ITS MORPHOGENETIC SIGNIFICANCE

Under certain conditions, it may be clearly shown that the peroxidase activity of the tissue, like the IAA oxidase activity and peroxide-generating capacity, rises in response to pretreatment with IAA. Dr. Siegel and I were able to show this with the excised 5 mm apices of 2-day-old pea seedling roots and also with young epicotyl tissue of week-old etiolated peas (Siegel and Galston, 1953). These experiments are carried out by incubating the appropriate tissue with *ca.* 10^{-7} M IAA for *ca.* 2 hours, then homogenizing the tissue and assaying the *brei* for peroxidase activity, using some appropriate substrate such as pyrogallol. In our best experiments, we were able to show about a 75 per cent increase in total peroxidase activity of pea root apices (*Figure 12*).

These experiments have been repeated and beautifully extended by Dr. W. A. Jensen (1955) working in our laboratories. Dr. Jensen had

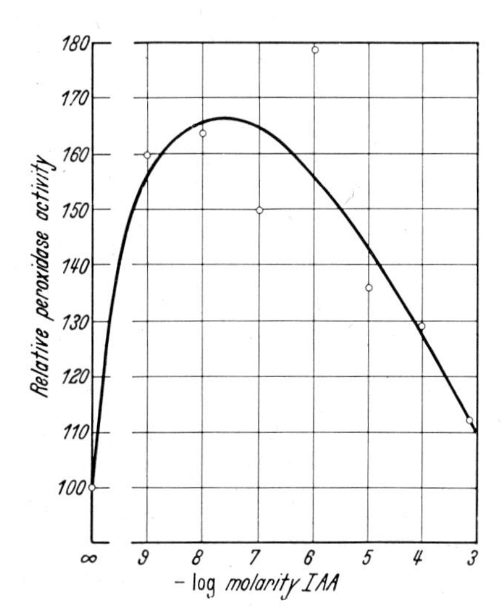

Figure 12. The effect of IAA pretreatment on the peroxidase activity of excised 5 mm apices of Pisum *roots.*

previously made a detailed anatomical analysis of the root of *Vicia faba* and so chose to work with this organ. Using successive 200 μ slices of the root, he was able to assay each for total peroxidase activity by the use of pyrogallol as a substrate. He was also able to carry out a histochemical localization of the peroxidase activity in the various slices of the root by employing as a substrate either benzidine or guaiacol, both of which produce insoluble, coloured end products of peroxidation. By the judicious application of both these techniques, he was able to determine which cells have peroxidase activity and how much activity each cell type has.

Dr. Jensen's results may be summarized as follows (*Figures 13* and *14*):

(*a*) The cells of the root cap are high in peroxidase activity, and this activity is not altered by preincubation of the root with IAA.

(*b*) The cells in the region of the general meristem are somewhat lower in peroxidase activity, but are likewise insensitive to IAA.

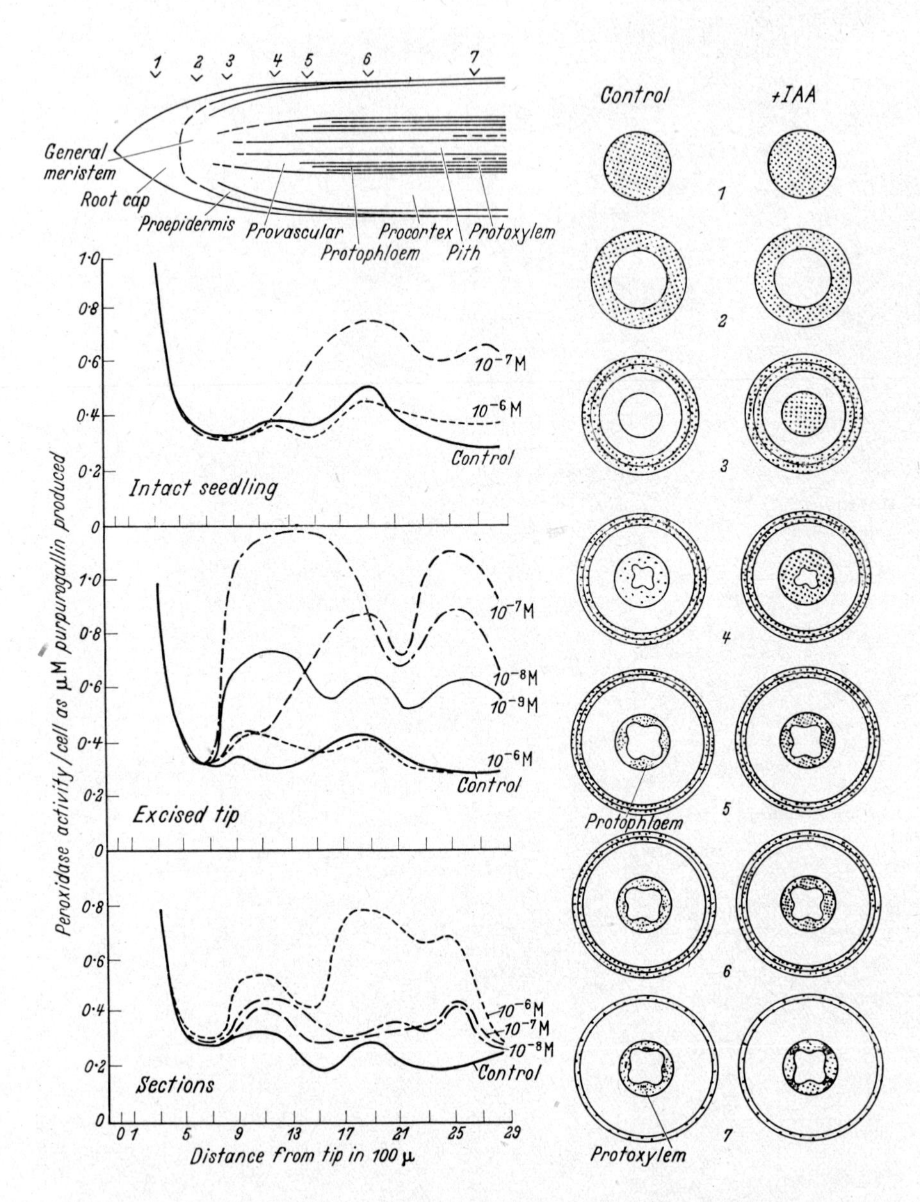

Figure 13. The effect of IAA pretreatment on the peroxidase activity of successive 200 μ *sections of* Vicia *roots. The IAA was applied to the roots either as the intact seedling (upper graph), as excised roots (middle graph) or as cut sections (lower graph). The figures at the right refer to the middle graph. They indicate relative peroxidase activity of sections cut at each of the* 7 *regions of the root shown by the numbers at the upper left. The darker the colouring, the greater is the peroxidase activity. Section* 1 *has only root cap; section* 2 *has root cap surrounding the meristem; the successive sections show root cap, cortex, and vascular tissues.*

(*c*) The cells in the region of elongation and early differentiation have a low level of peroxidase activity which may be dramatically increased by preincubation of the tissue with *ca.* 10^{-7} M IAA. Specifically, in these regions it is the potentially lignified cells of the xylem and phloem which show the marked increase in peroxidase activity, while cortex, epidermis, and pith show essentially no peroxidase activity either before or after treatment with IAA.

These results conform well with other recent discoveries. It has been demonstrated (Torrey, 1953) that administration of IAA to pea roots results in premature lignification, i.e. the occurrence of lignified cells closer to the root apex. It is also clear that IAA may promote the differentiation of xylem strands in a wounded stem of *Coleus* (Jacobs, 1952).

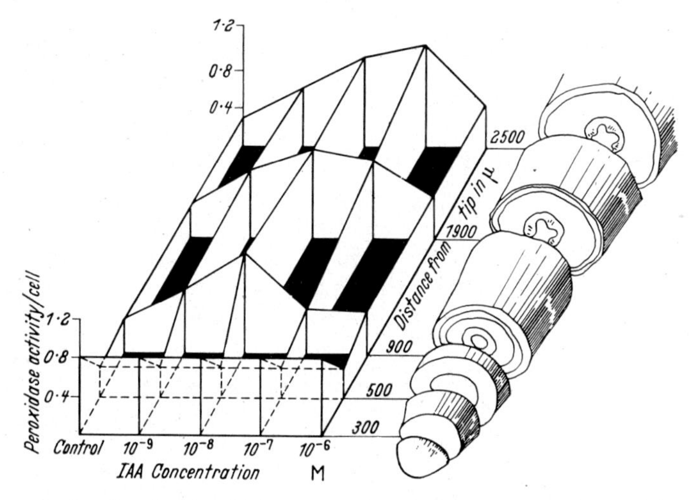

Figure 14. The effect of various IAA pretreatments on the subsequent peroxidase activity of successive sections of Vicia *roots. Note the marked effect of IAA on activity in the posterior sections, and the shift of the optimum from young to older tissues.*

How may the induced formation of peroxidase explain the lignogenic action of IAA? The answer is suggested by the work of Siegel (1955), who has demonstrated clearly that lignin is synthesized in certain plant cells by the action of peroxidase and H_2O_2 on hydroxyphenylpropane precursors such as eugenol. Fortified by this knowledge, Jensen was able to show, in his *Vicia* roots, that the same cells which are induced to higher peroxidase activity by IAA, have, after such induction, a greatly increased ability to convert eugenol to a lignin-like compound. *Thus, it appears that the morphogenetic action of IAA in promoting lignification is mediated by the induced formation, in certain cells, of a lignin-synthesizing peroxidase.*

Recently, Dr. I. B. Perlis, also working in our laboratories, has been making a study of the peroxidases of the etiolated pea seedling. He has found, as have others (Jermyn and Thomas, 1954; Kondo and Morita, 1952), that if one subjects the *brei* to chromatography or to paper electrophoresis, several (probably five) distinct peroxidases appear. These peroxidases differ not only in chromatographic and electrophoretic mobility, but also in substrate preference. We are now endeavouring to find which of these fractions responds inductively to IAA, both with regard to IAA destruction and to lignin biosynthesis.

SUMMARY

What emerges from these studies is a tentative picture of the ways in which the plant growth hormone, indoleacetic acid, may be responsible not only for the growth of a plant cell, but also for the cessation of growth, and for the differentiation of some cells into lignified elements. In the latter two processes, the metabolism of peroxides seems to play a major role.

REFERENCES

ANDREAE, W. A., and ANDREAE, S. R. (1953). Studies on indoleacetic acid metabolism. I. *Canad. J. Bot.* **31,** 426.

BEADLE, G. W., MITCHELL, H. K., and NYC, J. F. (1947). Kynurenine as an intermediate in the formation of nicotinic acid from tryptophane by *Neurospora*. *Proc. Nat. Acad. Sci., Wash.* **33,** 155.

GALSTON, A. W., and BAKER, R. S. (1951). Studies on the physiology of light action. III. Light activation of a flavoprotein enzyme by reversal of a naturally-occurring inhibition. *Amer. J. Bot.* **38,** 190.

GALSTON, A. W., and DALBERG, L. (1954). The adaptive formation and physiological significance of indoleacetic acid oxidase. *Amer. J. Bot.* **41,** 373.

GALSTON, A. W., BONNER, J., and BAKER, R. S. (1953). Flavoprotein and peroxidase as components of the indoleacetic acid oxidase system of peas. *Arch. Biochem. Biophys.* **42,** 456.

GOLDACRE, P. L. (1951). Hydrogen peroxide in the enzymic oxidation of heteroauxin. *Aust. J. Sci. Res.* **B4,** 293.

GOLDACRE, P. L., GALSTON, A. W., and WEINTRAUB, R. L. (1953). The effect of substituted phenols on the activity of the indoleacetic acid oxidase of peas. *Arch. Biochem. Biophys.* **43,** 358.

GORTNER, W. A., and KENT, M. (1953). Indoleacetic acid oxidase and an inhibitor in pineapple tissue. *J. biol. Chem.* **204,** 593.

JACOBS, W. P. (1952). The role of auxin in differentiation of xylem around a wound. *Amer. J. Bot.* **39,** 301.

JENSEN, W. A. (1955). The induction of peroxidase activity by indoleacetic acid. II. Histochemical localization. *Plant Physiol.* **30,** No. 5, 426.

JERMYN, M. A., and THOMAS, R. (1954). Multiple components in horseradish root peroxidase. *Biochem. J.* **56,** 631.

KONDO, K., and MORITA, Y. (1952). Phytoperoxidase II. *Bull. Res. Inst. Food Sci., Kyoto Univ.* **10,** 33.

LARSEN, P. (1951). Formation, occurrence and inactivation of growth substances. *Ann. Rev. Pl. Physiol.* **2,** 169.

LOCKHART, J. (1955). The role of 2:4-dichlorophenol in the destruction of indoleacetic acid by peroxidase. *Plant Physiol.* **30,** 86.

MANNING, D. T., and GALSTON, A. W. (1955). On the nature of the enzymatically catalysed oxidation products of indole-acetic acid. *Plant Physiol.* **30,** 225.

PILET, P. E., and GALSTON, A. W. (1955). Auxin destruction, peroxidase activity and peroxide genesis in the roots of *Lens culinaris*. *Physiol. Plant.* **8,** 888.

PLATT R. S., Jr. (1954). The inactivation of auxin in normal and tumorous tissues. *Ann. Biol.* **30,** 89.

SEQUEIRA, L., and STEEVES, T. (1954). Auxin inactivation and its relation to leaf drop caused by the fungus *Omphalia flavida*. *Plant Physiol.* **29,** 11.

SIEGEL, S. M. (1955). The biochemistry of lignin formation. *Physiol. Plant.* **8,** 20.
SIEGEL, S. M., and GALSTON, A. W. (1953). Experimental coupling of indoleacetic acid to pea root protein *in vivo* and *in vitro*. *Proc. Nat. Acad. Sci., Wash.* **39,** 1111.
SIEGEL, S. M., and GALSTON, A. W. (1955). Peroxide genesis in plant tissues and its relation to indoleacetic acid destruction. *Arch. Biochem. Biophys.* **54,** 102.
SWEDIN, B., and THEORELL, H. (1940). Dioxymaleic acid oxidase action of peroxidases. *Nature,* **145,** 71.
TANG, Y. W., and BONNER, J. (1947). The enzymatic inactivation of indoleacetic acid. I. Some characteristics of the enzyme contained in pea seedlings. *Arch. Biochem.* **13,** 11.
TONHAZY, N., and PELCZAR, M. J., Jr. (1954). Oxidation of indoleacetic acid by an extracellular enzyme from *Polyporus versicolor* and a similar oxidation catalyzed by nitrite. *Science,* **120,** 141.
TORREY, J. (1953). The effect of certain metabolic inhibitors on vascular tissue differentiation in isolated pea roots. *Amer. J. Bot.* **40,** 525.
WAGENKNECHT, A. C., and BURRIS, R. H. (1950). Indoleacetic acid inactivating enzymes from bean roots and pea seedlings. *Arch. Biochem.* **25,** 30.

Note added in proof

Since this manuscript was prepared for publication, several articles have appeared which bear on the subject matter discussed here.

(1) Auxin-protein formation in pea extracts has been independently demonstrated (Marré, 1955) with naphthylacetic acid.
(2) The formation of indoleacetylaspartic acid in pea seedlings has been unequivocally shown (Andreae and Good, 1955). This compound, which predominates over free IAA in the *brei* of IAA-treated tissues, resembles in several respects the IAA-complex split from the IAA-protein by the action of Coenzyme A.
(3) The fate of IAA exposed to various IAA oxidase preparations has been further investigated. In pea *brei*, 3-indolealdehyde has been isolated as a minor product of the reaction (Racusen, 1955). In *Omphalia* enzyme preparations, there is some evidence of oxindole formation (Ray and Thimann, 1955).
(4) The role of naturally-occurring phenols in the peroxidative destruction of IAA has been investigated (Kenten, 1955).
(5) The *in vivo* significance of auxin destruction in *Osmunda* has been challenged (Briggs *et al.*, 1955a, b) on the basis that auxin translocation occurs readily through tissues which, when converted to a *brei*, rapidly inactivate IAA.
(6) The xylogenic action of IAA has been confirmed in cultured callus tissues (Wetmore, 1955).
(7) Indirect confirmation of the induction of IAA oxidase activity by auxin has been obtained (Åberg and Jönsson, 1955).

REFERENCES

ÅBERG, B., and JÖNSSON, E. (1955). Studies on plant growth regulators. XI. Experiments with pea roots, including some observations on the destruction of indoleacetic acid by different types of roots. *LantbrHögsk. Ann.* **21,** 401.
ANDREAE, W. A., and GOOD, N. E. (1955). The formation of indoleacetylaspartic acid in pea seedlings. *Plant Physiol.* **30,** 380.
BRIGGS, W. R., MOREL, G., STEEVES, T. A., SUSSEX, I. M., and WETMORE, R. H. (1955a). Enzymatic auxin inactivation by extracts of the fern *Osmunda cinnamomea* L. *Plant Physiol.* **30,** 143.
BRIGGS, W. R., STEEVES, T. A., SUSSEX, I. M., and WETMORE, R. H. (1955b). A comparison of auxin destruction by tissue extracts and intact tissues of the fern *Osmunda cinnamomea* L. *Plant Physiol.* **30,** 148.
KENTEN, R. H. (1955). The oxidation of indolyl-3-acetic acid by waxpod bean root sap and peroxidase systems. *Biochem. J.* **59,** 110.
MARRÉ, E. (1955). Spectrophotometric demonstration of the formation of auxin-protein complexes by the sulfhydryl groups in vegetable enzyme preparations. *R. C. Accad. Lincei,* **18,** 88.
RACUSEN, D. (1955). Formation of indole-3-aldehyde by indoleacetic oxidase. *Arch. Biochem. Biophys.* **58,** 508.
RAY, P. M., and THIMANN, K. V. (1955). Steps in the oxidation of indoleacetic acid. *Science,* **122,** 187.
WETMORE, R. H. (1955). Differentiation of xylem in plants. *Science,* **121,** 626.

CHROMATOGRAPHIC INVESTIGATIONS ON THE METABOLISM OF CERTAIN INDOLE DERIVATIVES IN PLANT TISSUES†

R. C. Seeley
Chemistry Department, Wye College, University of London

and

C. H. Fawcett, R. L. Wain, and F. Wightman
Agricultural Research Council Unit on Plant Growth Substances and Systemic Fungicides, Wye College, University of London

INTRODUCTION

Of the indole derivatives known to be active as plant growth substances, indole-3-acetic acid has been shown to be widely distributed in plant tissues, while indole-3-acetonitrile, indole-3-acetaldehyde, and ethylindole-3-acetate have been identified in tissue extracts of several plant species. It is generally believed that indole-3-acetic acid has primary auxin activity, i.e. is active *per se*, but the mode of action of other indolyl derivatives is still a matter of conjecture. In the present investigations some information on the fate of indolyl compounds in various plant tissues was obtained by applying methods similar to those used at Wye in studies on the breakdown of ω-phenoxyalkanecarboxylic acids, amides, and nitriles in plants (Fawcett, Taylor, Wain, and Wightman, 1956). Briefly, the over-all procedure involved exposing solutions of indolyl derivatives to plant tissue with subsequent extraction and paper chromatographic separation of the products in the tissues and in the residual solution. After development, the chromatograms were examined by chromogenic and biological methods.

MATERIALS AND METHODS

The compounds examined were indole-3-acetic acid (IAA), indole-3-acetonitrile (IAN), indole-3-acetamide (IAAm), and methyl indole-3-acetate (IAMe). Solutions of pure samples of each of these substances were exposed separately to pea stem, wheat and maize coleoptile, and tomato and celery petiole tissues. In each treatment one hundred 1 cm segments of tissue were floated on 50 ml of aqueous solutions containing 500 μg (10 p.p.m.) of the substance. The solutions were incubated for 18 hours at 25°C, a water plus tissue control being included with each batch of treatments.

The solutions and tissues were extracted separately. Solutions were acidified to pH 6·5, extracted three times with peroxide-free ether, the combined ether layers dried over sodium sulphate, and the ether removed. The tissues were first washed several times with water and then immersed in peroxide-free ether at 10°C for 24 hours. The ether was then decanted off,

† This paper was read at the Conference by R. C. Seeley.

the segments washed with two further quantities of ether, and the combined ether extract treated as above.

Chromatography was carried out in all-glass apparatus at 20°C using the descending technique. All extracts were normally run in *n*-butanol/ammonia (0·880)/water (100 : 3 : 18) solvent, though sometimes *iso*-propanol/ammonia/ water (10:1:1) was employed. Chromatograms for chromogenic analysis were spotted with amounts of ether extract equivalent to 200 μg of the compound in the original solution. After development, the paper strips were dried in air and in most cases sprayed with Ehrlich's reagent applied as 1 per cent *p*-dimethylaminobenzaldehyde in alcohol followed by conc. HCl. Other sprays, such as 2 N HCl containing 0·05 per cent $NaNO_2$, and diazotized *p*-nitroaniline, were also used.

When preparing chromatograms for biological examination, ether extract equivalent to 1000 μg of original substance was evenly distributed over 20 spots on a sheet of Whatman No. 1 paper (8 in. wide). After development, a longitudinal strip containing 2 spots was removed from one side of the chromatogram and sprayed with Ehrlich's reagent to establish the position of indolyl compounds. The rest of the sheet was divided transversely into strips each corresponding to one tenth of the distance travelled by the solvent front. Two thirds of each strip ($\equiv$ 600 μg) was placed in a petri dish with 20 ml of water for assay in the pea curvature test. The remaining third ($\equiv$ 300 μg) was immersed in 5 ml of water in a 5 cm dish for the wheat elongation test.

The segments for the curvature test were taken from the third internode of pea plants (var. Alaska) grown for seven days under red light at a constant temperature of 25°C. Five segments were placed in each petri dish. The material for the elongation test was excised from 2 cm wheat coleoptiles (var. Eclipse) grown for 72 hours at 25°C in an atmosphere of high humidity. 10 mm segments were used in preliminary experiments to determine the growth-promoting activity of the four indolyl compounds (see *Figure 1*), but 5 mm segments were always used for the assay of chromatogram strips. The segments were threaded on glass rods, two segments per rod, ten segments being placed in each test solution.

Biological testing was restricted to solution extracts. This procedure was adopted because, although the colour chromatograms of tissue extracts revealed the presence of the same indolyl compounds as those observed on chromatograms of the corresponding solution extracts, the quantities present were always very small. Moreover, the presence of pigments and fatty substances extracted from the tissues tended to interfere with the chromatography.

EXPERIMENTAL RESULTS

The four compounds studied in this investigation are all active in the coleoptile extension test (*Figure 1*), although the activity of the amide is low. IAA, IAAm, and IAMe are active in the pea curvature test (*Figure 2*), but IAN is inactive at the usual physiological concentrations.

Chromatography of the extracts of solutions of all four compounds incubated for 18 hours at 25°C in the absence of tissue showed that they were effectively stable under these conditions.

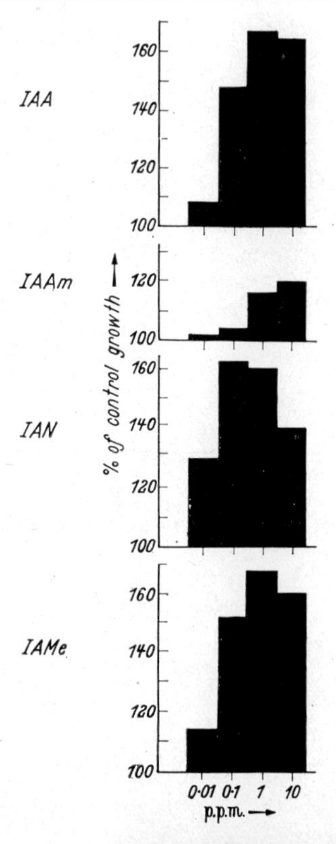

Figure 1. Histograms showing the activities of indole-3-acetic acid, -acetamide, -acetonitrile, and methyl ester in the wheat cylinder test.

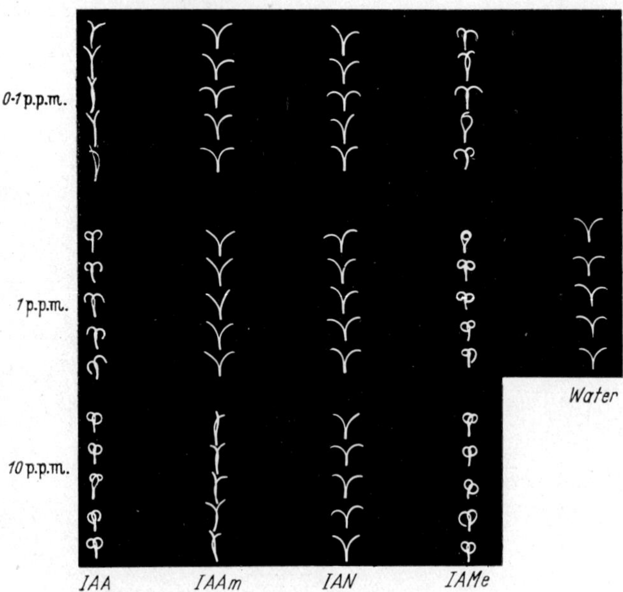

Figure 2. The activities of indole-3-acetic acid, -acetamide, and -acetonitrile and the methyl ester of indole-3-acetic acid in the pea curvature test.

Solutions treated with wheat coleoptile tissue

The colour chromatogram of the extracts from wheat treated solutions (*Figure 3*) showed no clear spots in the extract of the water control. Treated IAA gave rise to a large blue area, corresponding to that formed by authentic IAA, with a diffuse pink streak below; there was also an ill-defined dark area between R_f 0·8–1·0. The treated IAAm showed only the blue area corresponding to authentic IAAm, succeeded by a dark area, R_f 0·8–1·0, which was also apparent in the products of IAN treatment, below the

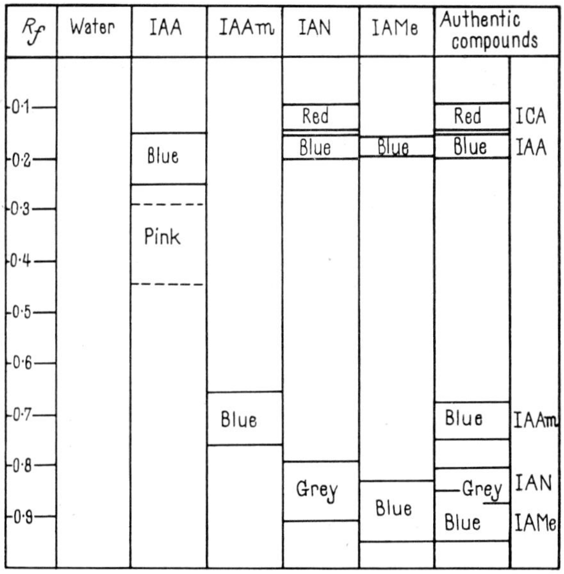

Figure 3. Diagrammatic representation of a colour chromatogram of extracts from solutions treated with wheat tissue. The chromatogram was developed in n-*butanol/ammonia/water* (100 : 3 : 18) *and subsequently sprayed with Ehrlich's reagent.*

IAN region of the chromatogram. Although there was no visible production of IAA from the amide, the nitrile gave rise to a blue area corresponding to that given by authentic IAA, with a red spot above corresponding in R_f to indole-3-carboxylic acid (ICA). The colour chromatogram of the methyl ester showed the formation of IAA.

Biological examination of another chromatogram of the same extracts substantiated the evidence shown by the colour chromatogram of the kinds of degradation occurring during treatment with wheat tissue. The histograms of the results obtained in the coleoptile elongation test (*Figure 4*) shows peak of activity corresponding to IAA, IAAm, IAN, and IAMe where they occur in the chromatograms. A slight peak of activity between R_f 0·1–0·2 in the IAAm chromatogram suggests the formation of a small amount of IAA not detected on the colour chromatogram. Activity in the region of R_f 0·8–1·0 in the water extract which is increasingly evident in the case of the IAA and IAAm extracts appears to correspond with dark areas in this region of the

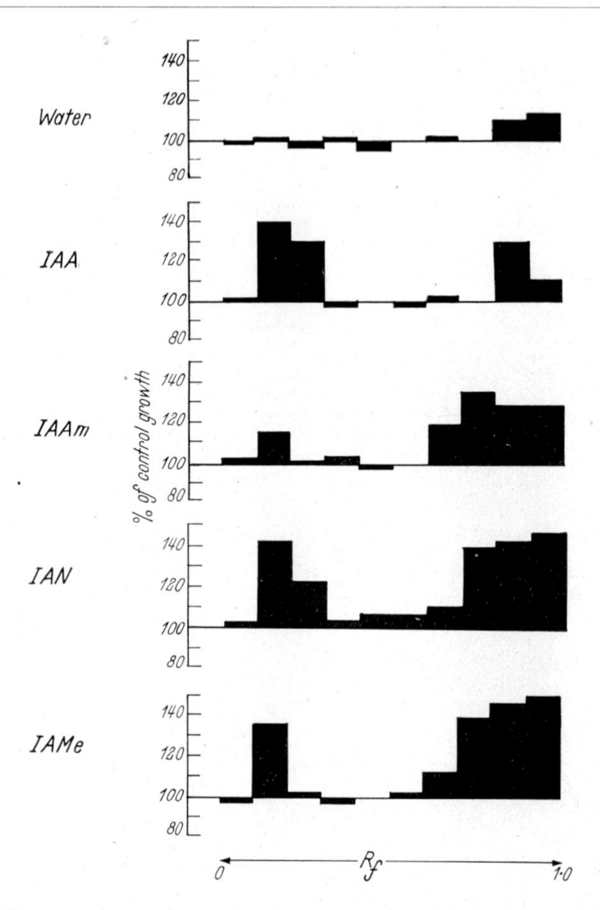

Figure 4. Histograms showing the activities in the wheat cylinder test of chromatograms of extracts from solutions treated with wheat tissue.

The chromatograms, developed in n-*butanol/ammonia/water* (100 : 3 : 18), *were divided into strips corresponding to one-tenth of the solvent flow.*

chromatogram previously noted. The results of the pea tests (*Figure 5*) show activity only in those regions where IAA, IAAm, or IAMe formed spots visible on the colour chromatograms.

Solutions treated with pea stem tissue

Examination of the colour chromatograms obtained from this treatment (*Figure 6*) showed that, as with wheat tissue, IAA gave rise to a pink area below the acid at R_f 0·2–0·35. The amide, however, behaved quite differently in this instance, giving rise to a well-marked IAA spot, whereas the nitrile gave no IAA and only a small amount of ICA. IAMe gave a distinct blue spot of IAA and a pink-staining degradation product running at R_f 0·2–0·3.

The histograms showing the results obtained in the coleoptile elongation test (*Figure 7*) indicate the presence of a small amount of IAA in the water extract. This loss of IAA from pea stem tissue is substantiated by the fact

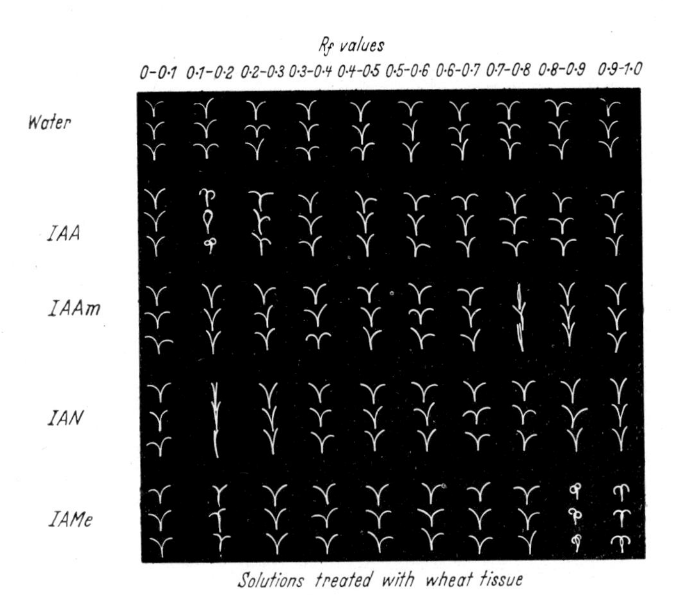

Figure 5. Bio-assay of chromatogram of extracts from wheat treated solutions using the pea curvature test.

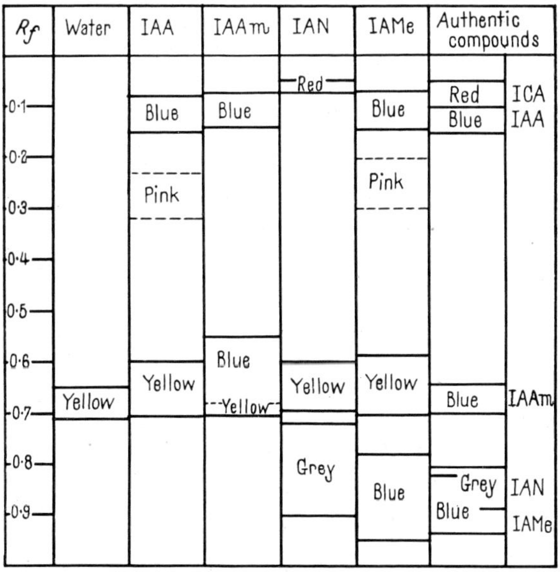

Rf | Water | IAA | IAAm | IAN | IAMe | Authentic compounds

0·1 0·2 0·3 0·4 0·5 0·6 0·7 0·8 0·9

Water: Yellow

IAA: Blue, Pink, Yellow

IAAm: Blue, Blue, Yellow

IAN: Red, Yellow, Grey

IAMe: Blue, Pink, Yellow, Blue

Authentic compounds: Red ICA, Blue IAA, Blue IAAm, Grey IAN, Blue IAMe

Figure 6. Diagrammatic representation of a colour chromatogram of extracts from solutions treated with pea tissue. The chromatogram was developed and treated as described in Figure 3.

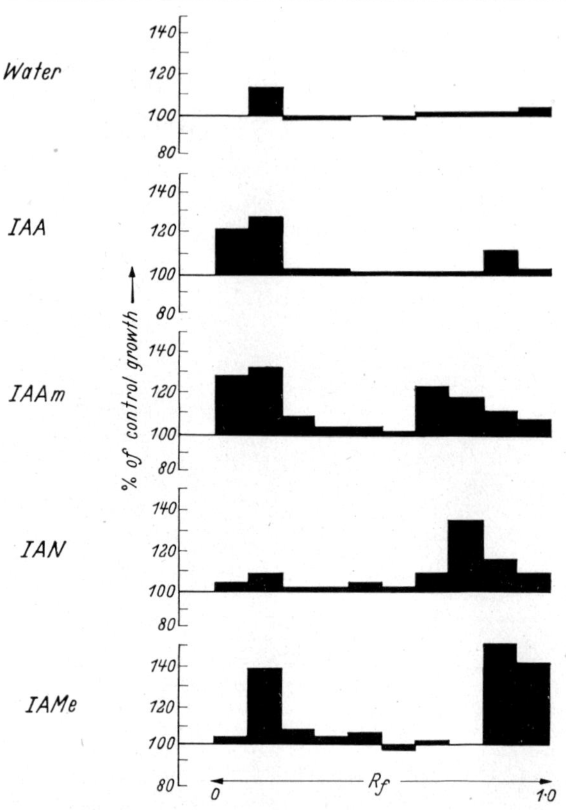

Figure 7. Histograms showing the activities in the wheat cylinder test of chromatograms of extracts from solutions treated with pea tissue.

The chromatograms were developed and segmented as described in Figure 4.

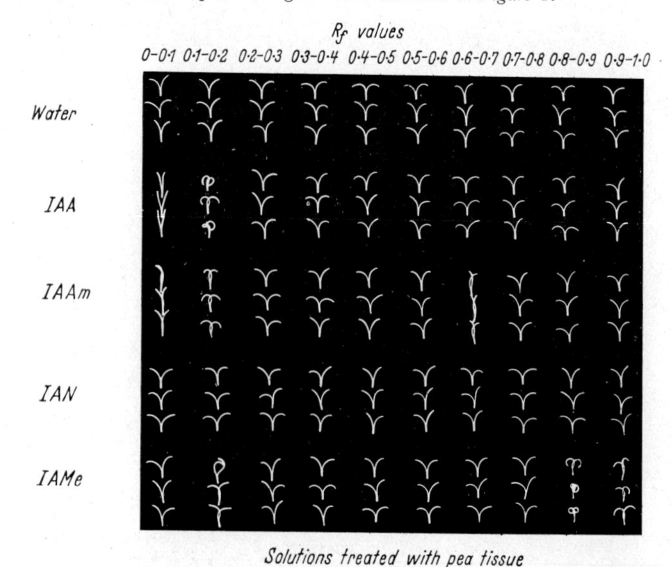

Figure 8. Bio-assay of chromatogram of extracts from pea-treated solutions using the pea curvature test.

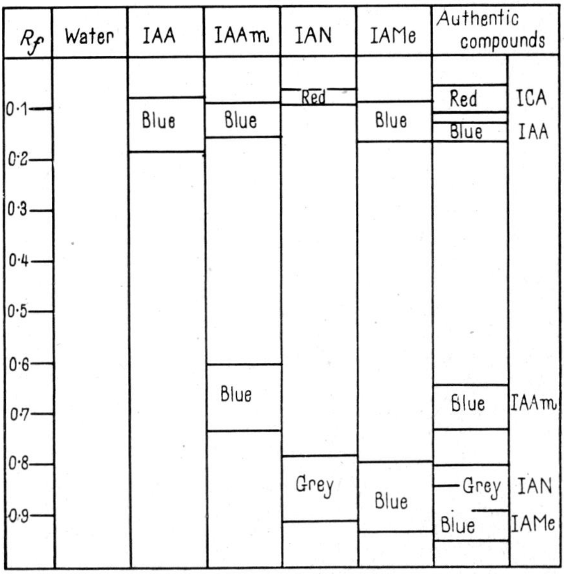

Figure 9.

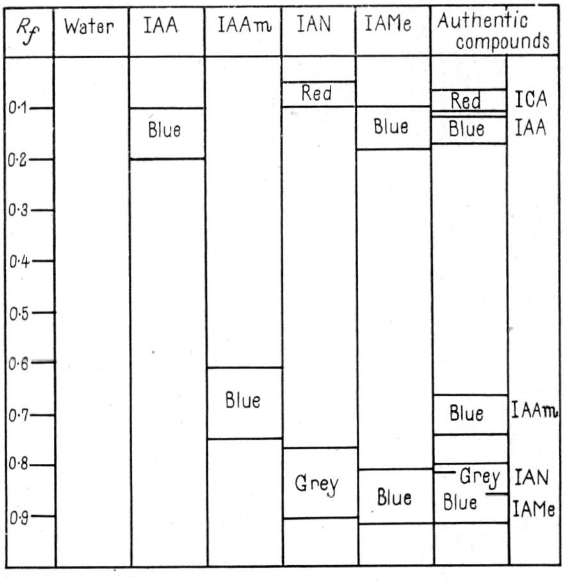

Figure 10.

Figures 9 and 10. Diagrammatic representations of colour chromatograms of extracts from solutions treated with tomato tissue (Figure 9) and celery tissue (Figure 10).

The chromatograms were developed and treated as described in Figure 3.

that a small amount of IAA was also evident in the extract of the AIN solution. With the extracts of all four compounds, peaks of activity occurred in the areas corresponding to the positions of unchanged acid, amide, nitrile, and ester. In the case of IAAm and IAMe, there is clear evidence of a second peak of activity between R_f 0·1–0·3 which strongly indicates the formation of IAA from these compounds. The results of the pea curvature test (*Figure 8*) support this conclusion for they confirm the presence of activity in the IAA region on chromatograms developed from pea-treated IAA, IAAm, and IAMe. Activity is also found in this test in the areas corresponding to unchanged IAAm and IAMe.

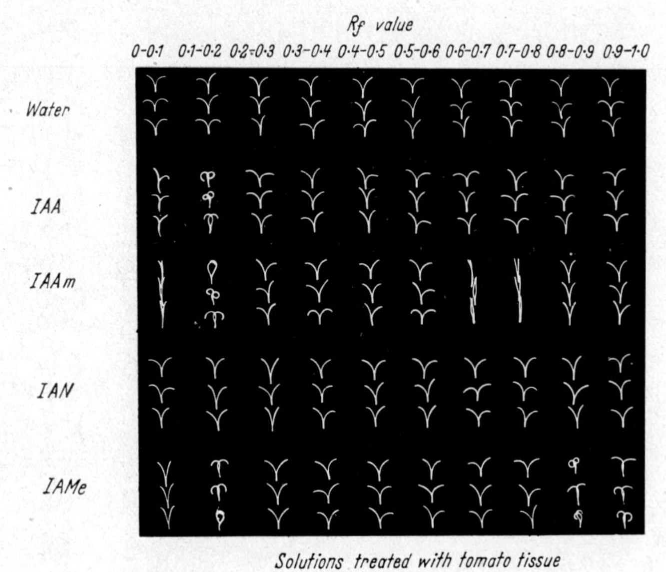

Figure 11. Bio-assay of chromatogram of extracts from tomato-treated solutions using the pea curvature test.

Solutions treated with tomato, celery, and maize tissues

The effects of tomato tissue treatment were essentially similar to those produced by pea tissue as is shown by the colour chromatograms (*Figure 9*), the histogram of the wheat cylinder test results (*Figure 12*), and the results of the pea test (*Figure 11*). Treatment with celery tissue, however, while producing some breakdown of IAN leading to the production of a trace of ICA but no IAA, also failed to produce enough IAA from IAAm to enable its detection on the colour chromatogram (*Figure 10*). The production of a little IAA from the amide is, however, suggested by the corresponding results in the wheat cylinder test (*Figure 13*), though the results in the pea test (*Figure 15*) show no trace of the acid. The methyl ester, on the other hand, was again readily converted to IAA.

The histograms of both tomato and celery treated IAN show less activity between R_f 0·8–0·9 than between 0·7–0·8 or 0·9–1·0. In these instances the elongation of the wheat segments used to determine the biological activity

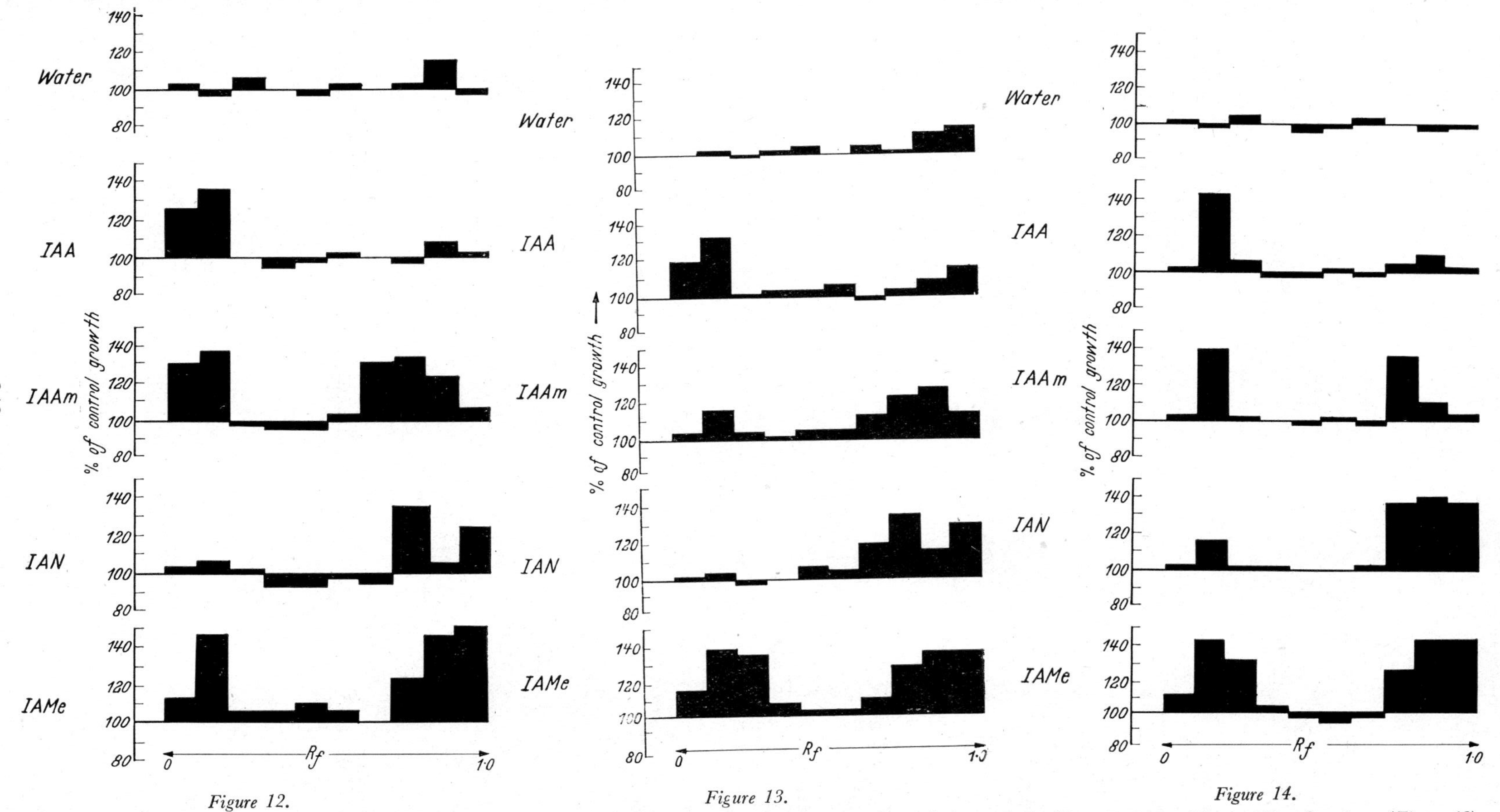

Figure 12.

Figure 13.

Figure 14.

Figures 12, 13, and 14. Histograms showing the activities in the wheat cylinder test of chromatograms of extracts from solutions treated with tomato tissue (Figure 12), celery tissue (Figure 13), and maize tissue (Figure 14). The chromatograms were developed and segmented as described in Figure 4.

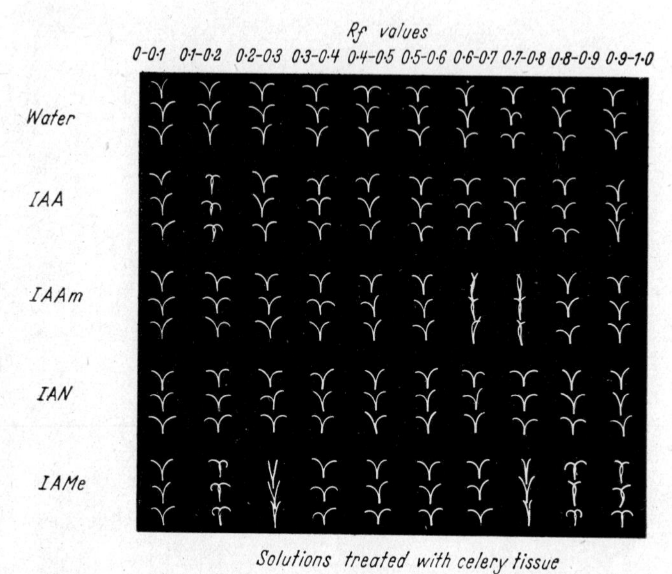

Figure 15. Bio-assay of chromatogram of extracts from celery-treated solutions using the pea curvature test.

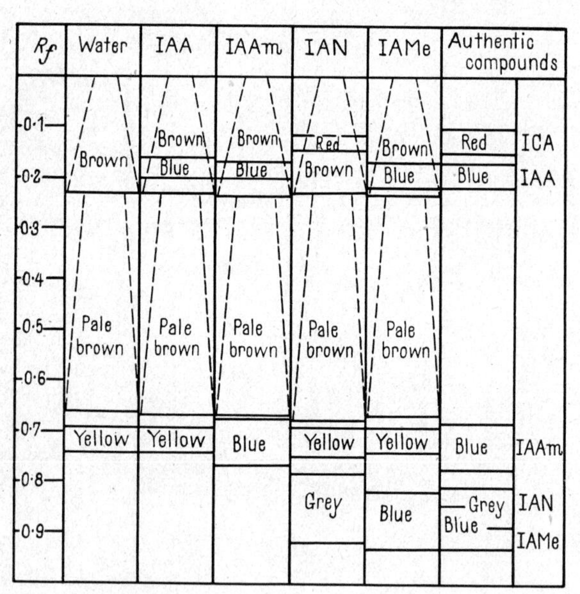

Figure 16. Diagrammatic representation of a colour chromatogram of extracts from solutions treated with maize tissue.
The chromatogram was developed and treated as described in Figure 3.

of the 0·8–0·9 portion of the paper was inhibited by toxicity which can be attributed to a high concentration of IAN.

The colour chromatogram of solutions treated with maize coleoptiles (*Figure 16*), although masked by brown pigments extracted from the tissue, shows extensive conversion of the amide to IAA, a small production of ICA from the nitrile with apparently no formation of IAA, and as with all other tissues so far employed, a considerable conversion of the methyl ester to the acid. These conclusions are supported in the main by the results in the wheat cylinder test (*Figure 14*) and in the pea test (*Figure 17*). The bio-assay of the IAN chromatogram, however, showed activity at R_f 0·1–0·2, which suggests that a small amount of IAA is formed from the nitrile.

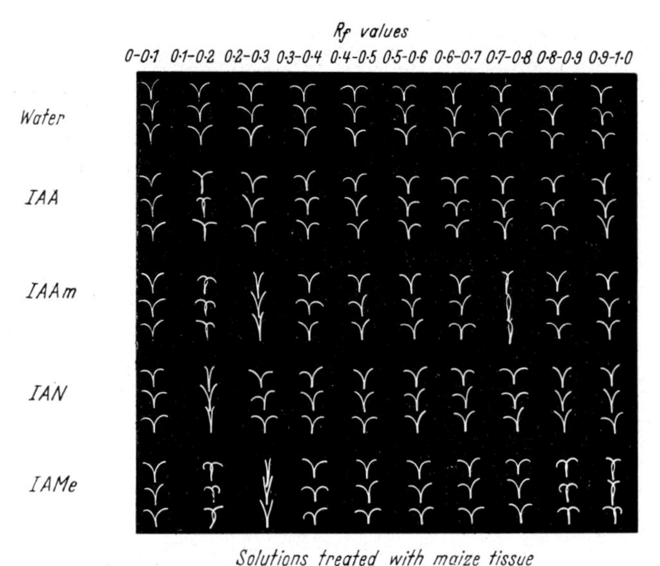

Figure 17. Bio-assay of chromatogram of extracts from maize-treated solutions using the pea curvature test.

DISCUSSION

The present series of results indicate that the activities of IAAm, IAN, and IAMe in the wheat cylinder and pea curvature tests are related to their hydrolysis to IAA within the tissues of the test material. The conversion of IAN to IAA by oat coleoptile tissue has been previously reported by Bentley and Housley (1952) and by Thimann (1953), although, as was shown by Jones *et al.* (1952), the amount of acid produced is quite small in relation to the activity of the nitrile. Wheat tissue seems to behave in essentially the same manner as oat tissue, though in this instance the amount of acid produced appears to be fairly substantial (see *Figure 4*). The inactivity of IAN in the pea test is explicable from the present results, which show no evidence of the production of IAA when solutions of the nitrile were exposed to pea stem tissue. This result was also found by Thimann (1953), who further reported that IAN showed slight growth-promoting activity in the split maize coleoptile test. The slight conversion of IAN to IAA by maize tissue shown in this investigation (*Figure 14*) would seem to confirm Thimann's result.

The amide has been suggested as a possible intermediate in the conversion of IAN to IAA (Bentley and Housley, 1952; Jones *et al.*, 1952), although it was not detected by Stowe and Thimann (1954) during their chromatographic study of the breakdown of IAN by oat tissue. The results from the present investigation show that pea and tomato tissues are unable to hydrolyse IAN to IAA, though they can convert the amide to the acid. Wheat tissue, on the other hand, is able to hydrolyse the nitrile to the acid, but apparently can only effect slight conversion of the amide to the acid (*Figures 3* and *4*). This evidence, coupled with the complete absence of any chromogenic indication of IAAm formation during the hydrolysis by IAN by wheat tissue, strongly indicates that free amide is not an intermediate in the hydrolysis of IAN in plant tissues.

The slight hydrolysis of the nitrile and ready conversion of the amide to IAA by maize tissue when compared with the effects of wheat tissue on these two compounds, suggests interesting differences in the enzymatic make-up of these closely related species. On the other hand, celery tissue which effects only slight hydrolysis of both amide and nitrile, appears to differ from all other tissues examined. All the tissues under discussion, however, appear to have one property in common, they are all capable of readily converting IAMe to IAA.

One of the most interesting observations recorded in this work is the appearance of a substance during the metabolism of IAN by wheat tissue which behaves on the chromatogram like indole-3-carboxylic acid. The identification of this substance, which is also produced, though to a lesser extent, when IAN is treated with the other tissues employed, has received further study. Since treatment with wheat tissue appears to effect the best conversion of IAN to this compound, extracts of nitrile solutions treated in this manner have been used to confirm its identity with indole-3-carboxylic acid.

It was shown, by chromogenic estimation, that the amount of this substance formed by a given amount of wheat tissue (50×1 cm coleoptile segments) markedly increased when the supply of IAN in the test solutions (50 ml) was increased (i.e. the amount formed was proportional to the concentration of IAN up to 4 mg/l.). Similarly, the compound was never formed from IAN in the absence of living tissue, maximum conversion being achieved with 50 coleoptile segments per 200 μg IAN.

When an extract of wheat-treated IAN was run in two different solvents (butanol:ammonia:water, and *iso*propanol:ammonia:water) and using two different types of chromatographic paper (Whatman No. 1 and 'Devon Valley' 431 Mill blotting paper) the compound always moved the same distance as authentic indole-3-carboxylic acid. Since blotting paper permits a fairly rapid movement of the solvent a wider separation of IAA and suspected ICA could be achieved by allowing the solvent front to flow off the paper. Using this technique, it has been possible to separate and extract *ca.* 0·1 mg of the suspected ICA from large volumes of wheat-treated IAN solutions. This extract was submitted to Professor E. A. Braude (Imperial College, London) for ultra-violet spectrographic analysis, the results of which strongly suggest its identity with indole-3-carboxylic acid. In a later experiment, the infra-red absorption spectrum was shown by Mr. J. G. Reynolds (Woodstock Research Station, Sittingbourne) to be identical with that of ICA. Finally, the *p*-phenylphenacyl ester of the acid in the extract was prepared and it was shown that its melting point was not depressed by admixture with the *p*-phenylphenacyl ester of indole-3-carboxylic acid. The identity of the acid in the extract was therefore fully established as indole-3-carboxylic acid. This same indole compound has recently been found in pea tissue by Cartwright, Sykes, and Wain (1956).

All these experiments then, strongly suggest that indole-3-carboxylic acid is a product of indole-3-acetonitrile metabolism in some plant tissues. This implies the loss of the —CN group and the oxidation of the α-carbon atom of the side-chain, a biochemical 'α-oxidation' mechanism which parallels that already suggested in an earlier paper of this volume (Fawcett *et al.*, 1956) to account for the activity of certain ω-2:4-dichlorophenoxyalkylnitriles in the wheat cylinder test.

REFERENCES

Bentley, J. A., and Housley, S. (1952). Studies on plant growth hormones. I. Biological activities of 3-indolylacetaldehyde and 3-indolylacetonitrile. *J. exp. Bot.* **3,** 393.

Cartwright, P. M., Sykes, J. T., and Wain, R. L. (1956). The distribution of natural auxins in germinating seeds and seedling plants. This volume, p. 32.

Fawcett, C. H., Taylor, H. F., Wain, R. L., and Wightman, F. (1956). The degradation of certain phenoxy acids, amides, and nitriles within plant tissues This volume, p. 187.

Jones, E. R. H., Henbest, H. B., Smith, G. F., and Bentley, J. A. (1952). 3-indolyl-acetonitrile: a naturally occurring plant growth hormone. *Nature,* **169,** 485.

Stowe, B. B., and Thimann, K. V. (1954). The paper chromatography of indole compounds and some indole containing auxins of plant tissues. *Arch. Biochem. Biophys.* **51,** 499.

Thimann, K. V. (1953). Hydrolysis of indoleacetonitrile in plants. *Arch. Biochem.* **44,** 242.

THE EFFECTS OF SYNTHETIC GROWTH SUBSTANCES IN THE LEVEL OF ENDOGENOUS AUXINS IN PLANTS†

L. J. Audus and Ruth Thresh
Bedford College, University of London

Currently fashionable theories of auxin and anti-auxin activity hinge on the assumption of direct actions of the active molecules at growth centres. The interactions of these substances in their effects on growth are thereby explained by competition for these specific sites of action. We wish, however, in this paper to revert to older, somewhat less fashionable, theories which suppose that synthetic organic molecules, having an effect on the growth of plant organs, may not be acting in this direct manner but that their activities may be due to a disturbance of the level of natural endogenous auxins. We recall the theory advanced by Skoog in 1947. It was then suggested that the activity of 2:4-dichlorophenoxyacetic acid (2:4-D) might be attributed to its competitive release of bound natural auxin from protein surfaces, where it was held inactive, so that it became free and available to affect growth. Theories involving a disturbance of native auxin metabolism have been put forward to account for the activity of certain supposed anti-auxins (e.g. maleic hydrazide; Åberg, 1953). In spite of considerable evidence to the contrary, it seemed to us some three years ago that these theories were still well worth considering and worth the effort of experimental testing. The obvious attack on the problem was to treat susceptible plants with synthetic growth 'regulators' at levels producing characteristic growth responses but well below toxicity limits. Subsequent paper partition chromatography of extracts and quantitative assay of the active compounds thus separated should reveal any disturbance of endogenous auxin levels and throw direct light on the validity of these early theories. During the progress of the work there have appeared papers dealing with the effects of 2:4-D (Weintraub, 1953; Henderson and Deese, 1954) and maleic hydrazide (Kulescha, 1953; Pilet, 1953) on endogenous auxin levels in various tissues. The accuracy of these assays, however, may have been completely vitiated by residual 2:4-D or maleic hydrazide (MH) in the extracts and so they need not be further considered. Chromatographic assays should be free from these objections.

EXPERIMENTAL

Three synthetic compounds were chosen for study, 2:4-D, on account of its very high 'auxin' activity, maleic hydrazide, because of its suspected action as a metabolic antagonist of auxin, and 2:3:5-triiodobenzoic acid (TIBA), because of its structural similarity to the growth-promoting substituted benzoic acids and the plausibility of its competitive action at a growth centre or at some other auxin-binding site in the cell.

† This paper was read at the Conference by L. J. Audus.

Plant material used consisted mainly of sunflower and garden pea seedlings, 2 to 3 weeks old, having been grown either in soil or in water culture at a constant temperature of 25°C in a fourteen-hour day of an intensity of 150 foot-candles.

2:4-D treatment took the form of painting the cotyledons or lower pair of foliage leaves with a 0·1 per cent solution of the ammonium salt. When growth responses had developed in the shoots (i.e. after about 24 hours) extracts were made of them for assay. Another treatment was to grow seedlings for a number of days in very dilute solutions (0·1 to 0·5 p.p.m.) of the ammonium salt. Considerable root growth inhibitions were thereby produced. Both roots and shoots were subsequently extracted and assayed. Similar root applications were made with the triethanolamine salt of maleic hydrazide and TIBA at concentrations of 10 to 30 p.p.m. The characteristic response to MH treatment was a marked suppression of lateral root production. TIBA, in addition to inhibiting root growth, modified the response of lateral roots to gravity so that many grew vertically upwards. After treatments varying from 6 to 12 days roots were extracted for assay.

Macerated material was extracted for 24 hours in ice-cold absolute ethanol followed by transference to peroxide-free ether as described by Kefford (1955). The volume of the extract was reduced by evaporation to about 0·5 ml and this was spotted directly onto the starting line of a Whatman No. 1 filter paper strip. The developing solvent for the chromatographic separation was an *iso*propyl alcohol–ammonia–water mixture (Kefford, 1955). After running, the paper was dried and then cut transversely into an appropriate number of portions. The growth substance content of each portion was then assayed by growing excised pea root segments laid directly upon it in 0·75 ml of $\frac{1}{2}$ per cent sucrose solution. Full details of this quantitative assay have already been published (Audus and Thresh, 1953). The position of indole-3-acetic acid (IAA) on the chromatogram was determined by a simultaneous running of synthetic IAA on a similar paper strip and identifying its position by spraying with ferric chloride–perchloric acid reagent. From the assay calibration curves (see Audus and Thresh, 1953) the quantities of IAA in the extracts could be directly calculated. Parallel assays of aliquots from the same extract showed that errors arising during running of the chromatogram and subsequent assay were of the order of 20–25 per cent. Assays of separate extracts of duplicate samples from the same plant material showed that errors due to variable extraction losses and plant sample differences gave variations between estimates of the order of 35–49 per cent. These latter errors necessitated a number of replicate experiments for each treatment in order to establish the significance of any differences observed.

RESULTS

(*a*) *Chromatograms of normal plants*

In sunflower shoots, in addition to IAA (R_f 0·3–0·4) three other active spots were consistently observed, a stimulatory spot at R_f 0·1–0·2 and inhibitory spots at R_f 0·65–0·8 and R_f 0·9. The inhibitor at R_f 0·65–0·8 corresponds closely with the inhibitor β of Bennet-Clark and Kefford (1953). In pea shoots these two inhibitors have also been consistently found. Further attempts at identification have not been made and in the experiments described above assays have been confined almost entirely to the IAA spots.

(*b*) *The effects of* 2:4-*D treatments*

Experiments on runner beans (leaf treatment), sunflowers (leaf or cotyledon treatment), and peas (applications to roots) showed no detectable effects of treatments on IAA levels in the bean or sunflower shoots or in pea roots and shoots. *Table 1* shows the mean values obtained for a number of sets of experiments. An analysis of variance of the data revealed no significant effect of treatment.

Table 1

Material	*Treatment*	*IAA content µg/kg F.W.*	
		Control	*Treated*
Broad bean shoots	0·1% 2:4-D to lower leaves	0·67	0·72
Sunflower shoots	0·1% 2:4-D to cotyledons	4·4	4·4
Sunflower shoots	0·01% 2:4-D to cotyledons	2·6	2·9
Pea roots	0·1 to 0·5 p.p.m. 2:4-D to roots	0·83	0·78
Pea shoots	0·1 to 0·5 p.p.m. 2:4-D to roots	0·64	0·68

These results are strongly opposed to the theory of Skoog and suggest also that 2:4-D has no significant effect on IAA metabolism. There seems little reason therefore to doubt that 2:4-D is an auxin in its own right and is exerting its growth-modifying actions directly at the growth centres.

2:4-D has an R_f of about 0·7 and in the chromatogram is superimposed on inhibitor-β, which could not then be assayed in treated extracts. In the neutral fractions of extracts from treated plants an inhibitor was found giving a spot on the chromatogram at the same R_f value as 2:4-D. It is suggested that 2:4-D in the plant forms a neutral complex with some cell constituent. This complex is extracted with alcohol and is decomposed to liberate 2:4-D during the running of the chromatogram.

(*c*) *The effects of maleic hydrazide treatment*

Maleic hydrazide has an R_f of about 0·2 in the solvent mixture used and so both IAA and inhibitor were assayed in these experiments. Only pea roots were studied. *Table 2* shows the results. Levels of inhibitor (in terms of

Table 2

Duration of treatment, days	*Conc. of MH, p.p.m.*	*IAA content, µg/kg F.W.*		*Inhibitor, IAA equivalents*	
		Control	*Treated*	*Control*	*Treated*
12	10	0·91	2·0	15·9	10·9
10	20	0·52	1·65	1·84	2·92
10	20	0·18	0·20	14·9	very high
5	20	0·74	0·37	1·6	5·1
6	20	0·18	0·97	3·4	2·1

IAA equivalents) showed erratic fluctuations and there were no consistent effects of treatment. With IAA, on the other hand, the table shows that, with one exception, levels in treated roots are higher than those in controls. A statistical analysis shows this effect to lie just on the 5 per cent level of significance, indicating the need for further confirmatory work. It seems unlikely, however, that these relatively small increases in free IAA content could account for the growth inhibitions produced by these maleic hydrazide treatments. Furthermore, they might be expected to promote rather than cause the inhibition of lateral root production, which was in fact observed.

In view of the other marked metabolic disturbances now known to be produced by this compound in plants, it seems logical to suppose that these altered auxin levels are additional expressions of these general disturbances and have no direct part to play in growth inhibitions by maleic hydrazide.

(d) The effect of TIBA treatment

This compound has an R_f the same as that of inhibitor-β and so only IAA levels have been followed in these experiments. The results of treatment of

Table 3

Duration of treatment, days	*Conc. of TIBA, p.p.m.*	*IAA content, μg/kg F.W.*	
		Control	*Treated*
6	10	1·3	0·0002
7	10	1·07	0·0002
7	10	1·89	0·5
8	10	1·40	0·35
9	10	0·77	0·0001
8	30	0·51	0 or 0·01

pea roots are shown in *Table 3* and chromatograms from a typical experiment in *Figure 1*. Here it will be seen that TIBA treatment has produced a dramatic

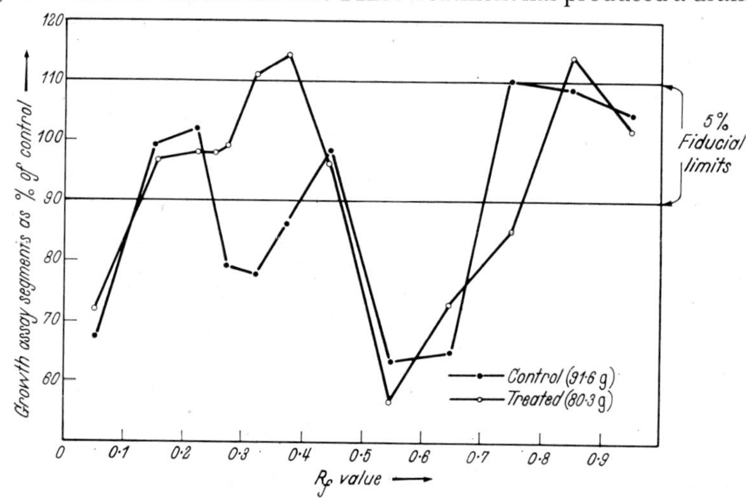

Figure 1. Pea roots (9 days from germination). Treatment—7 days in 10 p.p.m. 2:3:5-triiodobenzoic acid. Acid fraction.

and consistent lowering of free IAA levels, in most cases to vanishingly small values. Concentrations were thus reduced from levels markedly inhibiting root section growth to levels causing stimulation, i.e. a reduction to at least a thousandth of the control value. This effect is highly significant. These startling results offer an explanation of many of the observed physiological actions of TIBA. Its stimulating action on flower production, now established by many independent workers, coupled with this lowering of free auxin, supports the current theories associating flowering with low auxin levels. Its inhibition of extension growth in shoots could be due to the same lowering of auxin levels. On the other hand, such an effect might be expected to cause a stimulation of the growth of attached roots if endogenous auxins are at supra-optimal levels for growth in such roots. Such stimulations, however, have never been observed. It is, of course, possible that any such stimulation might be offset by a direct inhibitory action of TIBA at those concentrations. Its abolition of positive geotropic response is strong evidence that IAA plays an important role in geotropic phenomena in roots. Synergisms of IAA action by low concentrations of TIBA reported in coleoptiles and pea shoots by Thimann and Bonner (1948) and in roots by Åberg (1953) are difficult to reconcile with lowered auxin levels. The most rational explanation of these conflicting responses is that TIBA has a number of different and discrete actions in plant cells depending on the concentration employed. A slight synergism of auxin action at very low concentrations might well give way to this disturbance of free auxin levels as the concentration is raised, both effects being modified and sometimes swamped by a direct, and perhaps unspecific inhibiting action, particularly at the higher concentration levels. The next steps towards solution of these problems are obviously investigations on the relationship between the intensity of this auxin-lowering effect and the applied TIBA concentrations.

REFERENCES

Åberg, B. (1953). On the interaction of 2:3:5-tri-iodobenzoic acid and maleic hydrazide with auxins. *Physiol. Plant.* **6,** 277.

Audus, L. J., and Thresh, R. (1953). A method of plant growth substance assay for use in paper partition chromatography. *Physiol. Plant.* **6,** 451.

Bennet-Clark, T. A., and Kefford, N. P. (1953). Chromatography of the growth substances in plant extracts. *Nature,* **171,** 645.

Henderson, J. H. M., and Deese, D. C. (1954). Correlation between endogenous auxin and its destruction *in vivo* by 2:4-dichlorophenoxyacetic acid in plants. *Nature,* **174,** 967.

Kefford, N. P. (1955). The growth substances separated from plant extracts by chromatography, I. *J. exp. Bot.* **6,** 129.

Kulescha, Z. (1953). Action de l'hydrazide maléique sur la proliferation des tissus de Crown Gall de Scorsonère et sur leur teneur en auxine. *C. R. Acad. Sci. Paris,* **236,** 958.

Pilet, P-E. (1953). Étude de l'action de l'hydrazide maléique sur le developpement et la teneur en auxines des racines du *Lens culinaris Med. C. R. Acad. Sci. Paris,* **237,** 1430.

Skoog, F. (1947). Growth substances in higher plants. *Ann. Rev. Biochem.* **16,** 529.

Thimann, K. V., and Bonner, W. D. (1948). The action of tri-iodobenzoic acid on growth. *Plant Physiol.* **23,** 158.

Weintraub, R. L. (1953). 2:4-D, Mechanism of action. *Agric. Food Chem.* **1,** 250.

INTERRELATIONSHIPS BETWEEN THE UPTAKE OF 2:4-DICHLOROPHENOXYACETIC ACID, GROWTH, AND ION ABSORPTION

G. E. Blackman

Department of Agriculture, University of Oxford, and Agricultural Research Council
Unit of Experimental Agronomy

During the last five years research has been proceeding at Oxford on the interconnected problems of the factors governing the absorption of growth regulators and their influence in turn on the absorption of other compounds. Investigations concerned with the uptake of 3-indolylacetic acid have already been published (Reinhold, 1954) and this paper summarizes some of the work which has been proceeding on similar lines with 2:4-dichlorophenoxyacetic acid. Initially, the effects of this growth regulator on the absorption of nitrogen, phosphorus, and potassium were investigated by H. M. Squire (Part II Chemistry Thesis, 1952) and continued by E. F. Henzell (D. Phil. Thesis, 1955). Complementary experiments relating to mechanisms controlling the uptake of 2:4-dichlorophenoxyacetic acid were started by W. R. Birch (B.Sc. Thesis, 1955) and these are now being extended by G. Sen and C. C. McCready.

A number of workers, for example Nance (1949), Asana, Verma, and Mani (1950), Klingman and Ahlgren (1951) and Freiberg and Clark (1952), have reported that phytotoxic doses of 2:4-dichlorophenoxyacetic acid depress the absorption of nitrogen by a number of different species. Rhodes, Templeman, and Thruston (1950) and Rhodes (1952) have found that the effects of 2-methyl-4-chlorophenoxyacetic acid on the mineral uptake and mineral content are dependent on both the experimental conditions and the species. Thus, when tomatoes were grown in culture solution containing the growth regulator, the potassium uptake and the potassium content of the tops and lower stems were depressed but potassium accumulated in the roots; the trends for phosphorus and nitrogen were similar but less marked. If on the other hand the application of the growth regulator was made as a spray to the shoot, then on the basis of 'residual dry weight' the total uptakes of nitrogen and phosphorus were reduced, but there was no suppression of the absorption of potassium, calcium, or magnesium.

In the majority of these investigations the plants were either grown in the open or in a greenhouse and the observations were recorded over considerable periods subsequent to treatment with the growth regulator. In consequence, comparison is rendered difficult because of fluctuations in the environmental conditions and ontogenetical drifts in the composition of the plants. In order to eliminate these variables clonal populations of the aquatic plants *Lemna minor* and *Salvinia natans* were selected and grown under constant conditions of light (continuous illumination of 275 or

300 foot-candles) and temperature (25°C) in a complete nutrient solution (pH 5·1) containing varying concentrations of the growth regulator (for details see Blackman and Robertson-Cunninghame, 1954). Under such conditions control samples of both species will grow at a constant and high relative growth rate (*ca.* 22–27 g/g/day) and the contents of nitrogen, phosphorus, and potassium are largely independent of time.

In the *Lemna minor* experiments a wide range of concentrations of 2:4-dichlorophenoxyacetic acid were selected (0·125–48·0 p.p.m.) such that, even with the highest concentration, the growth rate, although exhibiting a cumulative depression below that of the control, is still considerable at the end of 12 days. After 12 days concentrations of 3 and 12 p.p.m. also cause significant reductions in the growth rate but no significant depressions occur at the end of 4 days.

At concentrations above 3 p.p.m. the total amounts of nitrogen, phosphorus, and potassium absorbed are progressively depressed with both time and concentration, the reductions being greatest for potassium. On either a fresh- or dry-weight basis the content of nitrogen and phosphorus is augmented by 3–48 p.p.m. and for 3 and 24 p.p.m. the gains increase up to 12 days. The results for potassium are in marked contrast. On a dry-weight basis the content is depressed and the order of the depression is positively correlated with both time and concentration. On a basis of fresh weight the content is initially depressed but returns to or above the level of the control at the end of 12 days.

When the concentrations of nitrogen, phosphorus, and potassium in the nutrient solution are varied there is little evidence of an interaction between the effects of the growth regulator and variations in the total amount of each nutrient, absorbed. Likewise, for both nitrogen and phosphorus content the interaction is not significant but for potassium content the depressive effect induced by the growth regulator is magnified when the external concentration is reduced.

For *Salvinia natans* the pattern of experimentation was on similar lines but, in this instance, the range of physiological concentrations which only partially suppressed growth at the end of 12 days did not exceed 24 p.p.m. At a lower concentration of 12 p.p.m. the relative growth rate of both the fresh and dry weights can be significantly *increased* (about 17 per cent) in the first three days. Subsequently, the growth rate falls off and by 9 days is below that of the control. Over all concentrations (6–24 p.p.m.) there is a cumulative depression in the uptake of nitrogen, phosphorus, and potassium and the depression is most marked for nitrogen. At 12 p.p.m., compared to the control, the absorption of potassium may be greater at 3 days, equal at 6, and less at 9 and 12 days.

On the criteria of dry and fresh weight the growth regulator during the 12 days of the experiment progressively reduces the nitrogen content. With phosphorus at and below 12 p.p.m. the content at first rises and then tends to return to the control level after 12 days; at a higher concentration of 24 p.p.m. the final content is below that of the control. The trends for potassium content resemble those for phosphorus. Initially, in the first 6–7 days at all concentrations the potassium content increases and on a fresh-weight basis this gain in content is maintained during the rest of the experimental period. However, on the basis of dry weight, in the second phase the higher concentrations (12 and 24 p.p.m.) depress the content so that the final percentage of potassium is less than that of the control.

When the external concentrations of nitrogen, phosphorus, and potassium are varied, for the uptake of phosphorus and potassium in the initial 4 days there are no significant interactions of concentration on the order of the effect induced by growth regulator. However, the depression caused by the phenoxyacetic acid is greater if the level of nitrogen in the culture solution is high. A similar interaction is found for the decrease in the nitrogen content, but with phosphorus and potassium there is no evidence of any such interactions.

From the two series of experiments it is apparent that the influence of 2:4-dichlorophenoxyacetic acid on the absorption processes in the two species are markedly divergent. On *a priori* grounds it would be expected that the uptake of mineral nutrients would be correlated with the growth rate and comparisons between the two species will be most valid when the effects of the phenoxyacetic acid on growth are of the same magnitude. Taking the whole experimental period, a concentration of 12 p.p.m. brings about a similar depression in growth in both species and yet the effects on uptake are quite different. For *Lemna minor* the inhibition of absorption is greatest for potassium and least for phosphorus, while for *Salvinia natans* the suppression is again least for phosphorus but in this instance maximal for nitrogen. Turning to the results for mineral content, it is clear that the growth regulator increases the nitrogen content of *Lemna minor* whereas it depresses the content in *Salvinia natans*. Again, although the potassium content of *Salvinia natans* is at first increased and then later decreased, the content in *Lemna minor* is initially reduced but the degree of reduction diminishes with time. From these contrasting results it must be concluded that the interacting effects of 2:4-dichlorophenoxyacetic acid on the processes responsible for growth and those relating to absorption are different in the two species.

The balance between the effects on growth and the effects on absorption will determine whether the content of a given nutrient will be increased or diminished and any shift in the balance with time may alter or reverse the trend. From the experimental evidence it seemed reasonable to suppose that this balance is correlated with the concentration of the growth regulator or of some derivative at cell level, and that this in turn will be linked with the rate of its absorption from the external solution. It was therefore decided that the next step was to investigate the absorption of 2:4-dichlorophenoxyacetic acid by *Lemna minor*.

The cultures of *Lemna minor* were grown under the same conditions as before with 2:4-dichlorophenoxyacetic acid labelled with C^{14} in the carboxyl group. All measurements of uptake were made by estimating the C^{14} in the tissue, and the following is a brief account of the technique. After the material had been washed and dried (12 hours at 95°C) it was oxidized with Van Slyke reagents in an evacuated system, and the collected carbon dioxide absorbed in a known amount of baryta. The barium carbonate was then filtered off and the filter paper after drying transferred to a planchette and counted under constant geometry. The recovery is of the order of 94 per cent.

The first experiment on absorption revealed a most unexpected result. At the end of the first four hours, over all five concentrations there were marked gains in the amounts of C^{14} present in the tissues, but between 4 and 24 hours the trend for absorption was dependent on the concentration. At 4 and 8 p.p.m. the amount present remained unchanged, but at 16 p.p.m. and more, particularly at 32 and 44 p.p.m., there was a sharp fall in the activity between 4 and 8 hours followed by a further but less steep decline between 8 and 24 hours. Thus, although at the end of 24 hours the amount of C^{14} in the sample was roughly proportional to the external concentration, these amounts bore little relation to the amounts present after 4 hours since the proportion 'lost' in the interval ranged from nought to two thirds.

The experiment was then repeated with observations at 1, 2, 3, and 4 hours and in this instance maximal values for C^{14} were recorded at either 1 (8 p.p.m.) or 2 hours (16 and 32 p.p.m.) followed by progressive declines up to 4 hours. In another experiment the time intervals were shortened to 20, 40, and 60 minutes and under these conditions, after 20 minutes the rate of uptake was roughly proportional to time and concentration. It was noted that when for each concentration the line was extrapolated back to zero time it did not pass through the origin.

It seemed that there were two possible explanations for the loss of C^{14} from the tissues. Firstly, that the phenoxyacetic acid was rapidly broken down and the C^{14} respired as carbon dioxide. Secondly, that either the compound itself or some breakdown product was transferred back to the solution. The first explanation appeared unlikely on account of the speed and the amounts which would have to be respired since where such respiratory losses have been reported the percentage lost has been small (e.g. Weintraub *et al.*, 1952). It was decided, therefore, to test the second hypothesis by placing *Lemna minor* in labelled 2:4-dichlorophenoxyacetic acid (16 and 56 p.p.m.) for a short period (0·75 hours) and then to transfer samples to (*a*) double distilled water, (*b*) culture solution at the same pH, and (*c*) culture solution containing the same concentration of the unlabelled growth regulator. It was found that at the end of 0·75 hours more than half of the original C^{14} was no longer present in the tissues and that at 3 hours the loss was *ca.* 90 per cent. This hyperbolic relationship between loss and time was the same irrespective of the composition of the external solution.

When a balance sheet was constructed between (*a*) the original C^{14} in the sample and (*b*) the amounts present either in the tissue or in the solution at the end of 3 hours, then over 99 per cent could be accounted for, thus demonstrating that any respiratory loss of C^{14} as carbon dioxide was negligible. To discover whether it was the compound itself which was transferred to the solution an aliquot of the final solution was concentrated, the residue spotted on to chromatogram paper, run in a mixture of *iso*propanol, ammonia, and water, and the paper placed in an electronic scanning device. Only one radioactive spot was recorded and this had the same R_f value as the original labelled 2:4-dichlorophenoxyacetic acid.

From these experiments it can be concluded that the absorption of 2:4-dichlorophenoxyacetic acid is characterized by a very rapid rate of entry during the first few minutes followed by a steady rate of accumulation for between 1 and 2 hours. Subsequently the rate falls off to zero and this is followed at higher concentrations by a phase when there is a net loss of the growth regulator to the external solution. By analogy with ion absorption (see for example review by Broyer, 1951), after the first few minutes the accumulation of the growth regulator will be energy-dependent while the final transference to the external solution is unlikely to be dominated by an exchange process, since the rate of transference is the same into water as it is into a solution containing the unlabelled growth regulator. On this basis, it would be expected that within the 'metabolic' phase uptake would be sensitive to changes of temperature and the nature of the transfer mechanism would be indicated by the magnitude of the Q_{10}. Accordingly the rate of uptake from solutions of 16 and 48 p.p.m. in the first 0·75 hours was measured at 24 and 3°C and it was found that the Q_{10} was of the order of 2·4. In the complementary transference experiment, batches of *Lemna minor* were placed in a mixture of 16 p.p.m. of the growth regulator and 1 p.p.m. of rubidium chloride labelled with Rb^{86} for two hours, and then transferred to water and the rate of loss measured at 0·5, 1·5, and 4·5 hours. Over the initial half hour the loss of rubidium was not temperature-dependent while for the growth regulator the Q_{10} was approximately 1·6. It was also observed that when at the end of 4·5 hours only a small proportion of the rubidium had been transferred to the external solution the loss of the growth regulator, even at 1·25°C, was more than half. Before any final conclusions can be drawn it will be necessary to repeat these experiments over a wider range of concentrations and smaller time and temperature intervals, but the evidence suggests that the mechanism of transference has a metabolic component.

There is one other aspect of the mechanism of absorption which has received preliminary study, namely the influence of pH on the rate of absorption. On the basis of other work with *Lemna minor* (Blackman and Robertson-Cunninghame, 1953) it had been concluded that above the pK value uptake is accelerated by lowering the pH and for the initial 2 hours this supposition has now been confirmed since between pH 6·1 and 4·6 the amount absorbed may change by a factor of 17. It cannot, however, be concluded that entry is wholly as undissociated molecules since the rate of absorption, although highly correlated with the calculated molecular concentration in the external solution, is not directly proportional.

To date, only a few experiments have been carried out on the effects of the dichlorophenoxyacetic acid on ion absorption in the first 24 hours. Enough has, however, been done to reveal that the effects are complex. For example, although relative to the control the growth regulator at 16 p.p.m. has only a small effect on the absorption of Rb^{86} at the end of 24 hours, after 1 and 4 hours the rate of uptake is greatly depressed. When samples are first treated with the growth regulator and then transferred to the rubidium solution the uptake is different from that of samples placed in a solution containing both the rubidium and the growth regulator. Moreover, such differences are dependent on the time of pretreatment.

Contemporaneously another series of experiments were started to investigate some of the factors controlling the absorption of the same growth regulator by coleoptile segments of *Avena* and *Triticum*. Because the concentrations which stimulate extension growth are so small and because the specific activity of the then available labelled material did not exceed 0·78 mc/mmol, it was not feasible, with the existing technique of assay, to estimate accurately uptake over short periods. Most of the measurements were made after 11–24 hours. As with *Lemna minor*, the amount absorbed in 21·5 hours is accelerated as the pH is reduced from 6 to 4, but once again the rate is not directly proportional to the calculated concentration of undissociated molecules in the solution. In *Avena* coleoptiles cultured in a buffered sucrose solution at concentrations up to 0·25 p.p.m., the gains in extension growth after 22 hours match the amounts absorbed, but at higher concentrations (up to 2 p.p.m.) this linearity no longer holds. When observations are made at 11 and 22 hours the rate of absorption by *Triticum* coleoptiles does not fall off appreciably with time. From this aspect it would seem that this tissue resembles artichoke discs more than *Lemna minor*, since Hanson and Bonner (1955) have reported that the uptake of 2:4-dichlorophenoxyacetic acid continues for 18 hours and that it is only when the discs are transferred to a solution containing unlabelled material that any loss takes place, and then it is only on a small scale. It may well be that such differences are not so much a question of a varying specific reaction but rather the physiological level of the growth regulator. In coleoptiles and artichoke discs the concentrations were such as to accelerate either extension growth or water uptake and it is possible that loss to the external solution only takes place at inhibitory concentrations. If this proves to be the case then a new approach to the interpretation of the toxic action of 2:4-dichloro- and other phenoxyacetic acids may be provided. In this connection it is significant that a concentration which induces in *Lemna minor* a loss to the external solution after 1–2 hours does not cause any detectable reduction in the growth rate for at least four days, by which time the plants have tripled in weight.

REFERENCES

ASANA, R. D., VERMA, G., and MANI, V. S. (1950). Some observations on the influence of 2:4-dichlorophenoxyacetic acid (2:4-D) on the growth and development of two varieties of wheat. *Physiol. Plant.* **3,** 334.

BLACKMAN, G. E., and ROBERTSON-CUNNINGHAME, R. C. (1953). The influence of pH on the phytotoxicity of 2:4-dichlorophenoxyacetic acid to *Lemna minor*. *New Phytol.* **52,** 71.

BLACKMAN, G.E., and ROBERTSON-CUNNINGHAME, R. C. (1954). Interactions in the physiological effects of growth substances on plant development. *J. exp. Bot.* **5,** 184.

BROYER, T. C. (1951). *Mineral Nutrition of Plants*, University of Wisconsin Press, p. 187.

FREIBERG, S. R., and CLARK, H. E. (1952). Effect of 2:4-dichlorophenoxyacetic acid upon the nitrogen metabolism and water relations of soybean plants grown at different nitrogen levels. *Bot. Gaz.* **113,** 322.

HANSON, J. B., and BONNER, J. (1955). The nature of the lag period in auxin-induced water uptake. *Amer. J. Bot.* **42,** 411.

KLINGMAN, G. C., and AHLGREN, G. H. (1951). Effects of 2:4-D on dry weight, reducing sugars, total sugars, polysaccharides, nitrogen and allyl sulfide in wild garlic. *Bot. Gaz.* **113,** 119.

NANCE, J. F. (1949). Inhibition of salt accumulation in excised wheat roots by 2:4-dichlorophenoxyacetic acid. *Science*, **109,** 174.

REINHOLD, L. (1954). The uptake of indole-3-acetic acid by pea epicotyl segments and carrot disks. *New Phytol.* **53,** 217.

RHODES, A. (1952). The influence of the plant growth-regulator, 2-methyl-4-chlorophenoxyacetic acid on the metabolism of carbohydrate, nitrogen and minerals in *Solanum lycopersicum* (tomato). *J. exp. Bot.* **3,** 129.

RHODES, A., TEMPLEMAN, W. G., and THRUSTON, M. N. (1950). The effect of the plant growth-regulator, 4-chloro, 2-methyl-phenoxyacetic acid on the mineral and nitrogen contents of plants. *Ann. Bot. Lond.* (*N.S.*) **14,** 181.

WEINTRAUB, R. L., BROWN, J. W., FIELDS, M., and ROHAN, J. (1952). Metabolism of 2:4-dichlorophenoxyacetic. I. $C^{14}O_2$ production by bean plants treated with labelled 2:4-dichlorophenoxyacetic acids. *Plant. Physiol.* **27,** 293.

AUXIN-INDUCED WATER UPTAKE †

J. Bonner, L. Ordin, and R. Cleland

Kerckhoff Biological Laboratories, California Institute of Technology, Pasadena, California

The increase in cell size which is induced in plant tissue by applied auxin is an expression of and intimately related to the net uptake of water by the tissue under the influence of the hormone. In order to find out how auxin increases cell size it is therefore necessary to find out how auxin brings about net water uptake. Three general kinds of suggestions have been made concerning mechanisms which might be involved in such auxin-induced net water uptake. One proposal is that auxin in some manner softens or plasticizes the cell wall. A second suggestion is that auxin causes deposition of cell-wall material. A third notion has been that auxin brings about non-osmotic transport of water into the plant cell. The first two suggestions

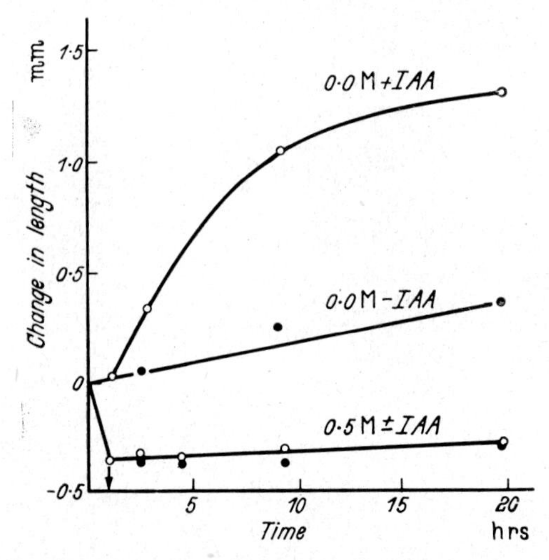

Figure 1. Elongation of Avena *coleoptile sections in the presence or absence of* 0·5 M *mannitol. Indole-acetic acid (IAA)* 5·0 *mg/l. added at arrow. After Ordin* et al. (1955).

envisage an osmotic entry of water into the cell in response to lowered wall pressure. The third suggestion envisages an actual active transport of water against an osmotic gradient. We have investigated the extent to which the auxin-induced net water uptake of *Avena* coleoptile sections is controlled by purely osmotic principles (Ordin, Applewhite, and Bonner, 1955). For this work, elongation of sections has been used as a measure of net water uptake. This is justifiable since diameter changes during auxin-induced elongation of coleoptile sections are negligible and since increases in length are closely correlated with increases in wet weight of this tissue.

Data on the time course of elongation of sections in media of two different osmotic concentrations are given in *Figure 1.* It may be noted that the osmotic concentration of the initial tissue is approximately 0·4 M. In the experiment of *Figure 1* the media in both cases contained potassium maleate buffer in low

† This paper was read at the Conference by J. Bonner.

concentration (0·0025 M), and to this mannitol was added as the non-permeating, osmotically active solute. It is clear from the data of *Figure 1* that sections elongate only in the hypotonic solution and that no elongation at all occurs in the hypertonic solution.

The rate of elongation of the sections of *Figure 1* decreases with time. It is known that the response of coleoptile sections to auxin is prolonged in time by the addition of sucrose or certain other substances to the medium. *Figure 2* gives data on the time course of the elongation response to auxin in medium containing an optimum concentration of sucrose (0·09 M) and mannitol added in appropriate concentration to produce varying total osmotic concentrations. The sections were first equilibrated in the medium for one hour after which auxin was added. In basal medium alone elongation

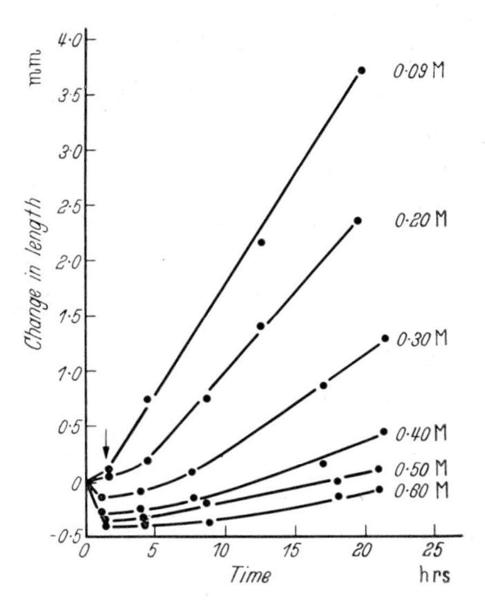

Figure 2. Elongation of Avena *coleoptile sections as a function of time in media containing* 0·09 M *sucrose and mannitol in varying concentration. IAA* (5·0 *mg/l*) *added at arrow. After Ordin* et al. (1955).

starts at once when IAA is added and continues at a constant rate through the 20 hours of the experiment. As the value of external osmotic concentration is increased a lag period in attainment of steady-state elongation rate becomes evident. This lag period increases in length as the external osmotic concentration is increased. The final steady-state rate of elongation also decreases regularly as external osmotic concentration is increased. *Figure 3* summarizes data on the relation of external osmotic concentration to elongation rate of coleoptile sections. The auxin-induced increment in elongation decreases sharply with increasing external osmotic concentration. None the less, elongation of tissue does occur in sections placed in solutions of osmotic concentration as high as 0·6 M. The cells of sections placed in such solutions are rapidly plasmolysed as will be discussed below. At the end of the 20-hour incubation period of the experiment of *Figure 2*, deplasmolysis has occurred. Elongation has then taken place in the presence of solutions initially hypertonic to the 0·4 M osmotic concentration of the initial section.

Burström (1953a) has shown that the extent to which wheat roots are irreversibly stretched by growing (irreversible extension) is independent of external osmotic concentration in the hypotonic region. This fact suggests that the cell elongation of such roots is not due to passive stretching of the cell wall but favours some hypothesis relating active wall synthesis to cell

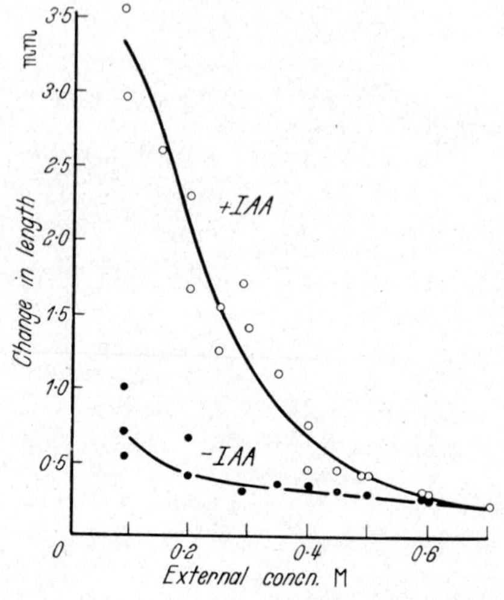

Figure 3. Elongation of Avena *coleoptile sections as a function of external osmotic concentration. All media contain* 0·09 M *sucrose and mannitol in varying concentration. Incubation time* 20 *hours. After Ordin* et al. (1955).

enlargement. The relations found by Burström do not obtain for *Avena* coleoptile sections. The irreversible component of elongation like the total elongation is an inverse function of external osmotic concentration. In the

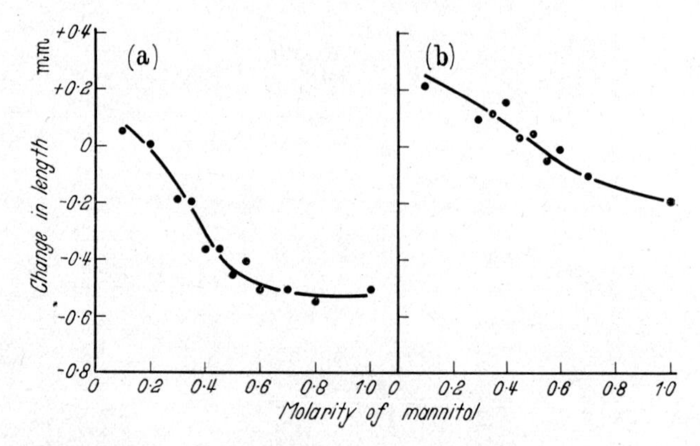

Figure 4. Length changes of Avena *coleoptile sections as a function of external mannitol concentration. Incubation for* 1–2 *hrs under anaerobic conditions. (a) Freshly cut sections. (b) Sections previously incubated for* 20 *hours in* 0·5 M *solution. After Ordin* et al. (1955).

case of the *Avena* coleoptile the greater the turgor pressure the greater the elongation rate. This implies that mere contact between protoplasm and cell wall is not of itself sufficient to support maximum elongation rate.

In order to ascertain to what extent purely osmotic considerations govern auxin-induced water uptake in the *Avena* coleoptile it is necessary to have measurements of diffusion pressure deficit (d.p.d.) and of internal osmotic concentration during the elongation process. The simplified method of

Ursprung (1923) was used for determination of the d.p.d. of coleoptile tissue. This method consists in the measurement of lengths of sections which have been equilibrated in a graded series of mannitol concentrations. The sections are held submerged in the solution in stainless steel baskets. Anaerobic conditions are maintained with argon in order to ensure that metabolic processes are kept at a minimum and do not contribute to the measured d.p.d. That group of sections which show no change in length is said to have been in a solution whose osmotic concentration equals the internal diffusion pressure deficit of the tissue.

According to classic osmotic theory, the simplified method of Ursprung should also be capable of yielding values of internal osmotic concentration for the tissue measured, since the curve which relates tissue length to external osmotic concentration should show a sharp inflection at the osmotic concentration of incipient plasmolysis. The data of *Figure 4* show, however, that with the coleoptile sections used in the present experiments such a sharp inflection is not found. The method is however suitable for the measurement of diffusion pressure deficit. The data of *Table 1* show that within the error

Table 1

Diffusion pressure deficits of Avena *coleoptile sections as a function of external osmotic concentration.* (*After Ordin* et al. (1955))

External concn., molar	*D.p.d. of section tissue, molar*		
	After 1 *hr*	*After* 20 *hrs* +*IAA*	*After* 20 *hrs* −*IAA*
0·25	0·25	0·27	0·28
0·50	0·47	0·52	0·45
0·59	0·60	0·54	0·56

of measurement (±0·05 M) the diffusion pressure deficit of the tissue is equal to that of the external solution in which the tissue has been incubated. This is true both in the presence and in the absence of auxin.

The present method of measurement of tissue d.p.d. excludes any possible metabolism dependent component of d.p.d. That coleoptile sections do not exhibit any such d.p.d. component to a measurable degree has been shown by transferring elongating sections to anaerobic conditions. The sections do not decrease in length under these conditions (*Figure 5*). IAA-induced elongation occurs in the absence of any apparent d.p.d. gradient over the entire range of external osmotic concentrations used. Since water enters the cell under the influence of auxin it must do so under the influence of a diffusion pressure deficit gradient. This is apparently infinitesimal and not detectable by present methods of measurement.

When sections are placed in hypertonic solution their cells are rapidly plasmolysed. The cells of such sections subsequently deplasmolyse under aerobic conditions. One might therefore conclude that absorption of solutes or production of solutes within the tissue has taken place. According to this view the section is deplasmolysed because internal osmotic concentration is increased and the solution is no longer hypertonic. At the same time wall pressure must increase above zero since tissue d.p.d. remains constant. Measurements of internal osmotic concentration were carried out in the present work by the plasmolytic method since the cryoscopic method has been shown by Le Gallais (1955) to be inaccurate and unsuitable. The plasmolytic method consists in examination of coleoptile sections from the d.p.d. determination solutions under the high power of the microscope. Internal osmotic concentration is taken as equal to the external osmotic concentration of that solution in which 50 per cent of the subepidermal cells of the section are plasmolysed. The internal osmotic concentration of the

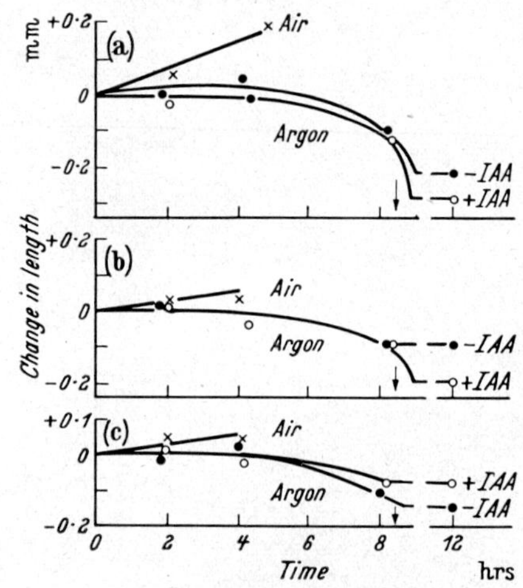

Figure 5. Avena *coleoptile sections do not lose water immediately they are transferred from aerobic to anaerobic conditions. (a) Sections previously incubated in* 0·4 M *solution in presence of IAA,* 5 *mg/l. (b) Sections previously incubated in* 0·5 M *solution in presence of IAA* 5 *mg/l. (c) Sections previously incubated in* 0·6 M *solution in presence of IAA* 5 *mg/l. Sections transferred to distilled water at arrow. Lack of elongation indicates death of section. After Ordin* et al. (1955).

cells of freshly excised coleoptile sections was found to be 0·42 M (corrected to initial volume). The internal osmotic concentrations of sections incubated for 20 hours under various conditions are summarized in *Table 2*. Sections

Table 2

Internal osmotic concentration of Avena *coleoptile sections after* 20 *hrs. Incubation in varied media. Initial osmotic concentration* 0·42 M

Treatment during incubation	*Internal osmotic concentration, molar*	
	+*IAA*	−*IAA*
Water alone	0·32	0·42
Sucrose 0·08 M	0·53	0·68
Mannitol 0·59 M	0·44	0·45
Mannitol 0·5 M and sucrose 0·08 M	0·69	0·69

incubated in IAA but in the absence of other external solute decrease in internal osmotic concentration. This effect is apparently due to dilution of the cell content by the water taken up under the influence of auxin. Sections incubated in mannitol alone show small increases in internal osmotic concentration over the 20-hour period. The addition of sucrose to the medium, however, permits very large increases in internal osmotic concentration to take place. This is true both for solutions which are initially hypotonic and for those which are initially hypertonic. The presence of sucrose in the medium evidently permits the tissue to adjust its internal osmotic concentration. This is clearly shown by the results of experiments in which sections were plasmolysed in mannitol and incubated either in mannitol alone or in mannitol and sucrose. Only in the presence of the sucrose did deplasmolysis take place and this was accompanied by an increase in tissue osmotic concentration.

It has been shown above (*Figure 2*) that when sections are incubated in solutions more concentrated than approximately 0·2 M there is a detectable lag period in establishment of steady-state elongation rate. The lag period

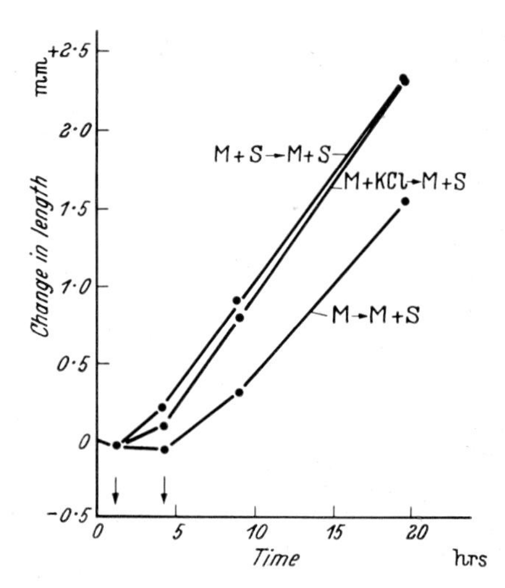

Figure 6. Effect of 4-hour pretreatment with mannitol alone (0·2 M) *or with mannitol plus absorbable solute on subsequent rate of coleoptile section elongation in* 0·2 M *medium containing mannitol and sucrose (total concentration* 0·2 M). *IAA* 5·0 *mg/l. added at first arrow. After Ordin* et al. (1955).

appears to represent the period needed by the cell to accumulate solutes and to increase in internal osmotic concentration. To study this matter, sections were placed in 0·2 M solutions containing IAA and mannitol or mixtures of mannitol and sucrose or KCl for 4 hours. The sections were then all transferred to a 0·2 M solution containing IAA, mannitol, and sucrose. The data of *Figure 6* show that the lag period in the second treatment is shortened or eliminated only if an absorbable solute is present externally in the pretreatment solution. The lag period is not shortened by a pretreatment in solutions containing indoleacetic acid and mannitol alone.

It is of interest to determine the effect of auxin upon the osmotic readjustment which occurs during the lag period. Sections were grown in 0·3 M solution containing mannitol and sucrose. Auxin was added periodically to successive lots of sections and the growth rates measured both before and after addition of the indoleacetic acid. The data of *Figure 7* show that the lag period, which is of about 7 hours duration under these conditions, is independent of the time of addition of auxin.

The important conclusion of this work is then that the auxin-induced uptake of water by *Avena* coleoptile sections follows osmotic principles and is not attended by any detectable metabolically controlled component of internal diffusion pressure deficit. It has long been known that sugars or potassium salts act as cofactors in auxin-induced elongation of coleoptile sections. The role of these substances is apparently in part an osmotic one. They contribute to the maintenance of internal osmotic concentration.

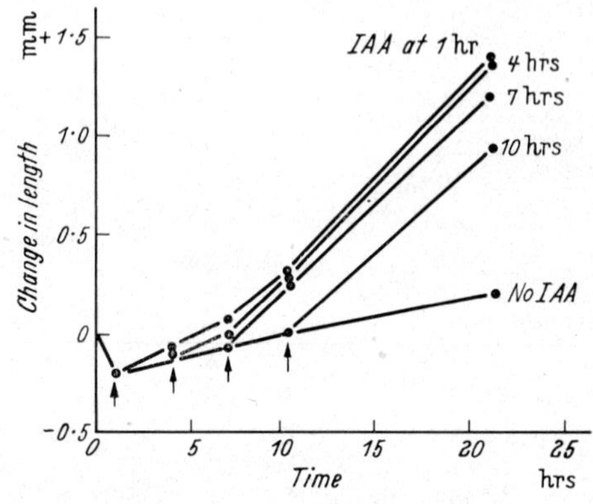

Figure 7. The presence of auxin (IAA, 5 mg/l.) is without effect on the length of the lag period in elongation of coleoptile sections in a medium composed of mannitol and sucrose (total concn. 0·3 M). *After Ordin* et al. (1955).

The presence of sucrose in the medium extends the period over which elongation is linear with time. The effect of sucrose on rate of water uptake may be in part due to the utilization of the material in respiration and support of cellular syntheses. In addition, however, sucrose clearly provides internal osmotically active material.

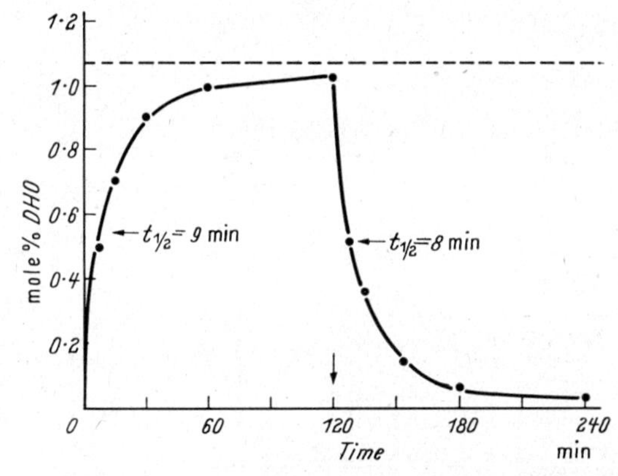

Figure 8. Time course of water movement into and out of Avena *coleoptile sections as followed with deuterium-labelled water, DHO. The ascending curve represents course of DHO movement into tissue from DHO labelled external solution. The descending curve represents the course of DHO loss by labelled tissue to unlabelled solution. After Ordin* (1955).

Further information concerning the role of auxin in the *Avena* coleoptile has been obtained by the study of absolute rate of water movement in this tissue (Ordin, 1955). This has been done with the help of dilute solutions of deuterium-labelled water, DHO. Groups of sections were placed in 1 per cent DHO solutions for various periods of time. After each desired time period a group of sections was dried superficially with filter paper, placed in a ground glass stoppered vial and water removed by lyophillization in a micro distillation apparatus. The water thus removed was analysed directly in a mass spectrometer. Data are presented as mole per cent DHO. Auxin has no influence on the course of either the inward or the outward diffusion of heavy water into *Avena* coleoptile sections. The data of *Figure 8* show that the half time of the diffusion in either direction is approximately 9 minutes. Other data similarly show that the rate of diffusion of water into the tissue is not detectably different as between plasmolysed and unplasmolysed tissue. In all of these cases water concentration approaches equilibrium in a logarithmic manner and we are apparently dealing with a diffusion process. In order to compare the diffusion constants measured by the isotopic method with the filtration constants as ordinarily obtained by osmotic methods, osmotic determinations of permeability have also been made (Ordin, 1955).

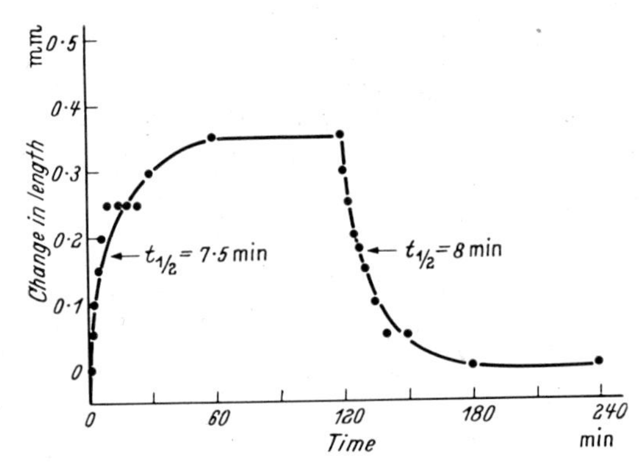

Figure 9. Time course of net water movement into and out of Avena *coleoptile sections as followed by changes in length of sections after transfer from* 0·4 M *mannitol to water and from the latter solution back to mannitol. After Ordin* (1955).

This involves measuring the rate of tissue elongation or shrinkage when sections are transferred from 0·4 M mannitol to distilled water and vice versa. The data of *Figure 9* show that the curves obtained are similar in shape to those obtained with DHO and that the half times are of the same order of magnitude, approximately 7·5 minutes in the present case.

The data of *Figure 2* indicate that for the *Avena* coleoptile section to increase by half in volume of water requires about 13 hours, i.e. the half time of net water movement is about 13 hours. This is to be contrasted with the half time for absolute water movement which is about 8 to 9 minutes. The rate of exchange is therefore approximately 90 times as great as the rate of net movement. It would appear that water can move relatively freely in and out of coleoptile cells and tissue but that net movements are governed primarily by classical osmotic relations.

Net water movement into the coleoptile under the influence of auxin is readily inhibited by varied metabolic inhibitors. Suitable experiments with isotopically labelled water have shown that this is not the case for water diffusion *per se*. That the net water movement into the coleoptile section is attended by an increase in respiratory rate of the tissue is indicated by the data of *Figure 10*. These data show that auxin, as is well known, increases rate of respiratory metabolism of the tissue. The auxin-induced increment in respiration diminishes however with increasing external osmotic concentration and disappears at an external osmotic concentration of 0·4 M in which elongation is reduced to a low value. These results parallel those obtained with Jerusalem artichoke storage tissue (Bonner, Bandurski, and Millerd, 1953).

It has been concluded that the *Avena* coleoptile is at all times essentially in diffusion pressure deficit equilibrium with the external medium. No movement of water against a d.p.d gradient appears to take place in coleoptile sections (Burström, 1953b). When non-absorbable solutes are used to constitute a hypertonic solution no elongation of the tissue takes place. Adjustments of osmotic concentration take place in the coleoptile provided that an absorbable solute is present in the external medium. These osmotic

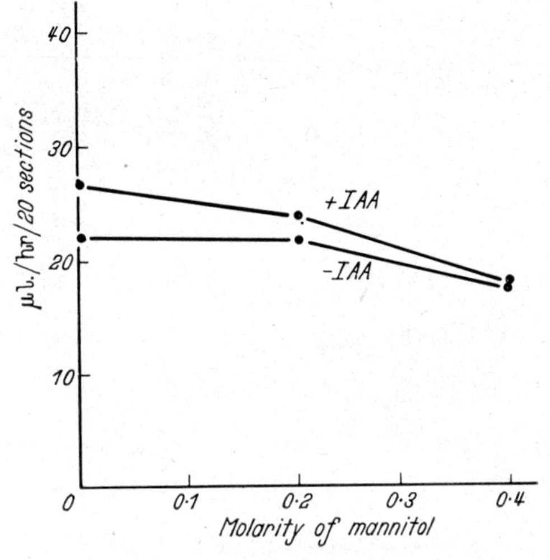

Figure 10. Rate of respiration of Avena *coleoptile sections in the presence or absence of IAA* (5 *mg/l.*) *as a function of external solute concentration. After Ordin* et al. (1955).

adjustments are, however, independent of auxin and occur in the absence as well as in the presence of added growth substances. Since auxin-induced water uptake by the section is a purely osmotic phenomenon it must take place in response to a d.p.d. gradient into the tissue, which is, however, so small as to be not measurable by the present methods. Classical osmotic lore tells us that the d.p.d. of a cell equals osmotic concentration less cell wall pressure. Auxin does not appear to directly influence internal osmotic concentration. It must be concluded therefore that auxin in some way decreases cell-wall pressure. We have arrived by a circuitous route at a conclusion reached by Heyn 24 years ago (Heyn, 1931). The hypothesis that auxin causes a metabolism mediated plasticization of cell walls of the coleoptile has found some experimental support, as for example in the work of Bonner (1935). The fact that auxin-induced water uptake is metabolism-dependent has, however, tended to focus our attention on the initial metabolic role of auxin. Net uptake of water by the coleoptile section is dependent upon auxin, on the metabolism of the section, and on the availability of water to the section. In the absence of any of these three factors auxin-induced elongation does not take place. It will now be shown that the metabolism-dependent auxin mediated effect upon the cell wall can be experimentally separated from the actual act of net water uptake (Cleland, 1955). For this purpose coleoptile sections were first treated with or without auxin for 45 minutes in aerated solution. The osmotic concentration of the solution was however so adjusted (0·3 M mannitol) that the sections showed no net water uptake. They were next transferred for 30 minutes to anaerobic conditions in 0·3 M solution. They were now transferred to water under anaerobic conditions. In this final treatment the sections can of course take up water and expand. The presence of auxin in the final solution does not

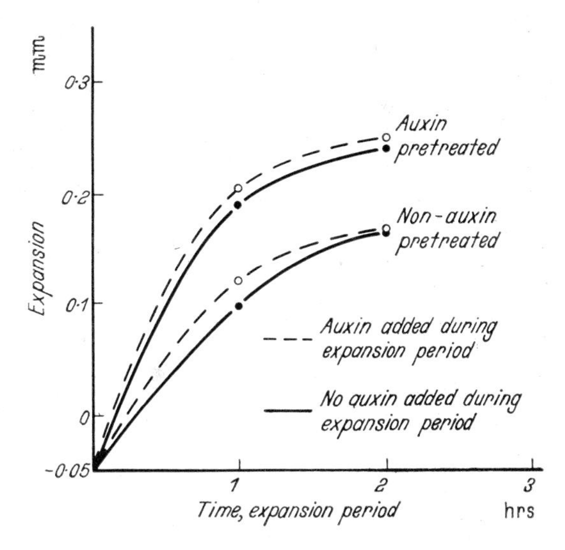

Figure 11. Effect of auxin during the anaerobic expansion period.

increase significantly this expansion (*Figure 11*) since the conditions are anaerobic. It is however evident from the data of *Figure 11* that pretreatment with auxin under aerobic circumstances markedly increases subsequent elongation under anaerobic conditions. Auxin brings about a change in the non-elongating section which can be subsequently expressed as a d.p.d. gradient and lead to a purely passive, net water uptake. The auxin-induced d.p.d. gradient has been shown above not to be due to changes in osmotic concentration. We must conclude again that auxin decreases cell-wall pressure and that this effect is to some degree a persistent one, separable from net water uptake itself.

CONCLUSION

The present work has shown that auxin-induced net water movement in the *Avena* coleoptile section follows osmotic principles and that net water movement into the section from truly hypertonic solution does not take place. The role of sucrose and of inorganic salts such as KCl, long known to increase auxin-induced elongation of coleoptile tissue, has been shown to be in part an osmotic one. These solutes by their absorption into the cells of the section serve to maintain or increase the osmotic concentration of the tissue and hence to maintain the turgor pressure upon which elongation rate is directly dependent. Osmotic concentration of coleoptile section tissue does not appear to be influenced in any direct way by auxin. Auxin appears rather to increase diffusion pressure deficit by lowering cell-wall pressure, although the d.p.d. gradient which governs water movement into the cell is so small that it has not been possible to measure it directly.

REFERENCES

BONNER, J. (1935). Zum Mechanismus der Zellstreckung auf Grund der Micellarlehre. *Jb. wiss. Bot.* **82,** 377.

BONNER, J., BANDURSKI, R., and MILLERD, A. (1953). Linkage of respiration to auxin-induced water uptake. *Physiol. Plant.* **6,** 511.

BURSTRÖM, H. (1953a). Studies on growth and metabolism of roots. IX. Cell elongation and water absorption. *Physiol. Plant.* **6,** 260.

BURSTRÖM, H. (1953b). Growth and water absorption of *Helianthus* tuber tissue. *Physiol. Plant.* **6,** 685.

CLELAND, R. (1955). *Abstr. Ann. Mtg Amer. Soc. Pl. Physiol., Western Section, Pasadena.*

HEYN, A. N. J. (1931). Der Mechanismus der Zellstreckung. *Rec. Trav. bot. néerl.* **28,** 113.

LE GALLAIS, D. R. (1955). Thesis, University of California, Berkeley.

ORDIN, L. (1955). *Abstr. Ann. Mtg Amer. Soc. Pl. Physiol., Western Section, Pasadena.*

ORDIN, L., APPLEWHITE, J., and BONNER, J. (1955). *Plant Physiol.* (in press).

URSPRUNG, A. (1923). Zur Kenntnis der Saugkraft. VII. Eine neue vereinfachte Methode zur Messung der Saugkraft. *Ber. dtsch. bot. Ges.* **41,** 338.

THE INFLUENCE OF GROWTH SUBSTANCES UPON SULPHYDRYL COMPOUNDS†

A. C. Leopold and C. A. Price

Department of Horticulture, University of Purdue

A wide variety of theories concerning the mechanism of auxin action have been proposed which include suggestions that sulphydryl materials may be specifically involved in auxin action within plants. It is the intention of this discussion to examine experimentally two of these theories in an effort to determine whether a positive role for sulphydryl reactions might be suggested.

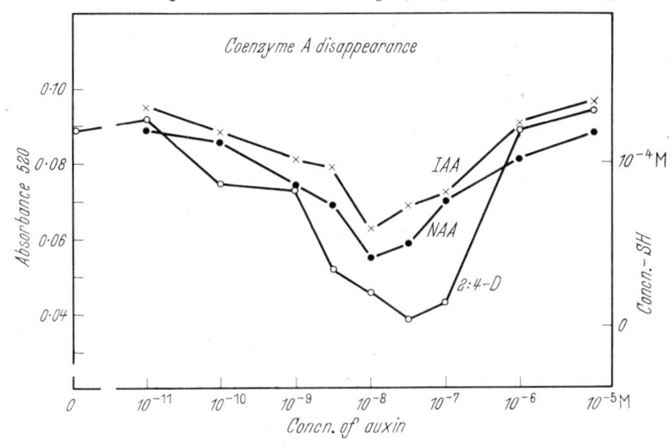

Figure 1. Coenzyme A disappearance as measured by the nitroprusside test (Leopold and Guernsey, 1953).

THE AUXIN CoA THEORY

In 1953 Leopold and Guernsey proposed a theory that the mechanism of auxin action might involve the formation of a thio-ester between auxins and CoA. Since the most active auxins are derivatives of acetic acid, it was suggested that they might form esters homologous to acetyl-CoA. Evidence was presented that such a reaction might occur, although the evidence was indirect in nature. Measurements were made showing a disappearance of sulphydryl groups in the presence of auxins, tomato mitochondrial preparations, and ATP. More direct evidence would result from the measurement of the actual formation of thio-esters. In the present study we have set about to make such measurements.

Turning first to the sulphydryl disappearance in the presence of auxins, some difficulties were encountered in repeating the experiments reported in 1953. In the earlier experiments the most active auxins brought about decreases of sulphydryl concentrations in the order of 10^{-4} M as shown in *Figure 1.* In some more recent experiments the extent of enzymatic sulphydryl

† This paper was read at the Conference by A. C. Leopold.

disappearance is of a considerably smaller degree. For example, experiments with mitochondrial preparations from castor bean are shown in *Figure 2.* Paired aliquots of CoA were incubated in the presence and in the absence of enzyme with different acid substrates. In the first place a non-enzymatic disappearance of CoA sulphydryl in the order of 10^{-4} M took place in all the preparations measured. When acetic acid was provided as a substrate,

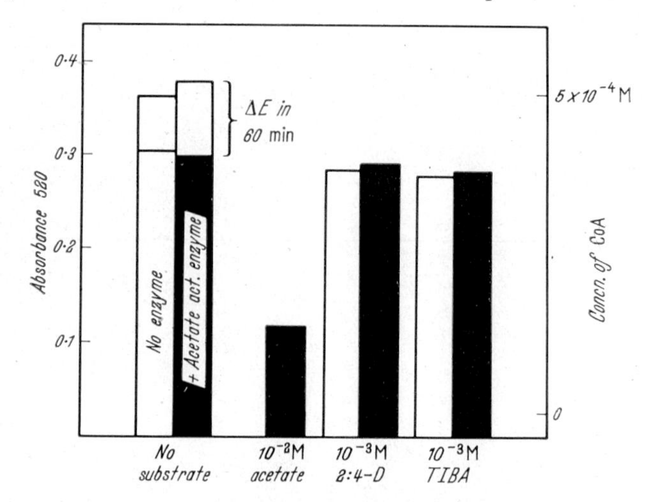

Figure 2. Sulphydryl disappearance with acetate activating enzyme. Final concentrations of constituents:
5×10^{-4} M *CoA reduced with* KBH_4
10^{-2} M *ATP*
10^{-1} M *TRIIS* pH 8
10^{-2} M $MgCl_2$
10^{-2} M KAc
ca. 0·4 *mg protein/ml where added.*
Incubation time: 60 *minutes except for portions of 'no substrate' as indicated.*
Temperature: 30°.
Volume: 0·5 *ml diluted immediately prior to assay with* 2·5 *ml sat.* NaCl *and* 0·3 *ml each of nitroprusside and sodium carbonate-cyanide.*
Concentration of free sulphydryl determined by E_{520}.

there followed an enzymatic disappearance of roughly 4×10^{-4} M sulphydryl concentration. The figure shows similar experiments with 2:4-D and TIBA, and it can be seen that the disappearance of sulphydryls in the presence of these growth substances was scarcely greater than the disappearance in the non-enzymatic circumstances.

This experiment warns us of the possible complication of the auto-oxidation of CoA. Not only is the extent of sulphydryl change due to auto-oxidation in the same order of magnitude as the greatest change reported by Leopold and Guernsey (1953), but it is somewhat larger than the change reported with 2:4-D by Millerd and Bonner (1954). Their experiments are roughly comparable in that, like ours, a relatively large disappearance of sulphydryl was obtained with acetate.

Turning to the measurement of thio-esters formed, a wide range of auxin concentrations was tested with a castor bean mitochondrial preparation which was active in the esterification of CoA. Results of such an experiment are shown in *Figure 3*. This work was done using acetate as a substrate. Naphthalene acetic acid was applied in varying concentrations in an effort to modify the rate of acetyl ester formation. The amount of esters produced was measured by the ferric hydroxamate assay. It can be seen from the figure that approximately 0·5 micromoles of ester was formed in the absence of any auxin, and the addition of auxin had no perceptible influence—either promotive or inhibitory. The same lack of auxin effect applied in the absence of acetate.

From these experiments we feel that the theory proposed by Leopold and Guernsey is inadequate in its original form.

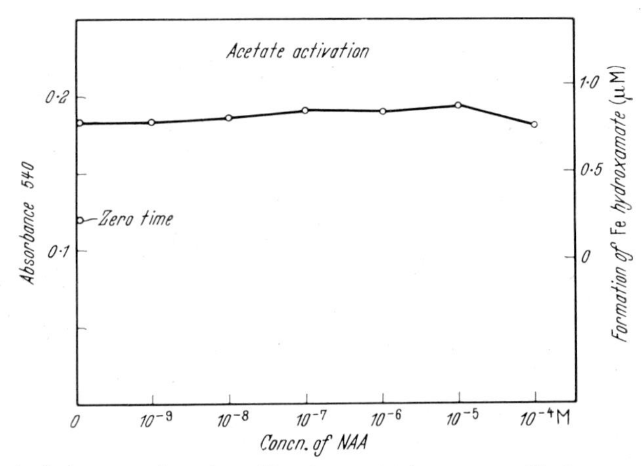

Figure 3. Acethydroxamate formation with acetate activating enzyme. Final concentrations of constituents (after Jones et al. (1953) *as in Figure 2, except CoA* = 10^{-4} M, *plus* 10^{-2} M *GSH and* 0·2 M NH_2OH.

Incubation time: 60 *minutes.*

Temperature: 30°.

Reaction product measured according to Jones et al. (1953).

INFLUENCE OF GROWTH SUBSTANCES UPON SULPHYDRYLS

If now we are unwilling to accept the scheme that auxins function through reaction with the sulphydryl of CoA, the question confronts us once again as to just what the role of sulphydryl compounds in growth substance action might be. It is well known that iodoacetate reacts directly with sulphydryl groups and in this manner inhibits a variety of enzymatic reactions essential for growth. Thimann (1951) pointed out that like iodoacetate, phenylpropionic acid may inhibit enzyme sulphydryl groups and suggested an analogy between this function of phenylpropionic acid and auxins. It was his idea that sulphydryl inhibitors occurring naturally in the tissues might be protected against by auxins. A more recent theory proposed by Muir *et al.* (1949) included an assumption that auxins react with sulphydryl groups at the *ortho* position of the ring. We would like to ask the question whether auxins or growth inhibitors might in fact react with sulphydryls *in vitro* in the manner of iodoacetate. It might be recalled here that lactones and quinones have each been considered as sulphydryl inactivating agents, and a number of growth substances are of these species.

Measurements of sulphydryl disappearance

The reactivity of sulphydryl with α-β unsaturated ketones was first described by Posner (1902). Dickens (1933) established the nature of the reaction of iodoacetic acid with sulphydryls, namely that the iodine was displaced by the sulphur resulting in the formation of a thio-ether. Geiger and Conn (1945) published some preliminary evidence that the activity of some antibiotics might be destroyed by cysteine, and in the same year Cavallito and Haskell (1945) published additional evidence for the reaction of some other lactones with cysteine. In no case, however, has the disappearance of the sulphydryl groups been measured quantitatively.

A simple system was used to follow sulphydryl disappearance. One-millilitre aliquots containing various concentrations of growth substances and

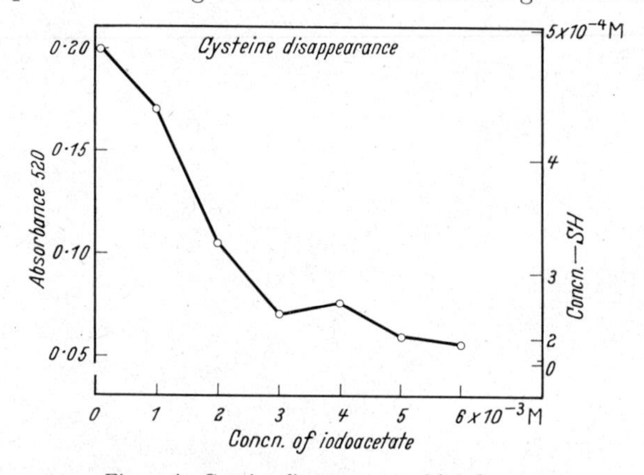

Figure 4. Cysteine disappearance with iodoacetate.

Volume: 1·1 *ml.*
Incubation time: 6 *hrs.*
Reactants adjusted to pH 6·5±0·3.
Free sulphydryl estimated by nitroprusside assay following dilution with 3·0 *ml sat.* NaCl.

including the sulphydryl compound cysteine were incubated *in vacuo* at approximately 28°C for 6 hours and the amount of free sulphydryl remaining was then measured by the nitroprusside test of Grunnert and Phillips (1951).

We proposed to begin following the disappearance of free sulphydryls in the presence of a model sulphydryl inactivating agent. We selected iodoacetic acid as the model substance and cysteine as the sulphydryl. The disappearance of sulphydryls with iodoacetate is presented in *Figure 4*. It can be seen that for each mole of iodoacetic acid there was a disappearance of approximately one-tenth of a mole of sulphydryl in 6 hours.

Turning to another halogenated acid, *Figure 5* shows the results obtained with TIBA. It is evident at once that this compound is at least as active as iodoacetate. For each mole of TIBA added approximately one-half of a mole of sulphydryl disappeared. The apparent reaction between TIBA and cysteine was followed in time as shown in *Figure 6*. The slow decrease of the sulphydryls in the control was presumably due to auto-oxidation.

If TIBA forms aryl-thio-ethers analogous to those formed by iodoacetate, it is interesting to compare the relative —SH activity of halogenated acetic acids to the growth regulator activity of halogenated benzoic acids. Dickens (1933) has reported that iodoacetic, bromoacetic, and chloroacetic acids show differential activities against sulphydryls of 100:60:1. Triiodo-, tribromo-, and trichlorobenzoic acids show differential activities in inducing stem abscission of 100:11:5 (Weintraub *et al.*, 1952).

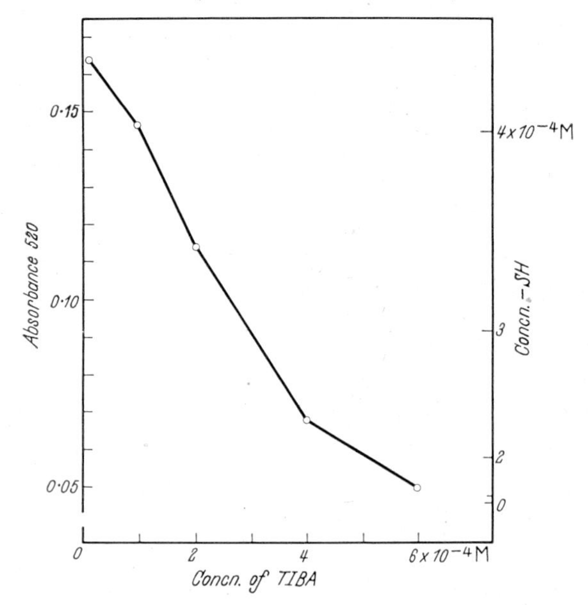

Figure 5. Cysteine disappearance with TIBA. Conditions as in Figure 4.

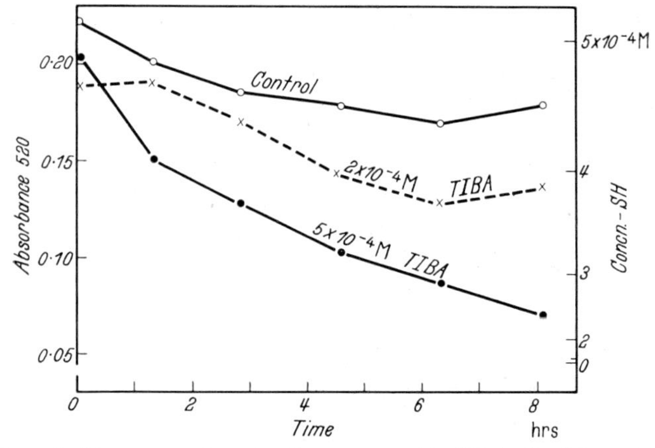

Figure 6. Time course of cysteine disappearance with TIBA. Conditions as in Figure 4.

Looking for a moment at TIBA as a growth substance, there are conflicting lines of evidence as to whether it acts competitively with auxin. In brief, it is not at all clear that TIBA competes with auxin for the same activity site. Hence it would be mistaken to interpret the present experiments with TIBA as evidence concerning the site of auxin attachment.

Veldstra and Havinga (1943) suggested that unsaturated lactones such as coumarin were sulphydryl inactivating agents. We have found in fact that coumarin incubated with cysteine brought about a disappearance of free sulphydryl as shown in *Figure 7*. Each mole of coumarin brought about the disappearance of about one-third of a mole of sulphydryl.

Turning to 2:4-D as a model auxin, it would be very interesting to know whether such a sulphydryl reaction might occur with this compound, particularly in view of the suggestion that auxin attaches to a cysteinyl group. It can be seen in this figure that 2:4-D gave only very small disappearance of sulphydryl. It would seem, therefore, that this auxin does not readily form a thiol bond under the conditions tested.

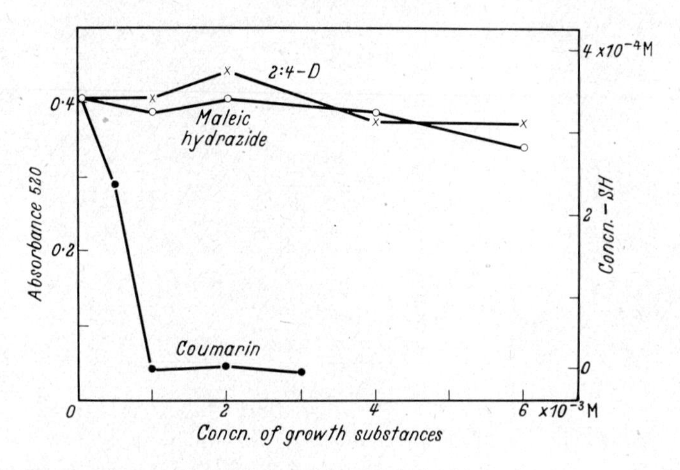

Figure 7. Cysteine disappearance with 2:4-*D, maleic hydrazide, and coumarin. Conditions as in Figure 4.*

Maleic hydrazide was also only weakly active at best in causing sulphydryl disappearance.

Another compound it would be interesting to examine for thiol reactivity is 2:4-dichloroanisole. Bonner (1949) first suggested this compound as a competitive inhibitor of auxin on the basis that it might satisfy the ring requirement for auxin (presumably by sulphydryl attachment) without satisfying the acid requirement. Consequently, it would be an anti-auxin by competitive inhibition. In *Figure 8*, it appears that 2:4-dichloroanisole may be quite effective in bringing about the disappearance of free sulphydryl, and this is in contrast to the relative inactivity of 2:4-D, and incidentally, of 2:4-dichlorophenol. Due to solubility limitations of the dichloroanisole, a small amount of ether was added to this experiment, and since this solvent interferes somewhat with the nitroprusside test, a part of this apparent sulphydryl disappearance may not be due to the growth substance.

While it is possible to assume that auxins may react with cysteine groups only through more complicated reaction conditions, the evidence presented here at least does not contribute to the scheme of *ortho* attachment of the auxin ring. The evidence that 2:4-dichloroanisole may be a competitive inhibitor of auxin has been criticized. Audus and Shipton (1952) were unable to show competitive interaction in root growth. Housley *et al.* (1954) have re-examined the evidence and suggested that this inhibitor was in reality non-competitive with auxin. The findings reported here, that the anisole may react with thiol groups whereas auxins do not, would seem to be in agreement with these criticisms.

Some data on indoleacetic acid and naphthalene acetic acid are also presented in *Figure 8*. We consider the changes with these reagents to be small.

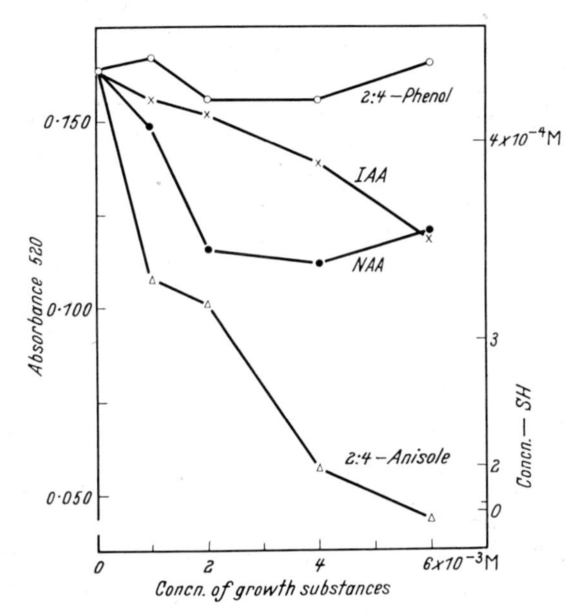

Figure 8. Cysteine disappearance with 2:4-*dichlorophenol, IAA, NAA, and* 2:4-*dichloroanisole. Conditions as in Figure 4.*

Sulphydryl reactions of enzymes and coenzymes

The evidence presented so far would suggest that some growth substances are able to react with sulphydryl groups and it is implied from this that by so doing they would influence some metabolic processes in a manner which would be reflected in growth. If this is true then the functioning of enzymes which require free sulphydryls for their activity should be inhibited by these growth substances. We selected amylase as being such an enzyme with which we might demonstrate sulphydryl inhibition.

Elliott and Leopold (1953) utilized the inhibition of amylase as an assay for a naturally occurring growth inhibitor in oats. Evidence was brought forward that this inhibitor might attack sulphydryl groups and apparently through this function it would inhibit growth. Since amylase activity is a function of its free sulphydryl groups, it could be utilized as a handy quantitative assay for the inhibitor. In the present experiments essentially the same scheme was used. Amylase was incubated at room temperature with TIBA at various concentrations ranging from 25 to $0{\cdot}5 \times 10^{-4}$ M. After this incubation period, the ability of the enzyme to hydrolyse starch was measured as shown in *Figure 9*. It is evident that in the control a rapid decline in starch was obtained as indicated with the iodine test. With increasing concentrations of TIBA both the amount of starch disappearing and the rate of disappearance were reduced. These data suggest then that the ability of TIBA to react with sulphydryl groups can actually bring about an alteration of activity of an enzyme requiring free sulphydryl groups.

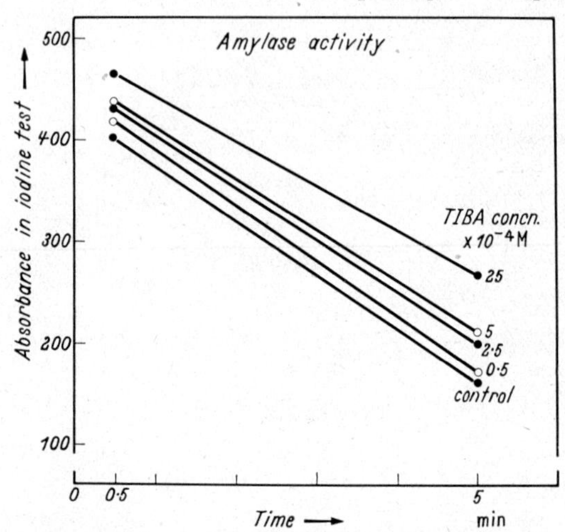

Figure 9. Effect of TIBA on amylase activity.

Order of addition of reagents:
1·0 *ml acetate buffer* pH 6·0
0·1 *ml* 10^{-3} M $CaSO_4$
De-ionized water to final volume of 10·0 *ml*
TIBA
Malt α-amylase at final concentration of 0·015 *mg/ml.*
Incubation time: 2 *hrs.*
Temperature: ca. 25°.
Enzyme reaction initiated by additions of substrate (0·05 *per cent final concentrations of soluble starch*).
Reaction stopped by removal of samples to KI_3 *reagent.*
Starch–iodine complex estimated by E_{525}.

One of the most important compounds in plant metabolism known to require a free sulphydryl group is CoA. If some growth substances inactivate sulphydryl groups, they may be able to inactivate CoA similarly. Experiments were therefore set up to investigate the possible inactivation of CoA with the growth substances TIBA and 2:4-D.

The method used involved the incubation of CoA and growth substance for periods up to an hour. The subsequent activity of the CoA in terms of its ability to form an acetyl ester was measured through the *trans*acetylase system of Stadtman (1952). The reactions involved were as follows:

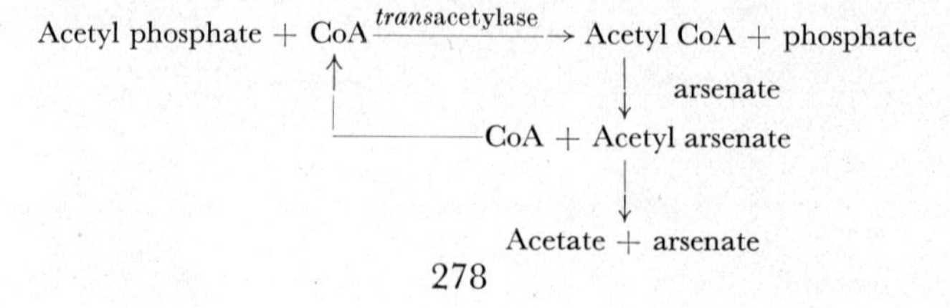

In this system acetate is transferred from acetyl phosphate to CoA enzymatically, and the rate of this acetylation is proportional to the amount of functional CoA present. A linear relationship between the disappearance of acetyl phosphate and the quantity of CoA present is obtained from 0 to 5×10^{-5} M CoA. Under the conditions utilized the acetyl phosphate remaining after 15 minutes was measured by the ferric hydroxamic acid test.

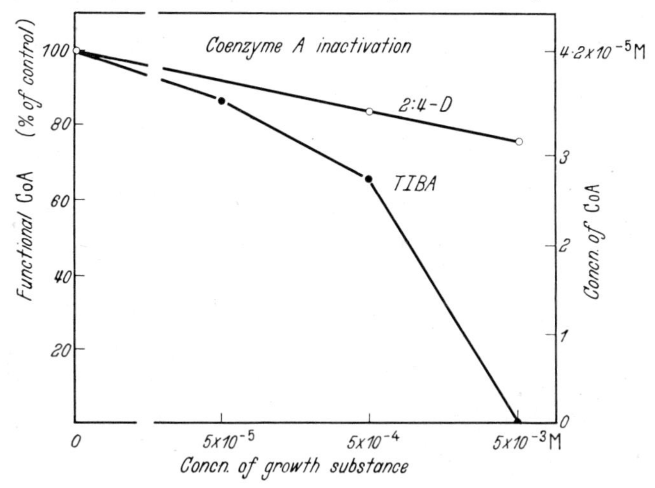

Figure 10. Reaction of CoA with TIBA and 2:4-*D.*

Final concentrations of constituents:

$2{\cdot}5 \times 10^{-4}$ M *CoA*

5×10^{-2} M *TRIS* pH 8

growth substances as indicated.

Volume: 0·2 *ml.*

Incubation time: 60 *minutes.*

Temperature: 30°.

Functional CoA remaining after incubation estimated according to Stadtman (1952), *except that the cysteine was deleted.*

The effects of TIBA and 2:4-D upon the reaction of CoA are shown in *Figure 10.* It can be seen that while 2:4-D was only slightly inhibitory, TIBA at 5×10^{-3} M completely destroyed the effectiveness of CoA in this reaction. There is approximately one hundred times as much of the growth substance as CoA present, but the time of incubation of the growth substance with CoA was only one hour. An increasing effectiveness of the growth substance TIBA with increasing time of incubation can be seen in *Figure 11.* It is strongly suggested from these data that TIBA may interfere with the acyl transfer functions of CoA through reaction with the sulphydryl group of the coenzyme.

Earlier work on sulphydryl inactivating agents has frequently shown a reversal of the inactivation with cysteine. Dickens (1933) reports such a reversal of iodoacetic acid inhibition of rat liver glyoxalase and suggests from his data that the iodoacetate attacks a prosthetic group rather than the enzyme itself. We were able to obtain a partial reversal of the inaction of CoA by TIBA as shown in *Figure 12.* This reversal, however, represents only a small fraction of the TIBA inhibition. In the case of 2:4-D, however, cysteine completely reversed the inhibition obtained. It is possible that cysteine may be able to restore the sulphydryls of CoA which have been oxidized to the disulphide form, but can not restore those sulphydryls which have been actually substituted by TIBA. The reversal effect of cysteine is quantitatively suggestive of the auto-oxidation effect evident in *Figure 2*.

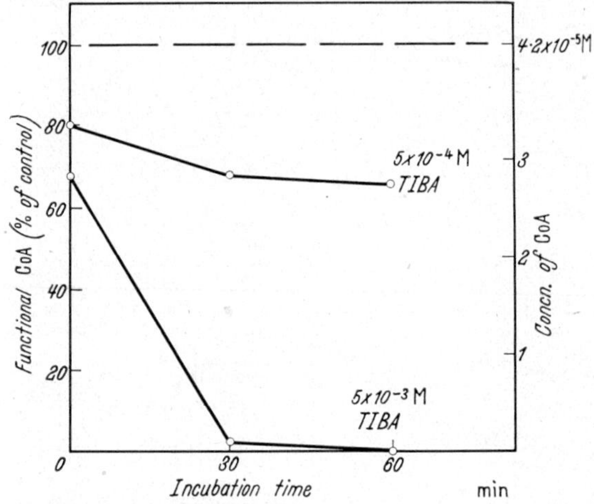

Figure 11. Time course of CoA inactivation with TIBA. Conditions as in Figure 10.

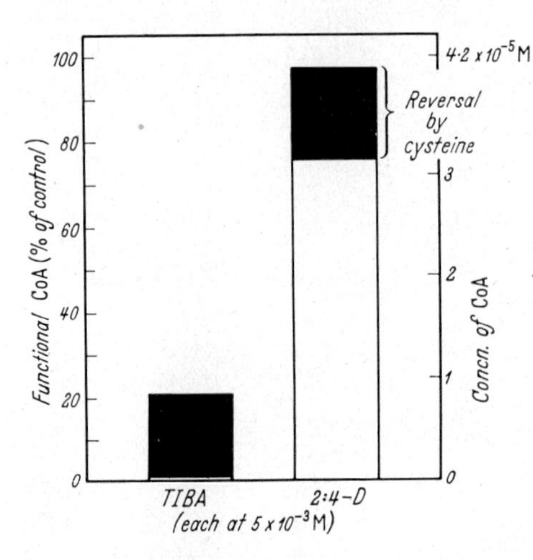

Figure 12. Effect of cysteine following incubation of CoA with growth substances. Conditions as in Figure 10, except that 10^{-2} M *cysteine added* 1 *minute before assay of CoA.*

Van Overbeek *et al.* (1955) devised a series of compounds which were assumed to be sulphydryl inactivators: the maleimides. The effects of these compounds upon abscission were of a much higher order of magnitude than the effects of TIBA. They did not measure the actual disappearance of sulphydryls in the presence of these maleimides but they did obtain a complete reversal of the effects with cysteine. Their findings suggest that the maleimides may inactivate some system in a chain of events which controls abscission but perhaps not inactivating directly the reaction at the precise site of abscission induction, for then one would not expect a complete reversal with cysteine.

DISCUSSION

In a re-examination of the possibility that auxin may form thio-esters with CoA, the experiments reported here cast some doubt on the possibility. The disappearance of sulphydryl groups in the presence of auxins may not be due to the formation of thio-esters. Direct examination of the amount of ester formation in the presence and absence of naphthalene acetic acid failed to show any increase in ester formation due to the auxin. For the present, then, we do not feel that the theory of Leopold and Guernsey (1953) is adequate.

Looking further into the possibility that growth regulators may alter sulphydryl reactivity, it has been found that TIBA, coumarin, and 2:4-dichloroanisole may react non-enzymatically with the sulphydryls of cysteine, a reactivity which may account in part for their activity as growth substances.

With regard to the action of iodoacetate, Thimann and Bonner (1948) interpreted the inhibition of auxin-induced growth by iodoacetate as indicating that there may be a growth enzyme requiring a free sulphydryl group for its activity, and that iodoacetate may thus be blocking auxin action in a fairly specific way. That iodoacetate may compete with auxin in some fairly close way is suggested further by the report of Reinhold (1954) that iodoacetate competes with indoleacetic acid for entrance into pea stem sections. Both of these instances, however, may be somewhat clouded by the fact that iodoacetate is affecting respiration itself, which may then alter the indoleacetic acid function.

Turning next to TIBA, this compound was early suggested to have properties antagonistic to auxin (Galston, 1947) and has since been shown to reverse the auxin inhibition of root growth by auxin (Minarik *et al.*, 1951), and to be reversed in its effects on abscission by auxin (Weintraub *et al.*, 1952). Its synergistic action with auxin in growth led Thimann and Bonner (1948) to suggest that it was sufficiently similar to auxins that it might be competing with auxins for the same sites. With respect to its spontaneous reactivity toward sulphydryl groups, TIBA shows strong reactivity where the auxins show very little.

The ability of coumarin to react with sulphydryl groups is in direct agreement with the early suggestion of Veldstra and Havinga (1945) that lactones of this sort may be sulphydryl inactivators andauxin antagonists. The ability of BAL (1:2-dithiopropanol) to prevent the coumarin inhibition of growth (Thimann and Bonner, 1949) is further support for their suggestion. The synergism of coumarin and auxin in growth and in seed germination (Thimann and Bonner, 1949; Mayer and Evanari, 1951) has opened the rather tenuous possibility that coumarin, too, may compete with auxins for the same site of action. Some new and interesting implications concerning coumarin have come recently from the work of Libbert (1955) who provides evidence that the lactones may be intimately involved in the ability of auxins to inhibit growth, particularly in relation to apical dominance. The work of Hemberg (1949, 1950) suggests too that growth inhibitors may be responsible for the bud inhibition involved in dormancy, and their inhibitions may be naturally relieved by the biosynthesis of glutathione. Von Guttenberg and Meinle (1954) provide some indirect evidence that the dormancy factors may be lactone type substances.

The apparent ability of 2:4-dichloroanisole to react with sulphydryls suggests that at least a part of the growth inhibition by that compound may be due to this characteristic. And since we have not found auxins to share this quality, it is not very surprising that some workers have not found it to inhibit growth in a manner competitive with auxin (Audus and Shipton, 1952; Housley *et al.*, 1954).

In conclusion, it would seem appropriate at this point to recall the caution given by Audus (1953) that there is no reason to believe *a priori* that growth inhibitors have a simple action in growth. Substances which we may think of as anti-auxins in the strictest sense may not act as good competitive inhibitors of auxin in many tests, for their ability to carry out side reactions may certainly alter the kinetics of their effects. We feel that the ability of TIBA, coumarin, and 2:4-dichloroanisole to react with sulphydryls may certainly contribute to their growth responses, though it is certainly not entirely responsible for them or iodoacetate would mimic them precisely.

REFERENCES

AUDUS, L. J. (1953). *Plant growth substances*, Leonard Hill Ltd., London.

AUDUS, L. J., and SHIPTON, M. C. (1952). 2-4-Dichloroanisole-auxin interactions in root growth. *Physiol. Plant.* **5,** 430.

BONNER, J. (1949). Limiting factors and growth inhibitors in the growth of *Avena* coleoptile. *Amer. J. Bot.* **36,** 323.

CAVALLITO, C. J., and HASKELL, T. H. (1945). The mechanism of action of antibiotics. The reaction of unsaturated lactones with cysteine and related compounds. *J. Amer. Chem. Soc.* **67,** 1991.

DICKENS, F. (1933). Interaction of halogenacetates and SH compounds. *Biochem. J.* **27,** 1141.

ELLIOTT, B. B., and LEOPOLD, A. C. (1953). An inhibitor of germination and of amylase activity in oat seeds. *Physiol. Plant.* **6,** 66.

GALSTON, A. W. (1947). Effect of 2:3:5-triiodobenzoic acid on growth and flowering of soybeans. *Amer. J. Bot.* **34,** 356.

GEIGER, W. B., and CONN, J. E. (1945). The mechanism of the antibiotic action of clavacin and penicillic acid. *J. Amer. chem. Soc.* **67,** 112.

GRUNNERT, R. R., and PHILLIPS, P. H. (1951). A modification of the nitroprusside method of analysis for glutathione. *Arch. Biochem. Biophys.* **30,** 217.

GUTTENBERG, H. VON, and MEINLE, G. (1954). Über die Veranderung der Wasserpermeabilitat von Kartoffolknollen wahrend der Lagerzeit und durch Cumarin. *Planta*, **43,** 571.

HEMBERG, T. (1949). Significance of growth inhibiting substances and auxins for rest period of potato. *Physiol. Plant.* **2,** 24.

HEMBERG, T. (1950). Effect of glutathione on growth inhibiting substances in resting potato tubers. *Physiol. Plant.* **3,** 17.

HOUSLEY, S., BENTLEY, J. A., and BICKLE, A. S. (1954). Studies on Plant Growth Hormones. III. Application of enzyme reaction kinetics to cell elongation in the *Avena* coleoptile. *J. exp. Bot.* **5,** 373.

JONES, M. E., BLACK, S., FLYNN, R. M., and LIPMANN, F. (1953). Acetyl CoA synthesis through pyrophosphoryl split of ATP. *Biochim. biophys. Acta*, **12,** 141.

LEOPOLD, A. C., and GUERNSEY, F. S. (1953). A theory of auxin action involving coenzyme A. *Proc. Nat. Acad. Sci., Wash.* **39,** 1105.

LIBBERT, E. (1955). Das Zusammenwirkung von Wuchs-und Hemmstoffen bei der korrelativen Knospenhemmung. *Planta*, **45,** 68.

MAYER, A. M., and EVANARI, M. (1951). The influence of two germination inhibitors (Coumarin and 2:4:D) on germination in conjunction with thiourea and cysteine. *Bull. Res. Coun. Israel*, **1,** 125.

MILLERD, A., and BONNER, J. (1954). Acetate activation and acetoacetate formation in plant systems. *Arch. Biochem. Biophys.* **49,** 343.

MINARIK, E. E., READY, D., NORMAN, A. G., THOMPSON, H. E., and OWINGS, J. F. (1951). New growth regulating compounds. II. Substituted benzoic acids. *Bot. Gaz.* **113,** 135.

MUIR, R. M., HANSCH, C. H., and GALLUP, A. H. (1949). Growth regulation by organic compounds. *Plant. Physiol.* **24,** 359.

OVERBEEK, J. VAN, BLONDEAU, R., and HORNE, V. (1955). Maleimides as auxin antagonists. *Amer. J. Bot.* **42,** 205.

POSNER, T. (1902). Zur Kenntnis der Disulfone. IX. *Ber. dtsch. chem. Ges.* **35,** 799.

REINHOLD, L. (1954). The uptake of indole-3-acetic acid by pea epicotyl segments and carrot disks. *New Phytol.* **53,** 217.

STADTMAN, E. R. (1952). The purification and properties of phosphotrans-acetylase. *J. biol. Chem.* **196,** 527.

THIMANN, K. V. (1951). The synthetic auxins: relation between structure and activity. In *Plant Growth Substances*, edited by F. Skoog, University of Wisconsin Press.

THIMANN, K. V., and BONNER, W. D. (1948). Experiments on the growth and inhibition of isolated plant parts. I. The action of iodoacetate and organic acids on the *Avena* coleoptile. *Amer. J. Bot.* **35,** 271.

THIMANN, K. V., and BONNER, W. D. (1948). The action of triiodobenzoic acid on growth. *Plant Physiol.* **23,** 158.

THIMANN, K. V., and BONNER, W. D. (1949). Inhibition of plant growth by proto-anemonin and coumarin and its prevention by BAL. *Proc. nat. Acad. Sci., Wash.* **35,** 272.

VELDSTRA, H., and HAVINGA, E. (1943). Untersuchungen über pflanzliche Wuchsstoffe. VII. Über struktur and Wirkungsmechanismus der pflanzlichen Wuchs- und Hemmstoffe. *Rec. Trav. chim. Pays-Bas*, **62,** 841.

VELDSTRA, H., and HAVINGA, E. (1945). On the physiological activity of unsaturated lactones. *Enzymologia*, **11,** 373.

WAARD, J. DE, and FLORSCHUTZ, P. A. (1948). On the interaction of 2:3:5-triiodobenzoic acid and indoleacetic acid in growth processes. *Proc. Acad. Sci. Amst.* **51,** 1317.

WEINTRAUB, R. L., BROWN, J. W., NICKERSON, J. C., and TAYLOR, K. N. (1952). Studies on the relation between molecular structure and physiological activity of plant growth regulators. I. Abscission-inducing activity. *Bot. Gaz.* **113,** 348.

SALT ACCUMULATION AND MODE OF ACTION OF AUXIN.

A PRELIMINARY HYPOTHESIS

T. A. Bennet-Clark

Botany Department, King's College, University of London

INTRODUCTION

Hypotheses on the mechanism of auxin action should, of course, provide explanations of the very numerous different effects which it seems to evoke: stem extension, bud inhibition, abscission delay, and the like. If, at the beginning, we consider stem elongation only, it may be said that three types of hypothesis have been advanced: (*a*) that the cell wall is rendered more plastic and is thus subjected to turgor stetching, (*b*) that active water and possibly solute uptake is promoted, (*c*) that polysaccharide synthesis is stimulated and the wall 'grows'.

The supporters of each of these types of hypothesis do not appear to have suggested or thought of any molecular mechanisms which would carry out the process involved. This may be explained or excused on the grounds that little or nothing is known of the mechanism of synthesis of the polysaccharide material of cell walls. This is true also of active water and solute uptake, apart from the Lundegårdh anion-respiration-cytochrome hypothesis and the contractile protein hypothesis of Goldacre; in neither case, however, are any precise molecular details specified, nor is there any reason to think that 3-indolylacetic acid (IAA) would be involved in either of these processes.

SUMMARY OF EXPERIMENTAL FINDINGS

It will be convenient before enunciating a working hypothesis, the aim of which is primarily to stimulate and direct research, to present the major series of experimental results suggesting this possibly novel view of the mechanism.

(i) Wightman (1955) has shown that considerable extension growth of wheat coleoptiles occurs under influence of IAA without corresponding production of cellulose. Our own results indicate also that in the absence of external supplies of sugar, wall extension occurs without appreciable gain of cellulose, 'hemicelluloses' or 'pectins' during a 10-hour period.

(ii) This extension is markedly influenced by the osmotic pressure of the medium and by the nature of the ions present in it. Results of typical experiments are given in *Figure 1*, which shows the extensions of 10-mm segments of oat coleoptiles plotted against time. The growth of segments treated with a series of solutions of different osmotic pressure to which IAA had been added at a concentration of 1 mg/l. are given together with that of corresponding controls without IAA.

The initial extension rates are negative (shrinkage) in the higher osmotic pressures. That o.p. which just balances the suction pressure (s.p.) of the tissue causes zero extension. It will be seen that a zero initial or negative initial extension is quite rapidly converted into a positive extension. The result is that one can only obtain crude estimates of the true initial s.p. of the tissue. The data of *Figure 1* suggest that in the absence of external IAA the s.p. is about 7·1 atm; with 1 mg/l. IAA it is about 9·8 atm and with 10 mg/l. 5·4 atm. In view of the experimental errors involved, it is uncertain how much significance should be attached to these differences in apparent s.p.,

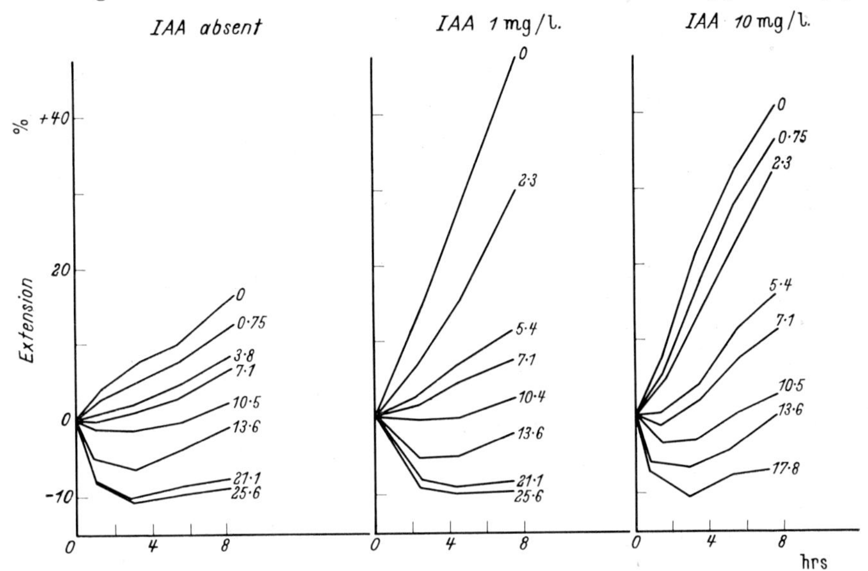

Figure 1. Per cent extensions of oat coleoptiles plotted against time in hours: without IAA, with IAA 1 mg/l. and IAA 10 mg/l. The figures at the right-hand side of each curve show the osmotic pressures of potassium chloride solutions in which the extension growth took place.

but one inclines to the view that the increase at low auxin concentrations is possibly due to increased wall plasticity and the reduction at higher concentrations may be explained on the basis of reduced activity of pumping mechanisms.

As it has been suggested that IAA *increases* water secretion, it may be well to record here that Dr. J. F. Sutcliffe (private communication) has shown that IAA, while having little effect on ion secretion at low concentrations, definitely *inhibits* ion uptake by actively absorbing beet tissue at higher concentrations such as 10^{-4} M and over.

The same set of data can be used to obtain estimates of the osmotic pressure of tissue by noting the external o.p. above which further shrinkage does not occur. Unfortunately, although one tends to expect that a plasmolysed tissue will not shrink on being placed in a hypertonic solution, considerable shrinkage does occur when plasmolysed cells are more strongly plasmolysed, especially in young extending tissues, though the increments of shrinkage are much less. One cannot therefore get an accurate estimate, but the data suggest values of around 18 atm at the lower auxin concentrations and 13 atm in the case where the concentration was 10 mg/l.

The difference (s.p.—o.p.) gives an estimate of the wall pressure. The very rapid change over from negative to positive extensions in the first 60 to 120 minutes of exposure to water or solutions makes detailed interpretations difficult; one can, however, be reasonably confident that initial suction pressures are of the order of 7 to 10 atm and it is consequently of interest to note the effects of very small external osmotic pressures of salts of bivalent or trivalent cations.

Figure 2 shows the extension against time of coleoptile sections placed either in solutions containing only IAA at 1 mg/l., or in solutions of the same IAA concentration with additions of calcium and praseodymium chlorides of various o.p. (the trivalent ion used was the commercially available mixture of praseodymium and neodymium chloride; hydrolysis of aluminium chloride was thought to offer a possible complication). Solutions of

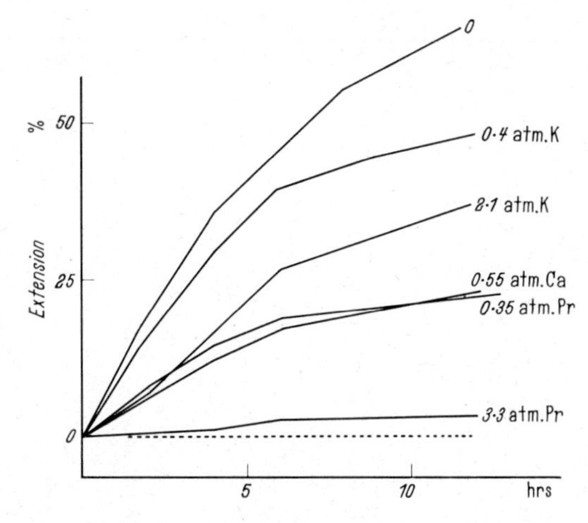

Figure 2. Extension growth of Avena *coleoptile plotted against time with* 1 *mg/l. IAA and additions of* KCl.$CaCl_2$ *and* $PrCl_3$ *of various osmotic pressures indicated at the right-hand side of the curves.*

$PrCl_3$ with an o.p. of 2 atm or over completely inhibit extension even though the internal s.p. has almost certainly a minimum value of the order of 7 to 10 atm. The effect is therefore almost certainly not osmotic.

The converse of these multivalent ion effects is also found. Substances which chelate such ions, like ethylenediaminetetraacetic acid (EDTA), not only counteract the effect of artificially added Ca^{++}, but act for a limited period of time as 'growth substances'. The initial growth-promoting effect is of rather short duration in the case of wheat coleoptile tissue, and thus bears some resemblance to the promoting effects observed with high concentrations of auxin. The falling off in growth rate and activity after some 6 to 8 hours may perhaps be ascribed to chelation and removal of essential ions of the respiration complex such as Mg^{++} and perhaps others. The falling off in growth rate with time is not very noticeable in oat coleoptile sections with EDTA concentrations of 10^{-3} M or lower.

Figure 3 shows the extension of oat coleoptiles in water (as control) and in EDTA. 10^{-4} or 10^{-5} M ammonium oxalate acts similarly as a 'growth substance' whereas the same concentrations of ammonium chloride give the same extension as water. These results, which will be published *in extenso* in the near future, strongly suggest interference with the pectins of cell walls. It will probably be agreed that the plastic and elastic extensibility of a polygalacturonic acid or in general of an oxidized hemicellulose will be markedly controlled by the condition of the carboxyl groups. If these long chain molecules are associated with multivalent cations, minimum extensibility will be found owing to electrovalent binding together of adjacent molecules. If the carboxyls are free, hydrogen bonding will provide considerable tensile strength but much less than that found in presence of cations and finally, when, or if, they are converted to methyl esters, there will be minimal tensile strength as hydrogen bonding will be replaced by van der Waals' forces and so extensibility will be maximal.

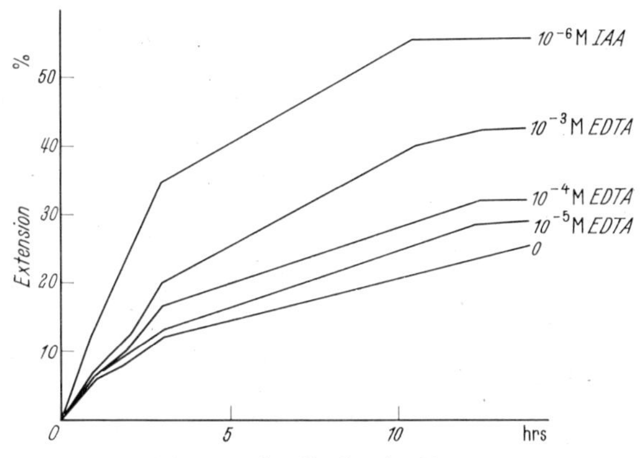

Figure 3. Extension growth of Avena *coleoptile plotted against time in the presence of IAA* 10^{-6} M *and in water as controls and with* 10^{-3}, 10^{-4}, *and* 10^{-5} M *EDTA.*

(iii) The percentage of methoxyl in the walls of coleoptiles before or during extension growth is readily determined. Fuller details will be published later. The critical data consist of ratios of uronic carboxyl to uronic methyl carboxylate. The fraction of total uronic carboxyl occurring as methyl ester in young extensible walls does not appear to exceed 50 per cent. The methoxyl content of such wall material is about 3 to 4 per cent of the dry weight, from which one can calculate a probable polyuronide content of 40 to 50 per cent of the total wall weight, as a minimum, in 70-hour-old coleoptiles.

(iv) It had been found by Brian and Rideal (1952) that strong interaction occurred between 2-methyl-4-chlorophenoxyacetic acid (MCPA) and surface films of phospholipids and lipoproteins. Similar interaction of IAA with such films was also found. This, coupled with results of some chromatography carried out in our laboratory, suggested complex formation of the choline moiety of the phospholipid with IAA.

The effect of IAA on acetylcholine-esterase was therefore examined and I am indebted to Dr. G. Brownlee for carrying out this study with a sphenic nerve-diaphragm preparation treated with tubocurarine. Reversal of the tubocurarine effect with physostigmine is well known and the explanation given and accepted by pharmacologists is that physostigmine is a specific inhibitor of acetylcholine-esterase and acts in this case by causing accumulation of acetylcholine.

Physostigmine is somewhat related in structure to IAA:

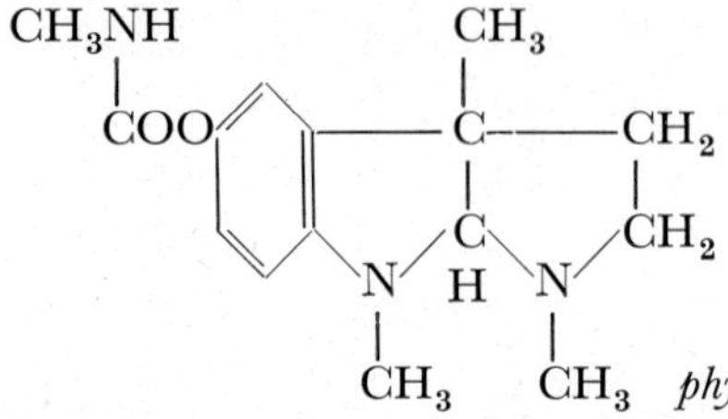

$$\begin{array}{l} CH_3NH \quad\quad CH_3 \\ | \quad\quad\quad\quad | \\ COO\text{-}C_6H_3\text{---}C\text{---}CH_2 \\ \quad\quad | \quad\quad | \quad\quad | \\ \quad\quad N\text{---}C(H)\text{---}N\text{---}CH_2 \\ \quad\quad | \quad\quad\quad\quad | \\ \quad\quad CH_3 \quad\quad CH_3 \end{array}$$

physostigmine

and the finding that IAA acted rather similarly as an apparent acetylcholine-esterase inhibitor in sphenic-diaphragm preparations was consequently not completely surprising. The concentration at which this inhibition was observed was relatively high, 5×10^{-4} M or around 100 p.p.m.

It has been shown by Koch (cf. review by him, 1954) that uptake of ions by gills of the crab, *Eriocheir*, is reversibly inhibited by physostigmine. The relatively irreversible choline-esterase inhibitor, tetraethylpyrophosphate (TEPP), similarly caused irreversible inhibition in this particular tissue, as did a rather less specific esterase inhibitor like rhodamine.

The situation in red blood cells may be similar. Greig, Faulkner, and Mayberry (1953) have shown that active transport or uptake of K^+ can be promoted by suitable metabolic energy sources and also by supply of acetylcholine in their absence, but that this transport is inhibited by physostigmine. There is some doubt regarding details of this situation as the concentration of physostigmine for inhibition of salt uptake is rather high, 2×10^{-3} M, while the isolated enzyme system is inhibited at 10^{-5} M (Strickland and Thompson, 1955). It is, however, of interest that concentrations of this order, 10^{-3} M IAA, cause roughly 50–60 per cent inhibition of uptake of NaCl from 0·02 M solutions by discs of beetroot tissue. Similar concentrations of IAA cause pronounced exosmosis of salts from coleoptile segments as shown by increase in conductivity of the water in which they are floating and also inhibition of salt uptake.

Rhodamine at a concentration of 10 mg/l. causes an 80 per cent reduction of NaCl uptake by beetroot discs.

(v) These facts do not, of course, show that salt uptake by plant tissue is mediated by an acetylcholine-esterase system. It is, moreover, necessary to show first the presence of an active choline esterase and here it is somewhat difficult to obtain really precise evidence. Discs of beetroot and roots of oat and of bean do cause marked decrease in pH of acetylcholine chloride supplied at 2×10^{-3} M at pH 7·3, but this could be explained as due to exosmosis of ions from the tissue. Parallel to this there is loss of acetylcholine from the external solution as determined colorimetrically after conversion to acethydroxamic acid; this loss, however, could be due to absorption of the acetylcholine chloride by the tissue. It is clearly necessary to obtain the isolated enzyme system before one can have confidence in its presence or consider very seriously its role in effecting ion uptake.

Dr. Bell of the Zoology Department of King's College has kindly carried out the histochemical test using acetylthiocholine chloride in a copper–glycine buffer. Crystals were formed at the surfaces of root hairs of broad bean, *Vicia faba*, but in material simultaneously treated with physostigmine or

IAA it could hardly be said that there was markedly less of this crystalline material and it is therefore very doubtful if these crystals really are the copper–thiocholine compound. It seems rather uncertain whether a choline-esterase *is* present. It should be noted that the apparent activity is very low in comparison with the esterase of neuro-muscular junctions, some 10 hours or more is needed to observe the apparent acetylcholine hydrolysis, and the pH changes are unspectacular compared with animal sources of choline-esterases.

A SUGGESTED MECHANISM OF ION UPTAKE

No clear mechanisms involving choline-esterases have been advanced though it seems highly probable that a role is played by these enzymes. Before enunciating a very tentative working hypothesis it should be mentioned that two other enzyme systems are known to be widespread. 'Choline-acetylase' is a mixture of enzymes requiring as co-factors, at least CoA and ATP. In presence of these factors and the enzyme-complex, acetylcholine is built up from acetate and choline.

This enzyme system exists in red blood cells and other tissues. It has not been reported and probably has not been looked for in plant tissues as yet.

Lecithinase-D is, however, widespread in particulate preparations from plants and from animal tissues. It causes hydrolysis of lecithin to phosphatidic acid and choline.

Finally, one must recall an important property of the phosphatides. Lecithins or phosphatidyl-cholines form complexes with salts which are soluble in non-polar solvents like benzene. The lecithin-$CdCl_2$ complex is probably the best known as its high solubility in benzene is used in preparing and purifying lecithin. Other salts also form complexes possibly as a result of the peculiar structure of the lecithin zwitterion.

The mechanism of ion uptake suggested is therefore as shown in the following diagram:

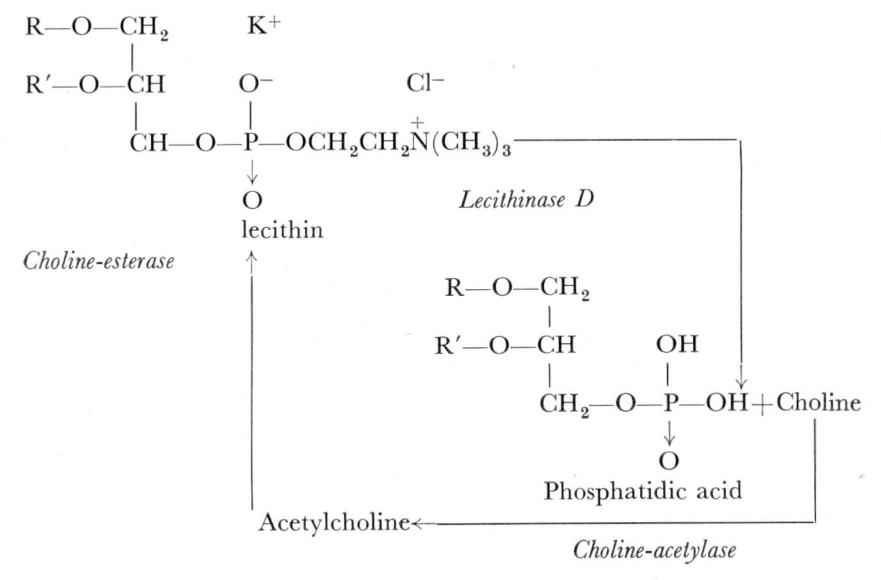

Lecithin or the corresponding lipoprotein at the outside of the lipoid boundary membrane (top left in diagram) at which accumulation is observed is supposed to form lipoid soluble complexes with salts and so act as the carrier which transfers the salt across the membrane to which as free salt it would be impermeable.

At the inside (or at the accumulation site; bottom right in diagram) lecithinase-D hydrolyses the complex to choline and phosphatidic acid, liberating the salt. The choline is then converted to acetylcholine by the acetylase system, the energy for this step being derived from ATP ultimately. Choline-esterase is known to act as a transferase in at least one reaction, i.e. acetylcholine+butyric acid $\rightleftharpoons$ butyrylcholine+acetic acid. It is suggested here that the choline-esterase of accumulating membranes similarly transfers choline from the acetyl to the phosphatidyl radical, thus resynthesising lecithin at the outside of the membrane.

A phosphatide cycle is thus postulated as the carrier mechanism. The cycle is obviously stopped by inhibitors of lecithinase, like rhodamine, by choline-esterase inhibition, and by interference with ATP phosphorylation such as is produced by dinitrophenal. All of these inhibitors apparently cause an inhibition in ion-uptake.

One should not over-emphasize any teleological argument, but it is noteworthy that choline-esterase is singularly active in the electric organ of *Electrophorus*, which must be a site of remarkable ion-secreting activity. Phosphatides are noteworthy structural constituents of plant and animal membranes. The enzyme systems referred to certainly exist and presumably have some function.

It is suggested that the phosphatide-cycle might also form a water-secreting system, as lecithin–water complexes are well known. Furthermore, carbohydrate complexes, particularly with inositol-phosphatides, have been isolated, and a corresponding carbohydrate accumulation system is conceivable which might be blocked by certain esterase inhibitors.

THE ACTION OF IAA ON COLEOPTILES

At high concentrations, 5×10^{-4} M and over, IAA causes a brief rapid extension which is replaced in short time, 2 to 4 hours, depending on the concentration, by either cessation of further extension or even by shrinkage. This 'toxic' effect, it is suggested, is due to paralysis of the water and salt accumulation system operated by the postulated phosphatide cycle. There is experimentally demonstrated paralysis of accumulation whatever the mechanism may happen to be.

The striking extensions produced at concentrations between 10^{-4} and 10^{-6} M are, it is suggested, due to interference with the pectin of the walls and removal of Ca^{++} and/or Mg^{++} and replacement of calcium pectate in part by free —COOH and in part by $—COOCH_3$.

One final point may be noted in this connection, we have found in this laboratory that 10^{-4} to 10^{-8} M dimethylthetin chloride, $[(CH_3)_2 \cdot S \cdot {}^{+}CH_2COOH]Cl'$, is an active promoter of extension growth during a limited period, behaving rather like a concentrated (10^{-3} M) IAA solution. This it seems may be related to its known behaviour as a methyl-donor.

The fact should again be emphasized that the chitin-containing and pectin-free walls of fungi are apparently not affected by IAA. A more extensive survey of IAA-stimulated cell walls is now projected; preliminary results suggest that pectin-rich walls are the type susceptible to stimulation by IAA.

It is emphasized that this preliminary hypothesis is an attempt to stimulate or open up new lines of research. As yet the secondary effects due to auxin have hardly been considered, though it may be remarked that the high concentrations required to induce bud dormancy may possibly be esterase or accumulation-inhibiting concentrations. Interference with abscission may be also connected with pectin metabolism.

ACKNOWLEDGEMENTS

I wish to thank Miss J. Turnham and Dr. B. Hazzi, who provided some of the experimental data quoted.

REFERENCES

BRIAN, R. C., and RIDEAL, E. K. (1952). On the action of plant growth-regulators. *Biochim. biophys. Acta*, **9**, 1.

GREIG, M. E., FAULKNER, J. S., and MAYBERRY, T. C. (1953). Studies on permeability. IX. Replacement of potassium in erythrocytes during cholinesterase activity. *Arch. Biochem. Biophys.* **43,** 39.

KOCH, H. J. (1954). Cholinesterase and active transport of sodium chloride through the isolated gills of *Eriocheir sinensis*. *Recent Developments in Cell Physiology*, Colston Research Society, Bristol.

STRICKLAND, K. P., and THOMPSON, R. H. S. (1955). Anti-cholinesterases and K loss from brain. *Biochem. J.* **60,** 468.

WIGHTMAN, F. (1955). Paper read at 98th conference of Society for Experimenta Biology, London, January, 1955.

IV

APPLICATIONS OF KINETICS TO AUXIN-INDUCED GROWTH

THE KINETICS OF AUXIN-INDUCED GROWTH†

J. Bonner and R. J. Foster

Kerckhoff Biological Laboratories, California Institute of Technology Pasadena California

When we supply auxin to a plant tissue we observe a response. This response in its most general terms consists of cell enlargement. Auxin goes into the tissue, some mysterious and unknown events take place, and growth appears. We can, however, find out a little about these obscure events in a very simple way. We can determine how the response of the plant tissue to auxin varies with auxin concentration, and from this we can deduce something about the nature of the reaction or reactions in which auxin participates. In this kind of study we deduce things about the mechanism of auxin action by measurements of the growth rate of tissue. We study the inside by measuring the outside.

If we wish to investigate the dependence of plant growth on auxin concentration, it will simplify matters to do it with a tissue which grows little in the absence of added auxin and responds greatly to the addition of the material. We may refer to the growth rate in the absence of added auxin as the endogenous growth. It is convenient to use a tissue which possesses a low level of endogenous growth but which responds greatly to added auxin. This situation is found with sections of the *Avena* coleoptile and this paper will refer only to work with such sections. That the growth of excised *Avena* coleoptile sections is increased by added auxin has been known for over twenty years (Bonner, 1933). In this time, it has become possible to grow sections in a moderately reproducible manner and the several factors in addition to auxin which determine growth rate have become known. The most important of these factors are:

(*a*) the pH of the medium, which must be kept constant since growth rate is dependent on pH (Bonner, 1936);

(*b*) the concentration of absorbable solutes such as glucose or sucrose in the external medium, since these solutes by their absorption into the tissue contribute to the osmotic concentration of the tissue which otherwise decreases by dilution during auxin-induced water uptake (Bonner, 1949; Ordin *et al.*, 1955);

(*c*) the ratio of external solution to tissue volume, which must be sufficiently large that the removal of auxin from the external solution does not appreciably influence the concentration of the material.

Suppose that we now place coleoptile sections in solutions containing varied auxin concentrations, bearing in mind the above three points of technique. The data of *Figure 1* show that growth rate of the tissue as measured by rate of elongation is constant with time over rather considerable periods. Each concentration of added auxin elicits a growth rate which is constant and therefore characteristic, for our conditions, of that auxin concentration. It is apparent that when the section is placed in an auxin solution the processes

† This paper was read at the Conference by J. Bonner.

which result in growth are quickly initiated and are then maintained in a steady-state condition for several hours. Our further analysis will deal only with the steady-state conditions.

Let us now proceed with the question of how section growth rate depends on auxin concentration. It has been known for some time (Bonner, 1933) that as the external auxin concentration is increased growth rate of the

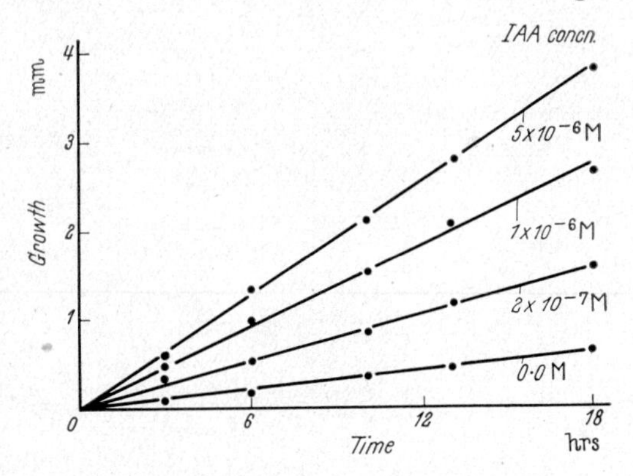

Figure 1. Elongation of Avena *coleoptile sections in different concentrations of indoleacetic acid* (*IAA*) *as a function of time. After Bonner and Foster* (1955).

section increases to a maximum and then drops off. We will first consider the low range of auxin concentrations, those below that which elicits maximum growth rate, often referred to as the physiological range of concentration. In *Figure 2*, the growth rates characteristic of each of a series of auxin concentrations are plotted as a function of auxin concentration for each of three auxins.

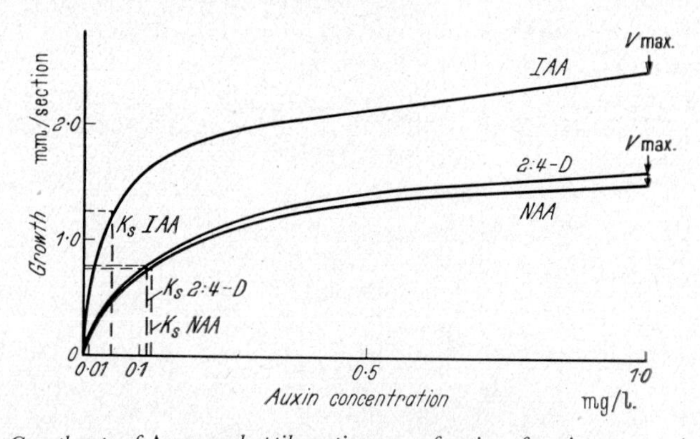

Figure 2. Growth rate of Avena *coleoptile sections as a function of auxin concentration. The three curves are, from top to bottom, for indoleacetic acid* (*IAA*), 2:4-*dichlorophenoxyacetic acid* (2:4-D), *and naphthalene acetic acid* (*NAA*). *After Foster, McRae, and Bonner* (1952).

It is evident that growth rate tends to increase towards a limiting value for each auxin and that the curves are hyperbolae such as are characteristic of saturation phenomena. They suggest that auxin interacts with something in the section, that growth rate is proportional to the amount of such interaction products, and that maximum growth rate is achieved when this something is fully occupied by auxin molecules. Let us see how we might formulate this hypothesis, which has been suggested by the data of *Figure 2*. Evidently

$$\text{auxin}+\text{coleoptile} \rightarrow (\text{auxin-coleoptile}), \qquad \ldots(1)$$

$$\text{growth rate} = k(\text{auxin-coleoptile}), \qquad \ldots(2)$$

or

$$(\text{auxin-coleoptile}) \xrightarrow{k} \text{growth}, \qquad \ldots(2a)$$

where k is a constant which relates growth rate to concentration of the auxin-coleoptile interaction product. This formulation may be expanded if we take note of the fact that reaction (1) is reversible, as is shown by the fact that a coleoptile in an auxin solution at one concentration quickly adjusts its growth rate to the appropriate level when transferred to a second auxin solution of different concentration. Combining this fact with equations (1) and (2a), we obtain

$$\text{auxin}+\text{coleoptile} \rightleftharpoons (\text{auxin-coleoptile}) \xrightarrow{k} \text{growth}. \qquad \ldots(3)$$

This equation is, of course, nothing more than a description in words, and not necessarily a unique description, of the relations of *Figure 2*. Equation (3) does, however, have certain attractive features. For one thing, its applicability may be tested. The central feature of our formulation is that auxin interacts with coleoptile to form something to which growth rate is proportional. We have further seen that the formation of the interaction product is a reversible reaction. Let us assign the dissociation constant K_{aux} to the dissociation of the interaction product:

$$\frac{(\text{auxin})(\text{coleoptile})}{(\text{auxin-coleoptile})} = K_{\text{aux}}. \qquad \ldots(4)$$

The total concentration of auxin-receptive interaction sites in the coleoptile is at all times equal to the sum of the auxin-occupied sites and the sites not so occupied:

$$(\text{coleoptile})_{\text{total}} = (\text{auxin-coleoptile})+(\text{coleoptile})_{\text{free}} \qquad \ldots(5)$$

From relations (4) and (5) we may solve for (auxin-coleoptile) in terms of (auxin), $(\text{coleoptile})_{\text{total}}$, and K_{aux}. Substituting the value of (auxin-coleoptile) thus obtained into equation (2), we obtain an expression for growth rate of the coleoptile as a function of auxin concentration:

$$\text{growth rate} = kC_{\text{total}} \Big/ \left(1+\frac{K_{\text{aux}}}{(\text{auxin})}\right). \qquad \ldots(6)$$

It will be evident that as auxin concentration is increased, growth rate will, according to expression (6), approach kC_{total} as a maximum value. Let us therefore replace kC_{total} by $(\text{growth rate})_{\text{max}}$, the growth rate in non-limiting auxin concentration:

$$\text{growth rate} = (\text{growth rate})_{\text{max}} \Big/ \left(1+\frac{K_{\text{aux}}}{(\text{auxin})}\right). \qquad \ldots(7)$$

The reciprocal of equation (7) is convenient to use in testing the applicability of our formulation to the coleoptile–auxin system:

$$\frac{1}{\text{growth rate}} = \frac{1}{(\text{growth rate})_{\text{max}}} + \frac{1}{(\text{auxin})}\,\frac{K_{\text{aux}}}{(\text{growth rate})_{\text{max}}} \quad \ldots\ldots(8)$$

The reciprocal of growth rate is expected to be a linear function of the reciprocal of auxin concentration for a system which follows the formulation of equation (8). The double reciprocal plot of *Figure 3* shows that our *Avena* growth rate data fulfil the expectations of equation (8) and are thus in agreement with our formulation. We see further that although each individual active auxin (indoleacetic acid, IAA; 2:4-dichlorophenoxyacetic acid,

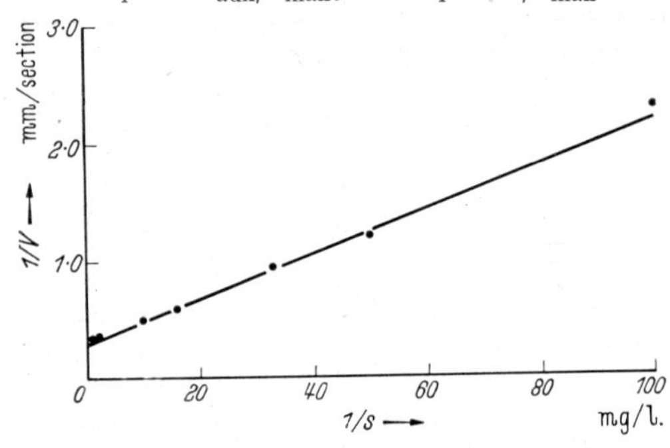

Figure 3. Growth rate of Avena *coleoptile sections as a function of auxin concentration. Reciprocal of growth rate* (V) *is plotted as reciprocal of auxin concentration* (S). *After Foster, McRae, and Bonner* (1952).

2:4-D) of those considered yield straight lines in agreement with the formulation, none the less the parameters (growth rate)$_{\text{max}}$ and K_{aux} are different for the different substances. These parameters afford us then a quantitative method for expressing differences in activity as between different auxins.

We have, in the paragraphs above, considered data on the concentration-dependence of auxin-induced coleoptile growth and found that these data suggest the hypothesis that auxin accomplishes its work by first interacting with some entity of the coleoptile to form a complex, the concentration of which determines growth rate. The relation between coleoptile growth rate and auxin concentration is in fact formally identical to the relation between rate of an enzymatic reaction and the concentration of substrate on which the reaction subsists. Our formulation (equation (3)) and the derived rate equation (equation (7)) are identical with those of Michaelis and Menten (1913) for the enzymatic case. The purpose of the present discussion is to show that we need not apply enzyme kinetics to the study of auxin-induced growth. We might equally well develop growth kinetics for our own problem, and the enzymologists might then try our growth kinetics and see how well they fit enzymatic reactions. Enzyme kinetics have however been delved into extensively already. They constitute a large body of lore. Our growth kinetics turn out to be identical with enzyme kinetics and we naturally use the prior experience of enzymologists in formulating our own problem. The discussion above has shown, however, that the application of the Michaelis–Menten equation to the coleoptile–auxin system makes no assumption about and implies nothing concerning the enzymatic nature of auxin-induced growth.

Formulation of the auxin-induced growth response in the terms of equation (3) has been useful. Thus it has been shown

(i) that chemically different auxins react within the plant as would be expected on the basis that they compete for a common site;

(ii) that certain substances related in structure to auxins but themselves inactive influence growth as would be expected on the basis that they compete with active auxins for the receptive sites.

Point (i) above has been established (McRae, Foster, and Bonner, 1953) by experiments with mixtures of active auxins. The growth rate of coleoptile sections in such a mixture has been shown with certain restrictions to be that expected on the basis of competition for a common receptive site. Point (ii) above, which involves the determination of which inhibitors of auxin-induced growth rigorously compete with auxin for the receptive sites of the plant, leads us to the concept of the multifunctionality of the auxin molecule

It has been shown by McRae and Bonner (1952, 1953) that among the substances structurally related to 2:4-D, for example, there are several which are devoid of growth-promoting activity, but which competitively inhibit the action of 2:4-D and of other active auxins. Competitive inhibition is used here to signify that the substance in question interacts with auxin in the coleoptile in accordance with the formulation

$$E+S \overset{K_S}{\rightleftharpoons} ES \rightarrow \text{growth}, \qquad \ldots.(9)$$

$$E+I \overset{K_I}{\rightleftharpoons} EI \text{ (inactive)}. \qquad \ldots.(10)$$

In this formulation we adopt the notation of enzyme kinetics. The auxin-receptive sites of the coleoptile are now designated as E, the auxin as S, and the inhibitor of auxin action as I. By considerations similar to those used in the development of equation (8), it can be shown that growth rate in the presence of auxin competitor I may be expected to follow the relation

$$\frac{1}{V} = \frac{1}{V_{\text{max}}}\left[K_S + \frac{K_S(I)}{K_I}\right]\frac{1}{S} + \frac{1}{V_{\text{max}}} \qquad \ldots.(11)$$

in which V_{max} replaces the term $(\text{growth rate})_{\text{max}}$. Substances which interact with auxin in the coleoptile in accordance with equation (11) are then substances which compete with the auxin for a common receptor site. The 2:4-D related inhibitors which fulfil the criteria of equation (11) include three broad classes, of which two are of particular interest here. These are typified by 2:4-dichloroanisole and related substances on the one hand, and by the di*ortho* substituted phenoxy acetic acids, 2:6-dichloro and 2:4:6-trichlorophenoxy acetic acid, on the other. The first class of compounds includes 2:4-D derivatives which lack the carboxyl group, a group which we know from other work to be essential to auxin activity. The second class includes those which lack a suitably reactive *ortho* position in the aromatic nucleus, a feature shown by Muir and Hansch (1951) to be essential to auxin activity. Evidently an active auxin molecule contains two functional groups. If we remove one but leave the other intact, we have a competitive inhibitor of auxin activity. But a competitive inhibitor inhibits by competing with auxin for the auxin-receptive site. We may conclude therefore that the auxin-receptive site contains two points of interaction, one suited to binding of the reactive *ortho* position, the other suited to binding of the carboxyl group. In the active auxin-receptor complex, a single auxin molecule would appear to be simultaneously bound at both points. Competitive inhibitors, which are capable only of single-point binding, may combine with either point but not with both.

The concept of the bifunctionality of the auxin molecule, of the growth-active auxin-receptor complex as consisting of a doubly attached auxin molecule, has been derived on the one hand by Muir and Hansch (1951) from the consideration of structure and activity among the auxins and on the other hand from the consideration of the chemical structure of competitive inhibitors of auxin action (McRae and Bonner, 1953). This concept has several corollaries which are of interest. The first has to do with the inhibition of growth which is induced by high auxin concentrations. If the growth functional form of auxin consists of a two-point attached auxin-receptor complex, then we must anticipate that at sufficiently high auxin concentrations, two molecules of auxin will simultaneously bind to the receptor entity, each remaining bound through but a single attachment point. This possibility is expressed by

$$E+2S \rightleftharpoons ES_1S_2 \text{ (growth inactive)}. \quad \ldots.(12)$$

Thus, as auxin concentration is increased, we should expect growth rate first to increase owing to the interaction, first order in auxin, between auxin and receptor, and then at still higher concentrations to decrease owing to the formation, second order in auxin, of inactive complexes. The kinetic consequences of equation (12) have been considered by Foster *et al.* (1952), who have shown that the concept of two-point attachment of auxin leads to the rate equation,

$$V=\frac{V_{\max}S}{K_S+S+S^2/C}. \quad \ldots.(13)$$

This equation is similar in principle to the rate expression of equation (7) with the addition that growth rate is now decreased as auxin concentration, S, increases, by a term in S^2. It has been shown by Foster *et al.* (1952) that the formulation of equation (13) fits the experimental data for coleoptile section growth with considerable precision over a concentration range of one hundred thousand-fold. Inhibition of growth by high auxin concentration would appear to be a natural and indeed an inescapable consequence of two-point binding of auxin to receptor at lower auxin concentrations.

Let us now turn to a further phenomenon which we can effectively describe in kinetic terms. This is the experimental fact that chemically different auxins elicit different maximum growth rates in the coleoptile system. The data of *Figure 1* show for example that if we supply 2:4-D in optimum concentrations, the growth rate or $V_{\max}$ which is elicited is only about two-thirds that elicited by an optimal concentration of IAA. Other auxins are characterized by even lower values of V_{max} in the coleoptile system. Thus the V_{max} for *para*chlorophenoxyacetic acid is about 0·4, that of *ortho*chlorophenoxyacetic acid about 0·14 of that found for the case of IAA. We can approach this matter as indicated in *Figure 4*.

Suppose that auxin, as we have already discussed, approaches the coleoptile and interacts, binds, with it. This initial binding may occur either through the carboxyl group (point 1) or the *ortho* position (point 2). Once the initial binding is consummated, the complex thus formed can proceed to consummate binding at the second position to form growth-active two-point attached auxin-receptor complex, or alternatively it may react with a second molecule of S to form inactive bimolecular complex ES_1S_2. We have already seen that the interaction of coleoptile with auxin to form growth-active

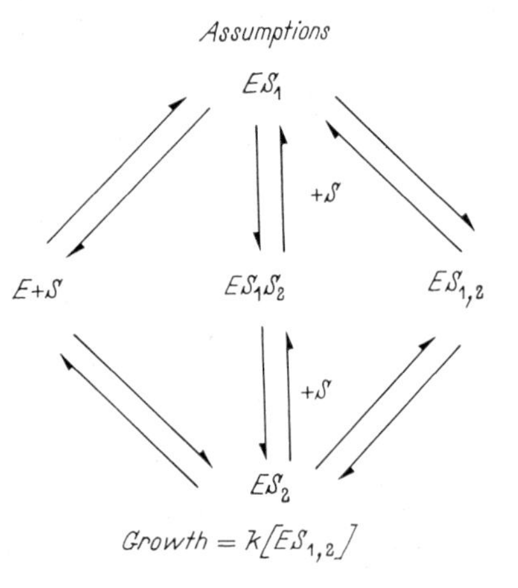

Figure 4. Equilibria relating the formation of growth-active auxin-receptor complex ($ES_{1,2}$) *to formation of other related complexes in the* Avena *coleoptile. After Foster, McRae, and Bonner* (1952).

complex is a reversible reaction, implying then that all of the component reactions are similarly reversible. Appropriate experiments (removal of coleoptiles from high to low auxin concentration) reveal that the formation of the ES_1S_2 complex must be similarly reversible. In the steady-state growth condition then the auxin receptor sites of the coleoptile would be expected according to our kinetic hypotheses to be partitioned between the various forms illustrated in *Figure 4*. The exact proportion of receptor in each form will be determined by the equilibrium constants which describe the tendency to formation of each complex. We will now show that auxins of low V_{max} are those auxins for which the tendency to formation of growth-active $ES_{1,2}$ is low relative to the tendency to formation of the growth-inactive precomplexes such as ES_1 so that at any given instant many of the total receptor sites of the coleoptile are tied up as inactive precomplexes.

It has been indicated above that the curves which relate growth rate to concentration of auxin are hyperbolae and that one parameter of such an hyperbola is the concentration, K_S, of auxin which elicits half maximum growth rate. This parameter signifies in our formulation that concentration of auxin which is needed to assure formation of one half as many $ES_{1,2}$ complexes as would be formed at substrate saturation. We have similarly seen that we can calculate for each inhibitor from our kinetic data a value

K_I which tells us what concentration of this inhibitor is needed to half-saturate available receptor sites with the substance. We will now make the assumption that the dissociation constants for the two precomplexes ES_1 and ES_2 are equal to the dissociation constants of the two related inhibitor complexes EI_1 and EI_2. This assumption, which has been shown by Foster

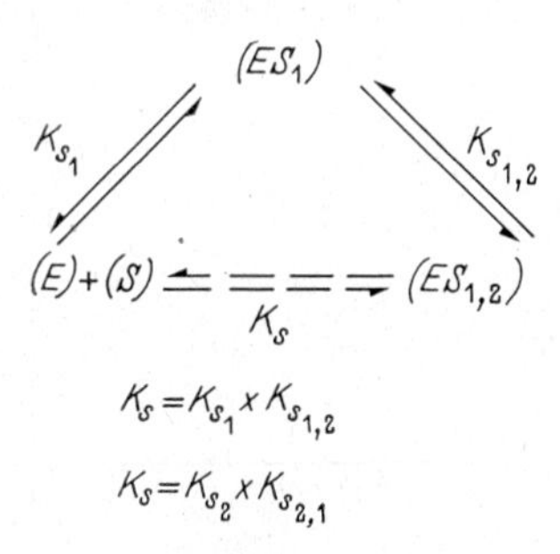

Figure 5. The equilibrium constant, K_S, for the formation of growth-active $ES_{1,2}$ is composed of the product of the two constants K_{S_1} (relating to the formation of complex ES_1) and $K_{S_{1,2}}$ relating to the conversion of ES_1 to $ES_{1,2}$.

et al. (1955) to be consistent with other data, provides us with a way of measuring the individual equilibria of *Figure 4*. This way is indicated in *Figure 5*.

The over-all constant K_S which describes the dissociation of growth-active doubly attached auxin-receptor, $ES_{1,2}$, is made up of the product of

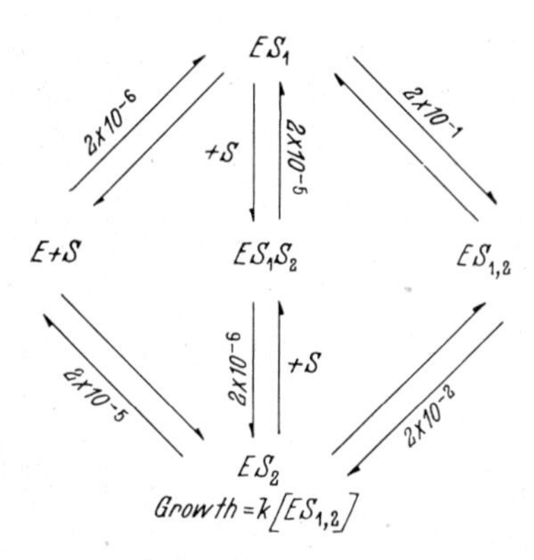

Figure 6. The equilibrium constants relating the varied auxin-receptor, ES, complexes in the Avena *coleoptile section as calculated for the case of* 2:4-D.

constants K_{S_1} and $K_{S_{1,2}}$ which characterize formation of singly attached ES_1 and conversion of ES_1 to $ES_{1,2}$ respectively. Since we can measure K_S for the over-all process as well as K_{S_1} (on the assumption made above), we can therefore calculate $K_{S_{1,2}}$. Similar considerations apply to K_{S_2} and to $K_{S_{1,2}}$. The equilibrium constants relating the varied species of ES complexes between 2:4-D and coleoptile as calculated on this basis are summarized in *Figure 6*.

We are now in the position to estimate the relative contributions of each form of complex for any given concentration of 2:4-D. We note that

$$(E_{\text{total}}) = (E_{\text{free}}) + (ES_1) + (ES_2) + (ES_{1,2}) + (ES_1S_2),$$
$$(E_{\text{free}}) = (ES_1)K_{S_1}/S, \qquad (ES_1) = (ES_{1,2})K_{S_{1,2}}, \qquad \text{etc.} \qquad \ldots.(14)$$

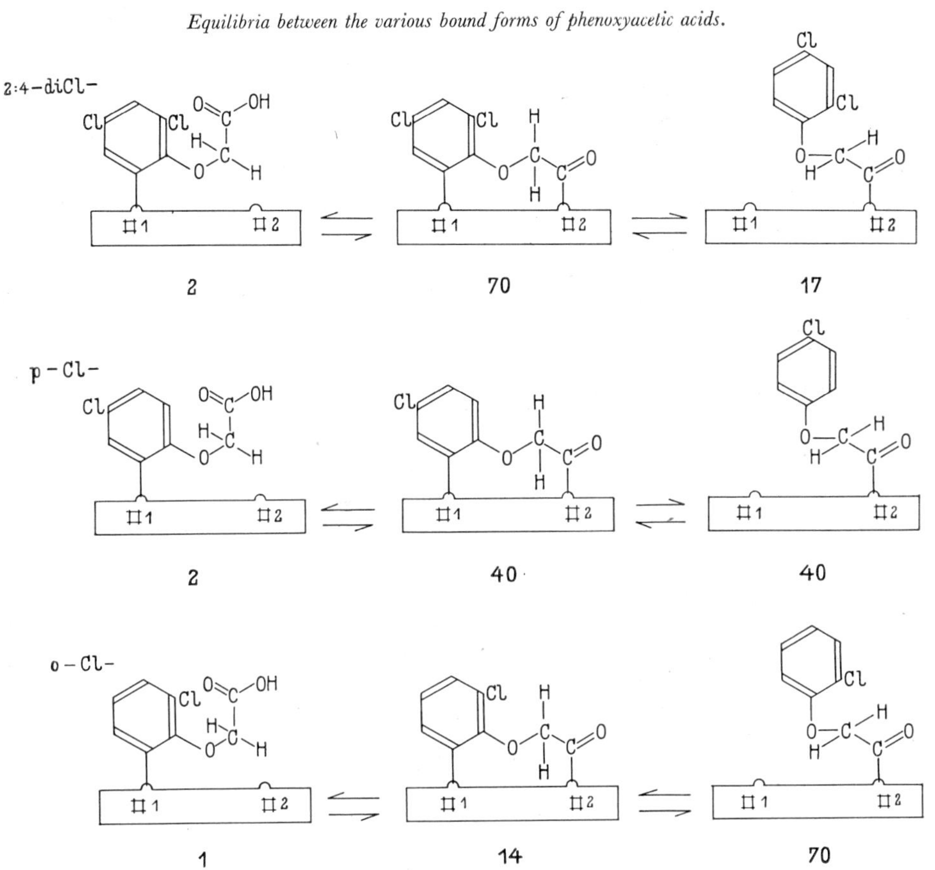

Figure 7. Distribution of auxin-receptor of the Avena *coleoptile section among the varied forms of auxin-receptor complex. Data for phenoxyacetic acids. The distributions are calculated for the optimal concentration of each growth substance. After Foster* (1953).

We may now determine the ratio of any one form of ES to E_{total} in terms of the several equilibrium constants K, and auxin concentration (S). For example, the expression relating growth active $ES_{1,2}$ to E_{total} is of the form

$$\frac{(ES_{1,2})}{(E_{total})} = \frac{1}{1+K_{S_{1,2}}+K_{S_{1,2}}+K_{S_{1,2}}K_{S_1}/S+K_{S_{1,2}}S/K_{S_1S_2}} \quad \ldots .(15)$$

We can now solve equation (15) for the numerical value of $ES_{1,2}/E_{total}$ for any given value of auxin concentration. Let us use that concentration of 2:4-D which yields maximum growth rate, i.e. 6×10^{-6} M. Expressions similar to that of equation (15) can be derived for each of the individual ES complexes and can be similarly solved. The results, summarized in *Figure 7*, indicate that for coleoptiles in steady-state growth in the optimum concentration of 2:4-D, approximately 70 per cent of receptor entities are combined in growth active $ES_{1,2}$ at any one moment, and that the remainder are distributed between varied growth inactive precomplexes, particularly the sinlgy attached (through the carboxyl group) ES_1.

We have compared the activities of the auxins *ortho*chlorophenoxyacetic acid and *para*chlorophenoxyacetic acid with that of 2:4-D. Estimates of the two single-point interaction affinities of *ortho*chlorophenoxyacetic acid were made with *ortho*chlorophenetole and 2:6-dichlorophenoxyacetic acid respectively. For determination of the single-point interaction affinities of *para*chlorophenoxyacetic acid we have used *para*chlorophenetole and 2:6-dichlorophenoxyacetic acid. The single-point interaction affinities as estimated from the appropriate K_I values are given in *Table 1*. The interaction constants for the carboxyl combining inhibitors do not vary greatly as

Table 1

Calculated equilibrium constants for Avena *coleoptile section–phenoxyacetic acid complexes.* (*After Foster* (1953).)

Compound	K_I *ortho*	K_I *carboxyl*	K_S	V_{max} *relative*
o-Cl phenoxyacetic acid	5×10^{-4} M	4×10^{-6} M	3×10^{-5} M	1
p-Cl phenoxyacetic acid	1×10^{-4} M	4×10^{-6} M	5×10^{-6} M	3
2:4-dichlorophenoxyacetic acid	2×10^{-5} M	2×10^{-6} M	5×10^{-7} M	5

between the differently substituted phenoxy compounds. The interaction constants for the *ortho* combining group vary, however, by more than an order of magnitude. Thus there is a five-fold increase in *ortho* attachment affinity as between *ortho*- and *para*phenetole and still another five-fold increase in affinity as between *para*chloro- and 2:4-dichloro-substituted *ortho* combining inhibitors. These changes are reflected in corresponding

Table 2

Distribution of receptor sites among the several complex species for Avena *coleoptile section–phenoxyacetic acid interaction.* (*After Foster* (1953).)

The distribution is calculated for each compound at its optimal growth-promoting concentration. POA = phenoxyacetic acid. 2:4-D = 2:4-dichlorophenoxyacetic acid.

Compound	*Per cent of* E_{total}				
	E_{free}	ES_1	ES_2	ES_1S_2	$ES_{1,2}$
o-Cl POA (5×10^{-5} M)	7·5	71	1	7·5	14
p-Cl POA (2×10^{-5} M)	8	41	2	8	41
2:4-D (6×10^{-6} M)	5·5	17	2	5·5	70

changes in the over-all values of K_S which increase as the *ortho* interaction affinities decrease. We may say that as the *ortho* interaction affinities decrease, the tendency of carboxyl group attached-auxin to complete two-point attachment, for ES_1 to go to $ES_{1,2}$, decreases. Our calculations, summarized in *Table 2*, indicate that for 2:4-D approximately four times as many receptor sites contain two-point attached as one-point attached auxin molecules at any one instant. For *para*chlorophenoxyacetic acid this ratio is reduced to approximately 1 to 1. For *ortho*chlorophenoxyacetic acid one such receptor entity in six bears a two-point attached auxin molecule; a reflection of the fact that singly attached (through the carboxyl group) *ortho*chlorophenoxyacetic acid is actually more stable than the doubly attached form.

We are now in a position to test the hypothesis that the maximum growth rate elicited by a particular auxin is determined by the extent to which the substance occupies the auxin-receptive sites of the plant with doubly attached auxin molecules. *Table 3* contains the appropriate comparison. This table contains firstly the ratios of $ES_{1,2}$ to E_{total} calculated as indicated above for each auxin and for the case of that concentration of each auxin which elicits maximum growth rate. It contains in addition the absolute rate of growth of coleoptile sections in the optimal concentration of each auxin. It is evident

Table 3

Comparison of maximum growth rates elicited by various auxins at optimal concentration with calculated ratios of $ES_{1,2}/E_{total}$

Auxin	$ES_{1,2}/E_{total}$	*Maximum growth rate*	
		mm/18 hrs	*Rel. to IAA*
o-Cl POA	0·14	0·5	0·14
p-Cl POA	0·41	1·5	0·43
2:4-D	0·70	2·4	0·69
IAA	1·00	3·5	1·00

that the relations between the absolute maximum growth rates elicited by each auxin are in good quantitative agreement with the ratios of $ES_{1,2}$ to E_{total} calculated for each auxin. *Table 3* includes data on the native auxin, IAA. Measurements of the individual single-point interaction affinities of IAA carried out as outlined above, have shown that with this auxin, given at its optimal concentration, the tendency to two-point attachment is so great that essentially all receptor sites are present as $ES_{1,2}$. The maximum growth rate elicited by IAA is larger than that elicited by 2:4-D by an amount which is precisely that expected on the basis of the kinetic calculations.

The above considerations have been extensive and involved. They have been carried through because they provide an elaborate test of the applicability of kinetic considerations to auxin-induced growth. The results of the test support the view that the auxin–coleoptile system does in fact behave quantitatively as expected of a system in which auxin interacts reversibly to form a variety of related auxin–coleoptile complexes which are in equilibrium with one another. The outcome of the investigation is also in agreement with the view that each auxin receptor site which becomes two-point attached to an auxin molecule contributes the same amount to the growth of the plant, regardless of the nature of the auxin which achieves two-point attachment.

We have thus far considered aspects of auxin–coleoptile interaction which may be treated in kinetic terms in a straightforward manner and with consistent results. There are, however, other experimental facts which do not appear to us to be capable of such treatment. A simple example is the fact that the apparent K_S of auxin in the coleoptile system is not constant as between one lot of seeds and another. We have found variations of two- to four-fold of the values of K_S in successive yearly harvests of *Avena* seeds of the variety Siegeshafer. A second example concerns interaction between IAA at low concentrations and some second auxin as for example 2:4-D. The latter auxin inhibits the growth-promoting effect of IAA as shown in *Figure 8.* This effect is not, as has already been noted (McRae *et al.*, 1953), interpretable with simple kinetic theory without further assumptions. Still another category of effects which appear to require further understanding for their interpretation are the synergisms between chemically different auxins and

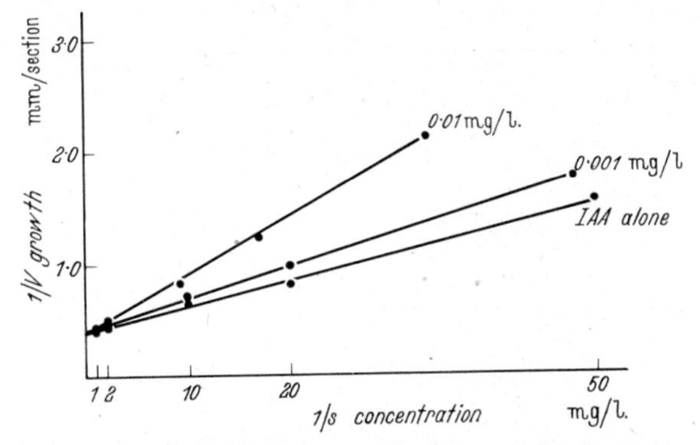

Competitive inhibition of IAA-induced Avena *coleoptile section growth by* 2:4-D.

Figure 8. The growth-promoting activity of indoleacetic acid in the Avena *coleoptile section is inhibited by low concentrations of* 2:4-*D. This effect, which is apparently a competitive one, needs an explanation. Data after McRae, Foster, and Bonner* (1953).

related substances. Such synergism has been frequently described in the literature. We will consider one specific case which illustrates the problems involved. The IAA derivative 2 methyl-5:7-dibromo-IAA is inactive as an auxin in the coleoptile system. It behaves as a carboxyl group-combining anti-auxin in the presence of 2:4-D. The same compound, however, enhances the growth-promoting effect of IAA. This effect is upon the apparent K_S of IAA which is decreased by a factor of 4. Maximum growth rate of coleoptile sections in the presence of IAA is unaffected by the addition of 2-methyl-5:7-dibromo-IAA. How can a substance decrease the apparent K_S of an auxin in our system? How can one and the same substance enhance the growth-promoting effect of IAA but inhibit that of 2:4-D? Discussion of these questions is not possible in terms of our simple kinetic model and appears to require additions to it. Answers to these questions will doubtless greatly amplify and deepen our understanding of auxin matters.

We have seen in the initial section of this discussion that to treat the auxin–coleoptile system in kinetic terms requires no assumptions as to what goes on inside the coleoptile and tells us nothing about the nature of the auxin–coleoptile interaction except that this process is growth-rate limiting. The nature of the substrate concentration growth rate relation suggests that the coleoptile possesses spots which can interact with auxin. We do not find out by our treatment where the spots are or what they do. It is necessary to try to find out what the spots are by other types of experiments. We have approached this problem with the aid of C^{14} carboxyl-labelled 2:4-D of high specific activity (10 millicuries/millimole). One might first ask whether the process whose kinetics we study when we study growth rate is simply the

Uptake of 2:4-*D* (0·5 *mg/l.*) *by* Avena *coleoptile sections with time.*

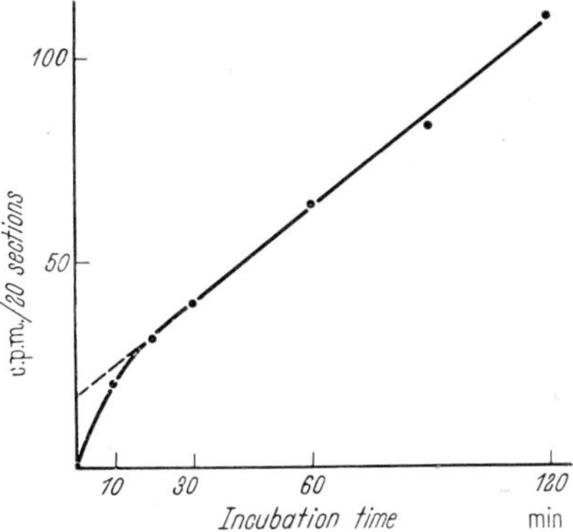

Figure 9. Time course of C^{14}*-labelled* 2:4-*D uptake by the* Avena *coleoptile section. Auxin supplied at a concentration of* 0·5 *mg/l. After Bonner and Johnson* (1955).

Uptake of 2:4-*D by* Avena *coleoptile sections as a function of* 2:4-*D concentration.*

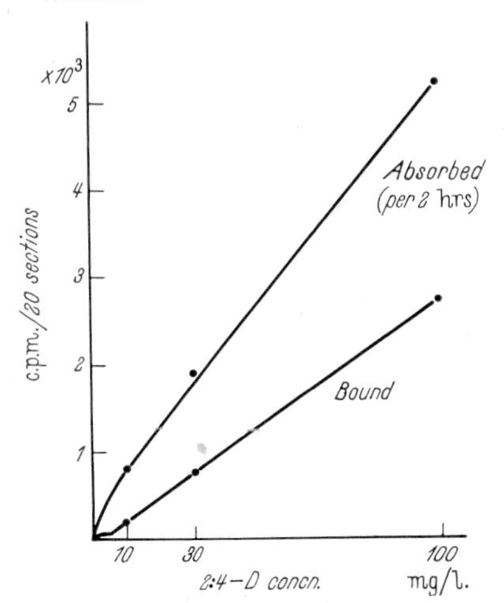

Figure 10. Concentration dependence of 2:4-*D uptake by* Avena *coleoptile sections. The upper curve refers to the amount of* 2:4-*D taken up by the continuing metabolically powered accumulation. The lower curve refers to that taken up in the initial* 20–30 *minutes. After Bonner and Johnson* (1955).

penetration of auxin into the tissue. The kinetics of penetration of 2:4-D into coleoptile tissue have therefore been investigated (Bonner and Johnson, 1955).

The data of *Figure 9* show that when coleoptile tissue is placed in 2:4-D of low concentration ($2{\cdot}5 \times 10^{-6}$ M), the 2:4-D is taken up at a rate which is constant with time over a prolonged period. Superimposed on this continuing uptake is, however, a rapid initial uptake which is consummated within 20–30 minutes. The continuing uptake, by which 2:4-D is actually accumulated in the tissue and which is a metabolism-dependent process, is not, however, related in any simple way to the auxin-dependent growth process. In the first place the total amount of 2:4-D accumulated by the tissue does not control growth rate, since uptake continues long after steady-state growth has been established. Rate of uptake cannot control the growth rate, since rate of 2:4-D uptake increases steadily with increasing external 2:4-D concentration and shows no tendency to saturate even at high concentrations (*Figure 10*).

The rapid initial uptake of 2:4-D by coleoptile tissue is a complex process and is made up of at least two separable components, the quantitatively more important of which is the diffusion of the auxin into the free space of the coleoptile. As might be expected this diffusion is but little dependent on metabolism, is linearly related to external concentration (*Figure 10*), and is not inhibited by other auxins. The significance of the remaining minor component of the initial uptake we have not yet assessed. It is clear in any case that neither the active accumulation nor the passive diffusion of 2:4-D into the coleoptile possesses kinetic characteristics similar to or of significant importance in the over-all control of growth rate by auxin.

SUMMARY

When auxin is added to a plant tissue such as the *Avena* coleoptile, the tissue grows. In the presence of different concentrations of auxin, the tissue grows at different rates. Analysis of the auxin concentration–growth rate relation suggests that some sort of saturation phenomenon is involved. The hypothesis may be made that auxin interacts with some receptor entity of the tissue and that growth rate is proportional to the amount of complex thus formed. This hypothesis has been shown to be a useful one because it encompasses and enables quantitative discussion of the interaction of two auxins in the plant, of the inhibition of growth by varied auxin derivatives and of the inhibition of plant growth by high auxin concentrations. The same hypothesis may be applied to predict quantitatively the relative growth-promoting activity of varied auxins. The supposition that auxin interacts with specific reactive sites of the plant tissue to promote growth and the kinetic consequences of this supposition cannot however embrace and render interpretable all interactions of plant and auxin. Neither does it tell us anything concerning the enzymology of auxin action.

REFERENCES

BONNER, J. (1933). The action of the plant growth hormone. *J. gen. Physiol.* **17,** 63.

BONNER, J. (1934). The relation of hydrogen ions to the growth rate of the *Avena* coleoptile. *Protoplasma*, **21,** 406.

BONNER, J. (1936). The growth and respiration of the *Avena* coleoptile. *J. gen. Physiol.* **20,** 1.

BONNER, J. (1949). Limiting factors and growth inhibitors in the growth of the *Avena* coleoptile. *Amer. J. Bot.* **36,** 323.

BONNER, J., and FOSTER, R. J. (1955). The growth–time relationships of the auxin-induced growth in *Avena* coleoptile sections. *J. exp. Bot.* **6,** 293.

BONNER, J., and JOHNSON, M. (1956). *Physiol. Plant.* (in press).

FOSTER, R. J. (1953). *Abstr. Ann. Mtg. Amer. Soc. Pl. Physiol.*

FOSTER, R. J., MCRAE, D. H., and BONNER, J. (1952). Auxin-induced growth inhibition, a natural consequence of two-point attachment. *Proc. nat. Acad. Sci., Wash.* **38,** 1014.

FOSTER, R. J., MCRAE, D. H., and BONNER, J. (1955). Auxin–antiauxin interaction at high auxin concentrations. *Plant Physiol.* **30,** 323.

MCRAE, D. H., and BONNER, J. (1952). Diortho substituted phenoxyacetic acids as antiauxins. *Plant Physiol.* **27,** 834.

MCRAE, D. H., and BONNER, J. (1953). Chemical structure and antiauxin activity. *Physiol. Plant.* **6,** 485.

MCRAE, D. H., FOSTER, R. J., and BONNER, J. (1953). Kinetics of auxin interaction. *Plant Physiol.* **28,** 343.

MICHAELIS, L., and MENTEN, M. L. (1913). Die Kinetik der Invertinwirkung. *Biochem. Z.* **49,** 333.

MUIR, R. M., and HANSCH, C. (1951). The relationship of structure and plant-growth activity of substituted benzoic and phenoxyacetic acids. *Plant Physiol.* **26,** 369.

ORDIN, L., APPLEWHITE, T., and BONNER, J. (1955). *Plant Physiol.* (in press).

THE KINETICS OF AUXIN-INDUCED GROWTH

T. A. Bennet-Clark

Botany Department, King's College, University of London

The treatment proposed by Bonner and Foster in the previous paper has aroused some controversy as it has not been universally admitted that simple enzyme kinetics are applicable to such a complex sequence of reactions as the 'growth process'. This treatment also takes no account of diffusion processes which the work of Housley, Bentley, and Bickle (1954) suggests may be of critical importance.

If, however, one agrees that there is a roughly hyperbolic relationship between initial extension in auxin and external auxin concentration, one possible explanation is that this extension rate is linearly proportional to the concentration of an auxin–tissue-component complex and that concentration of this complex is determined by a dissociation constant comparable to the Michaelis constant of an enzyme. This aspect of the Californian work taken alone would probably not have evoked any controversy. The major source of disagreement is concerned with the inhibiting action of high concentrations of auxin which the Californian workers regard as comparable in its nature to the inhibitions of certain enzymes, such as catalase and acetyl-choline-esterase, by high substrate concentrations. This they explain on the basis of a necessary two-point attachment of enzyme to substrate or auxin to cell complex.

The failure to agree on this point is entirely due to the inability of different groups of workers to obtain the same experimental results. The only rate of extension growth which can legitimately be used for this enzyme kinetic treatment is the *initial* rate. If the *initial* rate is maintained more or less unchanged for a period of several hours experimentation is, of course, made much simpler.

Bonner and Foster (1955) maintain that their experimental conditions provide a rate of extension which is constant over 12 to 18 hours both at low and at high auxin concentrations. Other workers (Bennet-Clark and Kefford, 1954; Housley, Bentley, and Bickle, 1954; Marinos, 1955; and Turnham (unpublished data)) find that the extension rate remains roughly constant for 12 to 18 hours when auxin concentrations are low and with relatively young coleoptiles, but that at high concentrations there is a rapid decrease in extension rate with time. These workers find that the initial rates at high concentrations have maximal values. In other words, the initial rate–auxin concentration curve is claimed by these workers to be roughly a hyperbola and the reciprocal plot is a straight line of the type shown as a continuous line in *Figure 1*. The Californian school, on the other hand, consider that the reciprocal plot resembles the dotted line of *Figure 1*, both when *initial* rates are taken and when one takes extensions over a 15-hour period.

Unpublished work (Bennet-Clark, Hurst, and Turnham, 1955) has shown that addition of salts and also of sugars to the buffered auxin solutions in which coleoptiles or mesocotyls are extending causes profound change in the course of extension. Relatively small osmotic pressures of non-electrolytes and still smaller external osmotic pressures of electrolytes cause marked

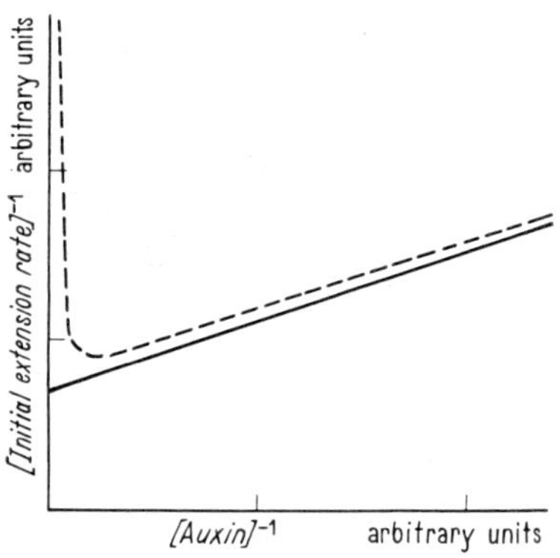

Figure 1. (Initial growth rate)$^{-1}$ plotted against (auxin concentrations)$^{-1}$. Our data are shown by a continuous line, Bonner's data by a dotted line.

reduction of the *initial* extension rate especially at high auxin levels. One can by suitable choice of external concentration, thus obtain curves convex or concave to the horizontal axis, or, at intermediate concentrations, nearly

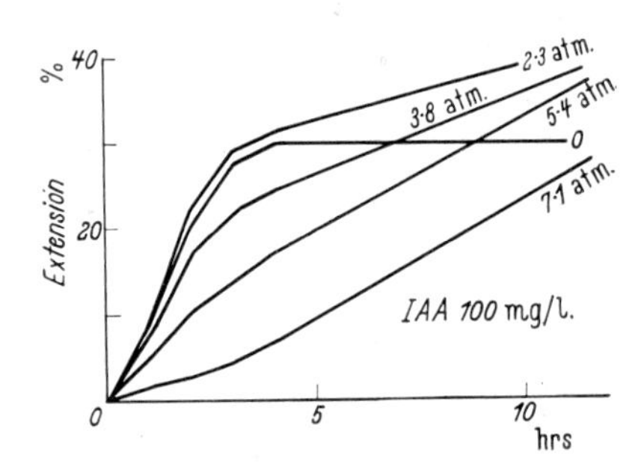

Figure 2. Per cent extension of Avena *coleoptiles plotted against time. The osmotic pressures of sugar solutions in which the auxin was dissolved are shown on the individual curves.*

linear relationships are found. This is shown clearly by the data of *Figure 2*, where sucrose only was added to the auxin to give solutions of the range of osmotic pressures shown.

It is, therefore, our claim that the reduced initial rates of extension and the linear extension–time curves at high auxin levels as found by Bonner and Foster (1955) are experimental artefacts due to the depressant action of external solutes. It has been shown by Marinos (1955) that the decrease with time in extension rate observed by him at high auxin levels is accompanied by a corresponding decrease in respiration rate and is associated with marked exosmosis of the cell contents. It seems probable that cell permeability or solute pumping mechanisms are progressively interfered with or destroyed when auxin concentration is high. In our laboratory we have confirmed Marinos' finding regarding this roughly exponential decrease in respiration rate; this and the corresponding decrease in extension rate may be looked upon as injury or toxicity phenomena, but they are not due to low pH of the medium as they occur at pH as high as 6.

It is difficult for the present writer to understand how the Californian workers find that initial extension rates in high auxin concentrations are *not* reduced by the presence of other solutes, sugars, maleate, etc. (cf. Bonner and Foster, 1955, *Figure 4*. In our experiments, using unbuffered auxin, auxin adjusted to pH 4·5 or 5·5 by NaOH, and similar solutions buffered either with maleate or citrate or with other additives, we invariably find that addition of buffer or other osmotica depresses initial extension rate and tends to flatten out the extension–time curve from concave to the horizontal axis towards linearity as shown in *Figure 2*.

Consequently, our view is that the inhibitions which develop at high auxin concentration are due to secondary destruction of part of the cell mechanism rather than to a competitive attachment to one of the postulated pair of auxin attracting centres. The lack of reversibility following injury due to high auxin concentration is consistent with this view.

REFERENCES

Bennet-Clark, T. A., and Kefford, N. P. (1954). The extension growth time relationship for *Avena* coleoptile sections. *J. exp. Bot.* **5,** 293–304.

Bonner, J., and Foster, R. J. (1955). The growth time relationships of the auxin-induced growth in *Avena* coleoptile sections. *J. exp. Bot.* **6,** 293–302.

Housley, S., Bentley, J. A., and Bickle, A. S. (1954). Studies on plant growth hormones. III. *J. exp. Bot.* **5,** 373–388.

Marinos, N. G. (1955). *Studies on cell elongation.* Ph.D. Thesis, University of Adelaide, S. Australia.